ASTRONOMY

THE NEW YORK UNIVERSITY LIBRARY OF SCIENCE

ASTRONOMY

EDITED BY

Samuel Rapport AND *Helen Wright*

ACADEMIC EDITORIAL ADVISER

SERGE A. KORFF

*Professor of Physics, University Heights Center,
New York University*

NEW YORK UNIVERSITY PRESS 1964

ACKNOWLEDGMENTS

"Copernicus and his Predecessors" from *The Scientific Adventure* by Herbert Dingle. Reprinted by permission of Sir Isaac Pitman & Sons, Ltd.

"Tycho Brahe" by Herbert Dingle from *Endeavour*. Reprinted by permission of the author and of the editors of *Endeavour*.

"Johannes Kepler" from *Makers of Science* by Ivor B. Hart. Reprinted by permission of The Clarendon Press.

"Isaac Newton" from *Men of Mathematics* by E. T. Bell. Copyright 1937 by E. T. Bell. Reprinted by permission of Simon & Schuster, Inc.

"Telescope, Spectroscope, and Camera" from *Palomar* by Helen Wright. Copyright 1952 by Helen Wright and reprinted by her permission.

"Radio Telescopes" from *The Exploration of Outer Space* by Sir Bernard Lovell. Copyright © 1962 by A. C. B. Lovell. Reprinted by permission of Harper & Row and of the Oxford University Press.

"Balloon Astronomy" by Martin and Barbara Schwarzschild. Copyright © 1959 by Scientific American, Inc. and reprinted by their permission. All rights reserved.

"The Heavens and the Earth" from Simon Newcomb's *Astronomy for Everybody* revised by Robert H. Baker. Copyright 1902, 1932 by Doubleday, Doran & Company, Inc.

"The Solar Family" from *Consider the Heavens* by Forest Ray Moulton. Copyright 1935 by Doubleday, Doran & Company, Inc. and reprinted by permission of the estate of Forest Ray Moulton.

"John Couch Adams and the Discovery of Neptune" by Sir Harold Spencer Jones. Reprinted by permission of the Cambridge University Press.

"The Exploration of the Moon" by Robert Jastrow. Copyright © 1960 by Scientific American, Inc. and reprinted by their permission. All rights reserved.

"Mariner: Mission to Venus" from *Mariner: Mission to Venus* by The Staff, Jet Propulsion Laboratory, California Institute of Technology. Copyright © 1963 by the Jet Propulsion Laboratory, California Institute of Technology. Reprinted by permission of McGraw-Hill Book Company, Inc.

"The Sun" from *Stars in the Making* by Cecilia Payne-Gaposchkin. Copyright 1952 by the President and Fellows of Harvard University and reprinted by permission of the Harvard University Press.

"Stars and Stellar Systems" from *Matter, Earth and Sky* by George Gamow. Copyright © 1958 by George Gamow. Reprinted by permission of Prentice Hall, Inc., Englewood Cliffs, New Jersey, and of Macmillan & Company, Ltd.

"Cepheid Variables" from *The Main Stream of Mathematics* by Edna E. Kramer. Copyright 1951 by Oxford University Press and reprinted by permission of the Press.

"Stars: Data and Classification" from *Physics of the Sun and Stars* by W. H. McCrea. Copyright 1950 by Hutchinson House. Reprinted by permission of the Hutchinson Publishing Group and of Curtis Brown, Ltd.

"The Birth and Death of a Star" by Allan Sandage, from *Frontiers of Science* edited by Edward Hutchings. Copyright 1958 by Basic Books and published by their permission.

"Galaxies" and "The Dust and Gas of Space" from *This Universe of Space* by Peter Millman. Copyright © 1962 by Schenkman Publishing Company, Inc. Reprinted by permission of Schenkman Publishing Company, Inc. and of Routledge & Kegan Paul, Ltd.

"Weighing Light" from *Space, Time and Gravitation* by Sir Arthur Eddington. Reprinted by permission of the Cambridge University Press.

"When Time Began" by Fred Hoyle. Copyright © 1959 by The Curtis Publishing Company. Reprinted by permission of the author.

"Life on Other Worlds" from *Of Stars and Men* by Harlow Shapley. Copyright © 1958 by Harlow Shapley. Reprinted by permission of Beacon Press.

CONTENTS

FOREWORD   ix

INTRODUCTION   xi

I. The Founders of Modern Astronomy

Copernicus and His Predecessors
    Herbert Dingle   6
Telescopic Observations *Galileo Galilei*   25
Tycho Brahe *Herbert Dingle*   35
Johannes Kepler *Ivor B. Hart*   43
Isaac Newton *E. T. Bell*   55

II. Tools and Techniques

Telescope, Spectroscope, and Camera
    Helen Wright   73
Radio Telescopes *A. C. B. Lovell*   100
Balloon Astronomy *Martin and Barbara
    Schwarzschild*   113

III. The Solar System

The Heavens and the Earth *Simon Newcomb*   128
The Solar Family *Forest Ray Moulton*   152
John Couch Adams and the Discovery of Nep-
    tune *Sir Harold Spencer Jones*   173
The Exploration of the Moon *Robert Jastrow*   186
Mariner: Mission to Venus *The Staff, Jet
    Propulsion Laboratory, California
    Institute of Technology*   198

IV. The Sun and Other Stars

The Sun   *Cecilia Payne-Gaposchkin*   224

Stars and Stellar Systems   *George Gamow*   239

Cepheid Variables   *Edna E. Kramer*   248

Stars: Data and Classification   *W. H. McCrea*   255

The Birth and Death of a Star   *Allan Sandage*   279

V. Galaxies, Cosmology, and Relativity

Galaxies   *Peter M. Millman*   294

The Dust and Gas of Space
          Peter M. Millman   307

Weighing Light   *Sir Arthur Eddington*   321

When Time Began   *Fred Hoyle*   331

Life on Other Worlds   *Harlow Shapley*   344

FOREWORD

THE PURPOSE of this book is to bring to the layman a brief introduction into a fascinating field. This field is the vastest imaginable, encompassing as it does the full extent of known time, billions of years, and the entirety of known space, billions of light years each way. This is the Universe in which we live, about which new techniques have revealed so much. The implications about the future are also a part of this study.

The approach adopted in the present series is to introduce the reader to a field of knowledge by quoting those people who have historically been the ones who developed the subject. In this way we have the points of view presented which the pioneers saw when they stood at the forefront of an expanding subject. The compilers of this book have chosen excerpts from the writings of the famous early originators of the modern era, including Galileo and Newton, as well as the well-known moderns, including such noted figures as Gamow and Sandage, Eddington and Hoyle. Each of these persons has actually carried forward the search for new knowledge and has added new territories to the advancing area of what is known and accepted. A number of these persons have enjoyed considerable reputations as successful popularizers as well as being important research men.

We stand today at the threshold of an era of new knowledge. We have formidable new tools which are just beginning to bring us new information. Today, new large optical telescopes are just entering their useful life-periods. Enormous radiotelescopes, able to see through optically opaque clouds of matter in the galaxy are becoming operational. The rapid advances in the understanding of nuclear physics, as well as the new NASA space probes, and especially the rocket and satellite-borne astronomical equipment are adding daily to our knowledge. A comprehension of what the outstanding problems are, of where we are going in our research, of what we know and of what we do not know, and of what we can hope to observe in the forseeable future, are topics of great interest, discussed in this volume by those at present active in doing the work.

Serge A. Korff

INTRODUCTION

ASTRONOMY IS THE OLDEST of the sciences. Hundreds, even thousands of years before the development of the other sciences, men were making surprisingly accurate measurements of the seasons, of lunar cycles, and planetary motions. They were predicting eclipses and estimating the sizes and distances of the sun and moon; they were wondering about the causes of all these celestial phenomena. Astronomy, indeed, is not only the oldest but in a way the father of all the other sciences. For through this sense of wonder arose the systematic examination of the workings of the external world which has resulted in modern science.

"Think how diminished humanity would be," said the great French mathematician Henri Poincaré, "if under heavens constantly overclouded, as Jupiter's must be, it had forever remained ignorant of the stars." Man's place in the universe would have remained unknown. Natural happenings would have been attributed to the whims of benign or angry gods. Conceivably, to this day, the rule of natural law would have remained unknown and in Poincaré's words, "a multitude of little genii, fantastic and exacting" would have been considered responsible for every occurrence.

It is in this appreciation of the orderliness of the universe, of its lack of capriciousness, of its obedience to natural laws which can be accurately determined by means of scientific technique, that astronomy has made perhaps its greatest contribution to civilization. From it have sprung the attempts to discover how the earth was created and how evolved, why the individual elements exist, how life first began, how plants and animals and man himself have developed from their primitive beginnings. Each of these problems, at first considered the result of supernatural caprice, has lent itself to scientific examination. The most profound of scientific problems, the origin of the universe, has become the subject of a study in which, as we shall see, specific astronomical theories are being tested by observation and analysis.

It is to astronomy also that we owe our modern concept of man's place in the universe. His eyes and his common sense at first seemed to tell him that the earth which was his home, was the center of the universe. His religion taught him that his destiny was the primary consideration of the Creator. The doctrine of Copernicus struck a shattering blow at this anthropocentric view. In successive stages man's place in the universe has been downgraded, until now the evidence indicates that he is the inhabitant of a minor planet revolving around one of the billions of stars in a system which is itself one among billions.

Hand in hand with this concept goes the realization that the universe is infinitely greater and more awe-inspiring than our forbears could conceive. The distances, velocities, and masses with which astronomy deals are of an order entirely different from those of our everyday world. The attempt to comprehend their nature staggers the imagination. Yet this attempt immeasurably extends our horizons and broadens our outlook. There is hardly an aspect of man's philosophical thinking on which astronomy has not had a profound effect.

The work of the astronomer may be divided into three classifications—observational, theoretical, and experimental. The earliest astronomers recorded what their eyes could see —the movements of the planets, sun and other stars. Their observations served both practical and supernatural ends. The observational approach is exemplified in the positional astronomy of Tycho Brahe and his successors, who included the meticulous observers of the nineteenth century. It continues to provide the data on which other methods of research depend. Theoretical astronomy was born in the attempts of early astronomers to explain the movements of the heavenly bodies. The origin of the solar system and of the universe, and the birth and death of stars are among the problems which concern the contemporary theoretical astronomer. The use of the adjective "experimental" in connection with astronomy may at first blush appear baffling to the layman. How is it possible to conduct experiments dealing with objects so utterly beyond man's control? Yet the modern science of astrophysics depends in large part on this scientific technique. A single example will illustrate the method and its possibilities.

George Ellery Hale, for whom the 200-inch Palomar telescope is named, formed the hypothesis that sunspots occur in connection with huge magnetic fields. In his laboratory in Holland, Pieter Zeeman had shown that when light is placed in a magnetic field its spectral lines are split and the light is polarized. To test his hypothesis, Hale carried these observations further in the Mt. Wilson Observatory laboratory. At the same time, in 1908, he used a new and powerful spectrograph with the 60-foot tower telescope on Mt. Wilson to examine a large sunspot. He found that the spectral lines were split and that the light was polarized, just as he had observed them in the laboratory. So, for the first time, an extraterrestrial, magnetic field had been detected and measured, and related to an observed experimental phenomenon.

In the following pages will be found further examples of work in all three of the classifications mentioned above. In recent years, due in large part to advances in related sciences, the field has grown exceedingly complex and in a book of this size, many outstanding developments must be omitted. However, it is hoped that the articles which follow will give the reader a broad general picture of the science and encourage him to further investigation.

The book is intended for educated laymen without specialized knowledge and references and footnotes have been omitted in large part. Because of limitations of space, it has been found necessary to present some articles in abbreviated form.

This book is one of a series entitled THE NEW YORK UNIVERSITY LIBRARY OF SCIENCE. Other volumes, dealing with individual sciences, are published or in preparation. This series as a whole will encompass much of the universe of modern man, for that universe has been shaped in greatest measure by science, the branch of human activity whose name is derived from the Latin *scire*—to know.

I. The Founders of Modern Astronomy

I. The Founders of Modern Astronomy

The beginnings of astronomy are hidden in the mists of pre-history. It began no doubt in a sense of wonder. Early man could not have failed to observe the rising and setting of the sun, the phases of the moon, the passing of the seasons, and the wheeling of the stars. In his attempts to measure these changes and discover their causes, astronomy had its birth.

At some early stage, the study received great impetus from the belief that celestial happenings were somehow related to those on earth. It was thought that the gods, who controlled all destinies, must dwell on high and that they could be identified with celestial objects. The sun-god traveled across the heavens in a golden chariot. The moon, the planets, the constellations represented other gods and goddesses whose whims and wishes were manifested in the skies. The appearance of an eclipse or a comet might presage disaster. The phases of the moon might somehow be related to the success or failure of crops. Kings and emperors, as well as common men, looked to the stars to foretell the future and guide them in their affairs. The psuedo-science of astrology was born and its practitioners wielded enormous powers. It continues to exist to the present day, despite all scientific evidence of its worthlessness.

Early astronomy had more practical aspects. Mariners sighted on the stars to determine their positions and guide their courses. The study of the heavens was a key to an accurate calendar, and the calendar played a vital role in the activities of early man. The yearly cycles were studied with great care. The results were of varying accuracy but some of them, for example those of the Aztecs, compare not unfavorably with modern measurements. Practical and supernatural considerations combined to empha-size the importance of astronomy.

Only legendary accounts exist of ancient Chinese astronomy, although Chinese literature ascribes great antiquity to the study of the subject. Prediction of eclipses was supposed to have been calculated as early as 4000 B.C. There is a famous legend that two astronomers, Ho and Hi, who were charged with this task, were taken with drink and failed in their duty, suffering decapitation as a penalty. Modern calculations indicate that the eclipse may have occurred on October 22, 2137 B.C., but the story is in all probability apocryphal. Later the Chinese developed a calendar of considerable accuracy, calculating the length of the year as 365¼ days. They considered that the center of the heavens was at the celestial pole. The center of the earth, which was presumed to be flat, was China itself. The four corners of the universe were related to the four seasons and to numerous other phenomena. A disturbance in the heavens, the appearance of a comet or a bright light which we now recognize to be a supernova, presaged war and pestilence on earth. Conversely, unwise or evil human actions could presumably cause disturbances among the stars.

Among the Egyptians, the most notable yearly event was the flooding of the Nile. It was noted that this flooding coincided with the first appearance of Sothis (Sirius) above the horizon at the capital at Memphis. Sothis became the divine star of the Empire, the symbol of fertility and plenty. The Sun-god, greatest of the deities, was supposed to travel daily on a river that surrounded the universe. The Egyptian year had 365 days. The loss of one day every four years, amounting to a month in 120 years, resulted in a complicated calendar with "wandering years" and shifting festival dates. The study of astronomy was in the hands of a powerful priestly class which was able even to defy the Emperor.

The most significant developments in astronomy before the Greeks took place in the plain of the Tigris and Euphrates. In artifacts which have been identified with the early Babylonian period, there is evidence of systematic observation of the phases of the moon and the cyclical movement of the stars. Stars and constellations were recognized and named. A tablet from the first Babylonian dynasty, preserved in the British Museum, contains descriptions of the movements of the planet Venus, linking them with rains and devastations, or with prospering crops.

This information was preserved after the early Babylonian dynasty had fallen to Hittite and Egyptian invaders. When the Assyrian Empire under Tiglath-pilesar (about 1100 B.C.) grew in power, and under his successors conquered Babylon, a considerable body of knowledge came into existence. The collection of systematic knowledge continued during the period when Assyria fell, when Babylon became the capital of a new empire, and when the Persian Cyrus conquered it in 539 B.C. Lists of fixed stars and their movements existed; prediction of lunar and possibly of solar eclipses was systematized. During the period when an empire whose capital was at the new Greek city of Seleucia was founded, tables expressing the motions of heavenly bodies in arithmetical terms were drawn up. A considerable knowledge of the perturbations of the moon existed.

In astronomy, as in other fields of knowledge, it was the Greeks whose accomplishments were greatest and who laid the foundations for later developments. Their most important contribution was the recognition of the fact that observed phenomena could be explained by a system of natural law. Thales of Miletus (about 600 B.C.) recognized the function of the moon in causing solar eclipses and from it developed the theory that the moon shone because of reflected sunlight and that its phases could thus be explained. His pupil, Anaximander, made the first, though mistaken, estimates of the sizes of the sun and moon. Anaximenes of Miletus held that the stars were embedded in a revolving crystal sphere, and the Pythagoreans recognized that the earth was a ball suspended in space. Indeed, Philolaus, a member of the school, believed that all heavenly bodies revolved around a fixed center not the earth, a startling departure from the geocentric theory. A later astronomer, Aristarchus of Samos, elaborated on this theory to state that it was the earth which revolved around the sun. His idea was of course rejected by the ancient Greeks. Instead, they held that the earth was the center of the universe and that the heavenly bodies were embedded in concentric crystal spheres revolving around it. This was the theory that Plato accepted. His pupil Eudoxus postulated more than a score of such spheres, and Aristotle, the most influential figure of ancient times, elaborated on it in a manner which is described in the following article. But the greatest astronomer of ancient times was undoubtedly Hipparchus, who made observations on the island of Rhodes during the second century. B.C. We know little about his life, but his accomplishments are set forth in the writings of Ptolemy. He was an observer of hitherto unequalled accuracy, developing the precession of the equinoxes (discussed in an article by Simon Newcomb appearing in a later section), and his system of the world served as the basis for Ptolemy's Almagest, which was written three centuries later and dominated astronomical thought for the succeeding fourteen centuries. The theory which overthrew the Ptolemaic system was that of Nicholas Copernicus, who is the subject of this article by Herbert Dingle, the English astronomer and astrophysicist. Born in London in 1890, Dingle became a reader of natural philosophy at the Imperial College of Science and Technology in 1918, and in 1946 professor of the history and philosophy of science at University College. He was a member of the British eclipse expeditions of 1927, 1932, and 1940, and he has written extensively on the history and philosophy of science.

COPERNICUS AND HIS PREDECESSORS

HERBERT DINGLE

AT THE JUNCTION of the fifteenth and sixteenth centuries two Churchmen from northern Europe went to Italy. One produced the Reformation: the other gave the Renaissance its most pregnant symbol. Truly, we see what our eyes are fitted to perceive.

At the time of this visit, Nicolaus Copernicus was twenty-three years old. He was born, the youngest of four children, on 19 February 1473, at Thorn (Torun) on the Vistula, then and now a town of Poland.

At the age of ten, on the death of his father, Nicolaus came under the care of his maternal uncle, Lucas Watzelrode, who was soon to become Bishop of Ermland, one of the four provinces of Prussia at that time. He continued at school in Thorn until 1491 when, at the age of eighteen, he entered the University of Cracow, then in the forefront of university education in mathematics and astronomy. Here he became a pupil of Brudzewski, one of the leading astronomers of the time, and acquired some proficiency in astronomical observation. There can be little doubt that the seeds of his future career were sown at this time, but they did not germinate immediately. After three years at Cracow, Nicolaus returned to his uncle's home at Heilsberg and entered the service of the Church. Bishop Watzelrode failed in his first attempt to secure for him a canonry at Frauenburg, and he was accordingly allowed to resume his university studies. This time he went to Bologna and entered the school of law, where he obtained the degree of Master of Arts. During his stay he formed a close friendship with Novara, the Professor of Astronomy, with whom we are told he worked "not so much a pupil as a helper and witness of the observations."

In 1500 Copernicus left Bologna for Rome, and remained there for twelve months, engaged in the private teaching of mathematics. It was then time to return home, where shortly after his departure for Bologna he had been elected a Canon of Frauenburg Cathedral. Almost immediately he sought and obtained further leave of absence to continue his legal studies, which he completed at Padua and Ferrara. At Padua also he studied medicine, and in 1506, after ten years of almost continuous study in Italy, he returned to Ermland to take up his clerical duties.

The remaining years of the life of Copernicus were outwardly full of arduous and varied activity. His official duties included not only those of a Churchman in the narrow sense, but also the medical care of a succession of moribund bishops and of the poor of the diocese, as well as much political work. This was no light matter in the circumstances of the time. Hostility between the Poles, the Prussians and the Teutonic Knights led to his assuming charge of the military defence of his district and the responsibility for its interests at the subsequent Peace Conference. A resulting debasement of the coinage drew from him an analysis of the principles of currency which formed the basis of the new legislation by which the evil was remedied. Difficulties arising from the spread of Lutheran ideas added further burdens, and altogether the life of Copernicus was anything but the placid stream of contemplation which it is often supposed to have been.

Nevertheless, although this succession of public activities

occupied the forefront of his life, in the background and much closer to his heart the development of his astronomica ideas pursued a steady and continuous course. His grea work, *De Revolutionibus Orbium Cœlestium*, published a the very end of his life, was compiled from notes on scraps of paper, margins of books, and even on walls, and the manu script itself is covered with amendments, insertions, and deletions made at various times as his ideas developed and new observations were made. He tells us in the Preface addressed to the Pope, Paul III, that he had worked at it not for nine years but well into the fourth period of that length, and when necessary (but only then, apparently, for he was no great observer) he supplied missing information by observations of his own. These were made with an in strument of his own construction, and he seemed to have no illusions about their accuracy.

"If only I can be correct to ten minutes of arc," he told his pupil, Rheticus, "I shall be no less elated than Pythagoras is said to have been when he discovered the law of the right-angled triangle."

Of his general character and temperament we know little save what can be inferred from the facts just outlined. No contemporary biography exists, and, apart from his published work, the only writings of his that remain are a few letters to his official superiors on matters of passing interest. His por traits suggest a man of thought rather than of action, reveal ing strongly-marked features on which sits a gravity befitting the countenance of one who had stopped the Sun and made the Earth to turn. On his basic devotion to astronomy, the superficial layer of his casual interests shows considerable variety. He was proficient in languages, and published a translation from Greek into Latin of the poems of Theo phylactus Simocatta. He was also an artist, of what skill we cannot judge, for the nearest existing approach to an ex ample of his work is a copy by other hands of his self portrait, which adorns the famous Cathedral clock-tower at Strasbourg.

Apart from a marked integrity and firmness of purpose, the one personal quality which I think we can deduce with some confidence is a certain humility or diffidence, which led him, on one hand, to shun publicity both for himself and for his work, and, on the other, to tend to depreciate his own worth in comparison with that of others. As a consequence, his work is an outstanding example of unaided individual thought; no interchange of opinion, no controversies disturbed or modified the gradual unfolding of his ideas. Not until four years before his death, when young Georg Joachim von Lauchen, better known as Rheticus, went on a pilgrimage to Frauenburg for a few weeks and remained for two years, had he even a pupil.

There is not a particle of evidence that he had any fear of making his views known, unless a shrinking from the ridicule of the unlearned may be so classed. The popular idea that he kept his thoughts secret from fear of persecution is entirely baseless. What he did shrink from was the laughter of those whose sense of the absurdity of supposing that the obviously stationary earth could be moving was unbalanced by the astronomical knowledge which would justify the supposition. He had, in fact, in 1531 been satirized on the stage near Frauenburg, and there was no lack of comment such as that of Luther, who called him the "new astrologer" —"the fool," he said, "would overturn the whole science of astronomy." His sensitive nature was hurt by such misunderstanding, and in his dedicatory letter to the Pope, prefaced to *De Revolutionibus*, he expressly says that it was this consideration which had kept him from publishing his views before.

De Revolutionibus is not primarily a polemical work. It is a complete treatise on astronomy—a new *Almagest*—in which, however, the centre of the Sun and not that of the Earth is taken as the stationary point of the universe. The arguments for the change occupy a relatively small part of the book, the greater part being concerned with descriptions of the movements of the celestial circles, with mathematical theorems and tables and astronomical tables intended to supersede earlier ones. The great observational work of Tycho Brahe, however, was soon to make the tables obsolete, and the main feature of interest for future generations was the substitution of the heliostatic for the geostatic universe.

To understand the significance of this it is necessary for us to look carefully into the state of astronomical thought in the days of Copernicus.

It is customary to think of pre-Copernican astronomy as a definite universally-accepted system of thought, whose principles were summarized once for all in Ptolemy's *Almagest* and which became more and more complicated in application as observations accumulated. Unfortunately the position was not so simple as that. We can best approach it by looking first at the Aristotelean and Ptolemaic systems in their original forms.

The principles of the Aristotelean physics which concern us are these. There was a fundamental distinction between sub-lunar and celestial matter. The former, consisting of the four elements, earth, water, air, fire, was subject to transformation, change, and corruption, while celestial matter was unchangeable and incorruptible. Motion was of two kinds— natural and violent—and bodies displaced by violence from their natural places in the universe sought those places again, so that violent motion was necessarily transient, while the natural motion of the imperturbable celestial spheres was eternal. This most perfect motion was uniform and circular, while the natural motion of displaced sub-lunar matter was rectilinear—either towards the centre of the universe (gravity) or away from it (levity). The universe was finite, so that rectilinear, unlike circular, motion necessarily terminated when the moving body had reached the centre or boundary of the universe.

These principles were exhibited in the operations of the universe, which was constructed in the following way. The Earth, which was spherical, was stationary at the centre: this was clearly so, since sub-lunar matter, which necessarily moved towards or away from the centre of the universe, is observed to move towards or away from the centre of the Earth. The stars were embedded in a sphere, concentric with the Earth, and, of course, of finite radius. The Sun, Moon, and planets had each a sphere of its own, on the equator of which it was fixed, and all the celestial spheres revolved round the Earth in various periods. The spheres were linked together, and several intermediate ones were provided to allow such of the motion of one sphere as was necessary to be transmitted to another, for each sphere by itself could have only one simple circular motion. Though all the spheres were concentric with the Earth, their axes were neither coincident nor necessarily constant in direction, and their revolution could be either from east to west or from west to east. In the whole system fifty-five spheres were found necessary to explain the observed motions.

In Aristotle's day (the fourth century B.C.) the recorded observations covered only a short period of time, and consequently the motions to be explained were relatively simple. This system of concentric spheres, which was originally designed by Eudoxus, accounted for them well enough. But the passage of time showed that its possibilities were too limited to cover the variations which gradually made themselves known, and new devices were necessary in order "to save the phenomena."

In the centuries after Aristotle, not only did the accuracy of observation improve, but the gradually lengthening list of data revealed details in the planetary motions which no multiplication of concentric spheres could deal with. New devices were needed, and when, five hundred years later, the facts and principles of astronomy were summarized by Ptolemy in the famous *Almagest,* the system described bore little apparent resemblance to the Aristotelean universe. Let us glance briefly at the chief phenomena to be explained before turning to the system itself.

The movements of the stars, which in Aristotle's day comprised only the uniform diurnal revolution, now included the precessional motion as well. The variations in distance and angular velocity of the Sun were known with some accuracy, as were the more irregular ones of the Moon, and with the Moon there were variations of latitude and of longitude of perigee also to be explained. The five known planets showed similar "inequalities," as they were called, and in addition a recurring retrograde movement; and for each planet the various inequalities had peculiarities of their own. In particular, the "inferior" planets, Venus and Mercury, were restricted within limited angular ranges from the Sun, while the others could move all around the Zodiac. These, in outline, were the facts to be accounted for.

Ptolemy acknowledged that the whole universe is enclosed within a spherical heaven, which revolves as a sphere; that the Earth also is spherical and is stationary at the centre of the heavenly sphere; and that the Earth is practically a point compared with the universe.

The way is now clear for the construction of a system of uniform circular motions, the resultants of which must agree with the observed paths of the heavenly bodies; or, in other words, the movements of the heavenly bodies must be analysed into a series of combinations of uniform circular motions. Concentric spheres were unequal to the task, but two other devices had come into use since the time of Aristotle, and of these Ptolemy took full advantage. The first was the "movable eccentric." A planet could be regarded as moving in a circle whose centre was not the centre of the Earth, and the phenomena required that the centre of this circle must always lie on the line joining the Earth and Sun, so that it was itself movable. The orbit of a planet referred to the Earth would then clearly be very different from a circle, but it would be compounded of uniform circular motions. The other device was that of "epicycles." Here the planet was fixed on a revolving circle, the centre of which was fixed on another revolving circle, and so on, until at last a circle was reached whose centre was stationary with respect to the Earth, though not necessarily in the Earth. This ultimate circle was called a *deferent* and the others *epicycles*.

Now these are not independent devices, for, as Ptolemy was well aware, for the superior planets any motion describable by a deferent and epicycle was describable also by a movable eccentric. As we should now say, the two analyses of the motion were geometrically equivalent. The epicyclic analysis, however, had the greater range of applicability and so, although he did not discard eccentrics altogether, Ptolemy usually adopted it. It can readily be imagined that astronomy under these conditions was the geometer's paradise. Notwithstanding the severe limitation imposed by the restriction to uniform circular motions, there remained ample scope for ingenuity. The circles could be as numerous as was necessary, their radii and periods of revolution could have any values, motion could be in either direction, and the planes of the circles could have any inclinations to one another. Viewing the problem as a whole, it is small wonder that men of the genius of Apollonius, Hipparchus, and Ptolemy succeeded in constructing a system adequate to save the crudely measured phenomena for many centuries. It is unnecessary to go further into the details of the Ptolemaic system, but we may note as an obvious example that the retrograde motions of the planets revealed the existence of an epicyclic movement periodically carrying the bodies in the opposite direction to that in which the deferents moved.

Between the Aristotelean and the Ptolemaic cosmologies there was thus little in common beyond the fundamental axioms and postulates. Ptolemy did not deny the spheres, but he ignored them, and by accepting eccentrics he went definitely beyond anything that Aristotle had contemplated. He was compelled to do so, however, if he was to save the phenomena, and in the centuries which followed, when the authority of Aristotle grew more and more absolute, and at the same time the phenomena grew more and more difficult to save even with the Ptolemaic liberties, the great problem was how to reconcile the two sets of ideas. One solution was to place the whole mechanism of deferent and epicycles for each body within the space between two spheres concentric with the earth, thus admitting the reality of the spheres without losing the advantages of the circles. A pair of spheres was conceived for each of the seven "planets" (including Sun and Moon), the lower being the "concave" and the upper the "convex." Owing to the great difference in the distances of perigee and apogee, the space between the spheres had to be granted considerable thickness, and in the absence of any means of measuring the distances, it was natural to assume that the concave of one body rested on the convex of that next beneath it.

This ingenious compromise appealed mainly to practical astronomers whose primary interest was in saving the phenomena, but philosophers, who valued above all things the Aristotelean principles, took another course. They insisted on a distinction between reality and mere calculating devices. The spheres were real, but inasmuch as they had failed to give an adequate account of the observations it was permitted to use mathematical artifices such as eccentrics and epicycles for purely practical purposes. This view was taken by, among others, men of such diverse types as Averroes and his great antagonist, Thomas Aquinas. It was a very convenient solution, for it not only avoided the immediate difficulties but gave absolute freedom to the mathematician to save the phenomena by any means he chose without having to consider the demands of reality. The result was that, as the centuries went by, astronomers, whether consciously or not, came to regard astronomy simply as pure geometry, and to isolate it not only from "reality" but even from other fields of experience as well. This was carried to such an extent that an astronomer, intent on solving the geometry of the heavens, could entirely forget that there were other phenomena to be saved, such as the brightness of the stars and planets, for example. Magnitude, originally a measure of brightness, had become a measure of apparent diameter. The stars were thought to appear as discs, and a definite angular diameter was assigned to each magnitude.

We note one other element in the intellectual atmosphere in which Copernicus was born, before coming to his own work. The speculations of the early Greeks had been preserved through the dark ages by Arabian astronomers, from whom the men of the Renaissance received it as a new revelation. The Arabs added little of value, but they saved it from oblivion. It is perhaps not surprising that European thinkers regarded their inheritance with a veneration approaching idolatry. The desire for absolute proof had awakened, but it still lay prone in the bed of authority. No new idea dared proclaim itself without the credentials of ancient sanction.

Both the old bottles of ancient learning and the new wine of re-awakened imagination were strange and charming, but they were ill fitted for one another. What men needed, but were not aware that they lacked, was a new outlook, a standpoint on attaining which the unperceived contradictions and complexities that confused their thinking would cease to operate, and a clear path to progress would become visible.

It was this that Copernicus supplied. Looked at in the light of present knowledge, what he did seems small enough, particularly when contrasted with what he did not do. He had all the medieval reverence for authority; he believed in a finite universe bounded by a sphere of fixed stars; he accepted—nay, almost worshipped—the Aristotelean principles of motion; and in support of his own views he advanced the most metaphysical of arguments. What he did was simply to assign the diurnal motion to the rotation of the Earth, and the annual motion to its revolution round the Sun, and work out, by the old devices of eccentrics and epicycles, the astronomical consequences of these postulates. When we contemplate to-day the enormous results of this change we can scarcely avoid the thought that never has so mighty a mountain issued from so minute a mouse. We need to return to the sixteenth century to realize the miracle needed for the creation of that mouse.

Before developing his system, Copernicus has to satisfy himself that he has authority for the liberty he is about to take; in an age of indulgences, he sought his from antiquity.

"Wherefore," he says, "I took upon myself the task of re-reading the books of all the philosophers which I could obtain. . . . And I found first that, according to Cicero, Nicetas had thought the Earth was moved. Then later I discovered, according to Plutarch, that certain others had held the same opinion. . . . When from this, therefore, I had conceived its possibility I myself also began to meditate upon the mobility of the Earth."

Consider first the Earth's rotation. It is clear that if the Earth rotates, a falling body no longer moves rectilinearly, for to its apparent rectilinear motion must be added the circular motion of the Earth. Copernicus counters this with the claim that although, as Aristotle had said, there were natural and violent motions, all natural motions were circular. Even a rectilinear motion, as Arab astronomers had shown and he himself had proved, could be represented by a combination of circular motions, and so long as a terrestrial body remained in its natural place it shared the circular motion of the Earth. When it was displaced, however, its motion was no longer natural but violent; hence its behaviour was not inconsistent with Aristotelean physics.

A second argument was that if the Earth rotated there would be a mighty east wind, clouds and objects thrown into the air would be left behind, birds would not be able to return to their nests, and so on. In reply to this Copernicus maintained that the air must share the Earth's rotation, and so carry along everything floating in it. A third argument, that rotation would result in the scattering and disruption of the Earth's surface by what we should now call centrifugal force, he was not able properly to answer; its refutation awaited the mechanics of Galileo. He could reply, however, that such an effect would have far more serious consequences for the stellar sphere if that moved, so that his system at least made the best of a bad job and was therefore to be preferred.

The annual motion offered less difficulty in principle, though in practice it took much longer to win general assent. Ptolemy had argued that the Earth must be at the centre of the universe chiefly for two reasons. First, bodies which must move towards the centre of the universe move towards the centre of the Earth. Secondly, the celestial sphere appears equally far off in all directions all through the year; or, in other words, the stars show no parallax. On the first point, Copernicus conjectures that gravity is a local phenomenon, representing the tendency to consolidation of any astronomical body; thus, objects on the surface of the Sun would similarly move towards the centre of the Sun, and not necessarily towards the centre of the universe. This was a remarkable anticipation of universal gravitation, but it was, of course, a mere guess for which no evidence was offered. The absence of observable stellar parallax Copernicus attributes to the great distance of the stellar sphere compared with the dimensions of the Earth's orbit, but here again he could offer no independent evidence to support his contention.

Having thus at least shown that there was no fatal objection to the Earth's mobility, Copernicus proceeds to develop the details of his system, of which we need only glance at a few typical features. The diurnal motion having been transferred to the Earth, the stellar sphere was reduced to rest; its

radius, though unknowably great, was finite, and its original
unity was restored by giving to the Earth also the precessional and trepidational movements. The Earth thus had
three motions assigned to it—a great stumbling-block to
many who might have been prepared to grant it one. The
first motion—the daily rotation—accounted for the rising and
setting of the heavenly bodies, and the second, an eccentric
circle round the Sun, for the passage of the Sun along the
ecliptic and the retrograde motions of the planets. The third
motion was necessary in the first instance because, since
celestial revolutions were always conceived as belonging to
the *orbes* in which the heavenly bodies were fixed, the
celestial pole would move in an annual circle unless a coun-
teracting movement were provided. Other birds were killed
with the same stone by making this movement such as to
account also for precession and its illusory variations.

The Sun, of course, like the sphere of stars, was now at
rest, and for the Moon and planets Copernicus provided
eccentrics, deferents, and epicycles of the traditional kinds.
His system had, however, a great advantage over rivals in
that the first inequalities—the retrograde motions—of all the
planets were now accounted for as mere appearances due to
a single movement of the Earth—the parallactic motion, in
fact, which the stars were too far off to show. As a consequence he was able to reduce the number of circles required
for the whole universe from about eighty to thirty-four.
Moreover, he had, for the first time, a definite criterion for
assigning relative distances to the planets, for the amplitude
of the retrograde motion would clearly depend on the distance of the body showing it. It was now immediately
obvious also why the superior planets should be in perigee
when in opposition, and why the periods of the epicycles
which had previously accounted for the retrograde motions
should have been so curiously related to the period of the
Sun. His treatment of the Moon is interesting, for it gives us
a good example of his mathematical skill. His problem here
was directly comparable with that of Ptolemy, for both held
that the Moon revolved round the Earth. Copernicus, however, was at a disadvantage, for his conscience would not
allow him an equant; yet he succeeded in representing the

Moon's motion with a variation in apparent diameter indistinguishable with his instrument from the actual one, in contrast to the inadmissibly great variations of Ptolemy. As an appropriate reward for his faithful observance of the rule of uniform motion he was elated to find that in his system all circles moved in the same direction.

Such was the system to the construction of which Copernicus devoted the greater part of his life. Notwithstanding the enthusiasm of his friends and disciples, what he feared was only too well realized. For many years, except among the few who were both willing and able to appraise its worth, the strange new doctrine was an object of contemptuous amusement scarcely deserving the compliment of disproof. Galileo tells us that, half a century after the death of Copernicus, he himself thought the whole idea a foolish whim, until he noticed that the few who praised it well understood Ptolemy and could give reasons for their belief, whereas the many who scoffed knew nothing of the system except that it was clearly absurd.

We must, however, avoid the common illusion that there was at first any appreciable opposition to Copernicanism on religious grounds. So far as any notice was taken of it at all, the initial reaction was on the whole favourable in Roman Catholic circles and contemptuously antagonistic among the reformers, but no attempt at suppression or persecution was made for many years. And, indeed, there was nothing in the new astronomy itself to call for such action; the danger lay in its potentialities, and these were not at first realized. Whitehead has said that Pope Urban, when faced with the *Dialogues* of Galileo, even if his infallibility tottered, was assisted by the gift of prophecy and smelt Voltaire. Pope Paul was less richly endowed, and failed to smell Bruno. Such religious objection as was made to the hypothesis was based on its supposed incompatibility with the sacred Scriptures, but these were broad enough to imply, as well as deny, the Earth's mobility, and no one foresaw the wider issues of the new idea. The relegation of man to a subordinate place in the universe was not an early menace. There had never been any lack of appreciation of the physical insignificance of man compared with the material universe. "When I consider the heavens, the work of thy fingers, the moon and the stars, which thou hast ordained; what is man?" Moreover, the change introduced by Copernicus was not the substitution of a heliocentric for a geocentric, but of a heliostatic for a geostatic view. In the successive forms of the Ptolemaic system the Earth had never been at the centre of either position or uniform motion of any celestial body except the sphere of the fixed stars, and in the Copernican system the sun was eccentric to the planetary orbits. The significance of Copernicus's work was that it changed the *state of motion*, not the *position*, of the Earth. There is no reason to think that the mobility of the earth was in itself objectionable on religious grounds; it was rejected not because it was impious but because it was absurd.

It was when new philosophies arose which challenged the existing philosophy of Christianity that the trouble began. It was seen that the apparently harmless mathematical *capriccio* that Copernicus had perpetrated was a potential source of the gravest heresies. In particular, it was but a step from the new astronomical ideas to the notion of an infinite universe. Copernicus had not taken that step, but he had removed the insuperable obstacle to it—namely, that if the universe were infinite the stars would have to travel with infinite velocity to complete their diurnal course. By transferring the diurnal motion to the earth Copernicus had opened the door to infinite space. Now an infinite material universe, with no abode of the blessed beyond the outermost sphere, could not be tolerated. The Church had overruled even Aristotle with respect to infinite time; it needed its creation and judgment day. It was not prepared, after rejecting eternity, to accept infinity. Consequently, when the removal of Bruno was followed by the discoveries and unanswerable polemics of Galileo, the evil had to be destroyed at its source. In 1616, seventy-three years after its publication, *De Revolutionibus* was placed on the Index. It remained there until 1835.

Did Copernicus regard his system as a real account of the universe or merely as a calculating device? I do not think we have sufficient data to answer this question definitely, even if we could fully understand what the alternatives meant to him. Certainly, if the question had been: "Is the Ptolemaic doctrine of a stationary Earth the real truth, and the hypothesis that the Earth moves merely a convenient artifice for solving astronomical problems?" (the question, it may be noted, to which Galileo was later compelled to give a particular answer), Copernicus would have answered emphatically in the negative. He would not have acknowledged his system inferior to Ptolemy's in any respect. We know also that he sometimes spoke of the "real" movement of the Earth, according to his system, in contrast to certain "apparent" movements of the heavenly bodies arising therefrom. But to the larger question, "Are all geometrical descriptions of the universe valid only for purposes of calculation, the real truth of the matter being inaccessible by geometrical analysis?" we have, so far as I can gather, no evidence as to what answer he would have given. He makes no definite statement on the point, and the fact that he describes his system as a "hypothesis" tells us nothing since we cannot be sure what he means by that word. The evidence that he might have regarded his system as falling short of reality seems to me at least as strong as that to the contrary.

Whatever may have been Copernicus's view of his work, however, we, who look back at it across four hundred years of astronomical progress, see it as one of the greatest landmarks in scientific history. Without it the work of Kepler and Newton, and hence the whole of modern dynamical astronomy, would have been impossible. It did not mark the beginning of a new era, but the logical closure of the old. Medieval astronomy was like a restless ghost,

> Wandering between two worlds, one dead,
> The other powerless to be born.

Copernicus made the birth of the new world possible.

"Through the Middle Ages," wrote John Addington Symonds in his well-known *Encyclopaedia Britannica* article on the Renaissance, "there were by no means lacking elements of native vigour ready to burst forth. What was wanting was not vitality and licence, not audacity of speculation, not lawless instinct or rebellious impulse. It

was rather the right touch on life . . . the right way of approaching the materials of philosophy . . . that failed. . . .
The path from darkness to light was lost."

It was the right touch that Copernicus supplied. He was no audacious speculator; he accepted implicitly and rigorously the Aristotelean metaphysics; but within the framework of that system he found the right way of approaching the materials of astronomy, and made visible, though he did not tread, the path from darkness to light. The elements of the astronomical universe could not break the shell of Aristotelean physics until they were formed into a living, organic system, and it was Copernicus who organized them. Then, and only then, could modern science be born.

It is always harder to acknowledge the stature of those who make great achievements possible than to pay homage to the authors of those achievements. The foundation of "scientific method" by Galileo and Newton has, by the very magnitude of its consequences, cast a shadow of quaintness and immaturity on the thought of the preceding time. How is it, we ask, that if Copernicus was really an original thinker he could accept so implicitly the metaphysical principles which to us seem so baseless? We cannot, perhaps, give a complete answer to this question, but we can say with certainty that if consistency is to be a requirement of greatness, the first great man has yet to be born.

To form a just estimate of the greatness of Copernicus we must turn to his contemporaries or to the generations which immediately followed, for whether or not greatness is an absolute quality, it can be determined only in relation to its immediate surroundings. Tycho, the outstanding dissenter from the Copernican doctrine, whose system was nevertheless mathematically equivalent to that of Copernicus, wrote: "The earth has not produced his equal for many centuries. . . . He has done what it has not been given to any mortal to accomplish since the beginning of the world. Who is his superior?" Kepler calls him "a man of the greatest genius, a free spirit, who, in the struggle against prejudice, is of great significance." And Galileo wrote: "I cannot find any bounds for my admiration, how that reason was able in

Aristarchus and *Copernicus,* to commit such a rape upon their Sences, as in despight thereof, to make her self mistress of their credulity."

In the light of this testimony we cannot deny to Copernicus a place among the great original thinkers of history. Seen across the centuries, through the smoke arising from three hundred years of scientific activity, his figure looks a little dim and strange, but its greatness survives our scrutiny. Others had asserted the mobility of the Earth, but none had so transcended the prejudices of their day and made the new idea the inevitable basis of future astronomy. It was one thing to adventure, like Aristarchus, in the freedom of ancient speculation; another to break a path through the petrified Greek philosophy of the Middle Ages. It was one thing to follow uncontrolled imagination, like Nicholas of Cusa; it was quite another to keep within the bounds of accepted principles and save the details of phenomena by a complete astronomical system. Great astronomers, like Regiomontanus, had caught a glimpse of the truth and had rejected it as impossible; he alone in his day made his reason mistress of his credulity. And what he undertook was the complete reform of astronomy; the erasure of the product of two thousand years of toil, and a rebuilding of the whole edifice. Such a task had never been attempted before; it has not needed to be attempted since.

In any list of the greatest scientists, or indeed of the greatest men in any category, the name of Galileo would stand near the top. He constructed the first thermometer, discovered the isochronism of the pendulum, designed the first pendulum clock for timing the pulse, and invented the microscope. Any one of these achievements would have secured a scientist's fame. In the life of Galileo they played only a relatively minor part. His contributions to both physics and astronomy were of the highest order. They revolutionized the knowledge of his day. Moreover, in his recognition of the fundamental methods of all scientific activity, he made a con-

tribution of overwhelming importance to human progress.
He looked on nature with complete objectivity, rejecting the
á priori reasoning which had stemmed from the Greeks and
which was one of the stultifying influences on his predecessors
and contemporaries. In his application of the experimental
method to prove the truth or falsity of hypotheses, competent
judges have seen the birth of modern scientific thought.

Galileo was born at Pisa in 1564, also the year of Shake-
speare's birth, the son of an impoverished Florentine nobleman.
At his father's insistence, he became a medical student at the
University of Pisa, but his interests soon shifted to mathematics
and physics, in part through reading Euclid and Archimedes.
His brilliance was soon recognized, and at the age of 26 he
was appointed to the University chair of mathematics at Pisa.
But with his brilliance went an arbitrary and contentious
disposition. He was of course surrounded by unswerving
disciples of Aristotle, for whom he made no effort to conceal
his contempt. By this time, he had already begun the
experiments which were to result in the founding of dynamics.
There is a legend, probably untrue, that he dropped two
shots of unequal weight from the Leaning Tower and established that they fell with equal speed, thus disproving an Aristotelian dictum and further incurring the enmity of his col-
leagues. He apparently made a more important enemy by ridi-
culing an invention of Giovanni de Medici and as a result was
forced to resign. He withdrew first to Florence and then to
Padua, where he was offered a professorship by the Venetian
Senate. His reputation had spread, his lectures were extraordinarily brilliant, and students attended them in hordes. In 1604
a new star appeared and Galileo gave a course of three lectures
on it, pointing out that its appearance rebutted the Aristotelian doctrine of the immutability of the heavens. The crowds
were so great that he adjourned first to a hall holding a
thousand persons and then to the open air. Again he was the
center of raging controversy, which was aggravated
by his polemical attitude.

In 1609, as he explains in the following selection from
The Sidereal Messenger, he heard rumors of the invention of
a telescope by one Hans Lippershey, a Dutchman. Immediately
recognizing the principle involved, he made numbers of
instruments of superior quality. The telescope was hailed for

its importance in military tactics. More important, it enabled Galileo to make observations which revolutionized the science of astronomy. Wherever he turned his magic glass, new vistas never before observed by man appeared. The Milky Way was resolved into individual stars. The face of the moon no longer exhibited Aristotelian perfection. The stars appeared in infinite multitudes. The moons of Jupiter, "never seen from the very beginning of the world up to our own times," as he proudly states, formed a miniature solar system which greatly strengthened the Copernican hypothesis.
His observation of sun spots proved that the sun revolved on its axis. These and other discoveries made a sensation. Some who looked through his telescope disbelieved the evidence of their eyes; others declared that the sights were due to reflected rays and optical illusions; still others refused to look. Kepler, on hearing the news, was thrown into a "fit of wonder."

Galileo's fame now spread to the corners of the Western World. His salary was doubled by the Venetian senate. But a more attractive post as professor and court philosopher was offered him by Cosmo II, Grand Duke of Tuscany, and he accepted. It was an unfortunate move. Venice, a free state, had defied the Pope. Florence was under the strong influence of the church. Galileo was a deeply religious man who had no desire to come into conflict with the Papacy. His defense of Copernicus, however, made such conflict inevitable, and his own position was compromised by a quarrel with the Pope. He was forced to recant and to adopt a life of strict seclusion, but he retained his intellectual vigor and made additional new discoveries in physics. After suffering blindness in his later years, he died in 1642, the year of Newton's birth.

TELESCOPIC OBSERVATIONS

GALILEO GALILEI

INTRODUCTION.   In the present small treatise I set forth some matters of great interest for all observers of natural phenomena to look at and consider. They are of great interest, I think, first from their intrinsic excellence; secondly, from their absolute novelty; and lastly, also on account of the instrument by the aid of which they have been presented to my apprehension.

The number of the Fixed Stars which observers have been able to see without artificial powers of sight up to this day can be counted. It is therefore decidedly a great feat to add to their number, and to set distinctly before the eyes other stars in myriads, which have never been seen before, and which surpass the old, previously known, stars in number more than ten times.

Again, it is a most beautiful and delightful sight to behold the body of the Moon, which is distant from us nearly sixty semidiameters of the Earth, as near as if it was at a distance of only two of the same measures; so that the diameter of this same Moon appears about thirty times larger, its surface about nine hundred times, and its solid mass nearly 27,000 times larger than when it is viewed only with the naked eye: and consequently any one may know with the certainty that is due to the use of our senses, that the Moon certainly does not possess a smooth and polished surface, but one rough and uneven, and, just like the face of the Earth itself, is everywhere full of vast protuberances, deep chasms, and sinuosities.

Then to have got rid of disputes about the Galaxy or Milky Way, and to have made its nature clear to the very senses, not to say to the understanding, seems by no means a matter which ought to be considered of slight importance.

In addition to this, to point out, as with one's finger, the nature of those stars which every one of the astronomers up to this time has called *nebulous,* and to demonstrate that it is very different from what has hitherto been believed, will be pleasant, and very fine. But that which will excite the greatest astonishment by far, and which indeed especially moved me to call the attention of all astronomers and philosophers, is this, namely, that I have discovered four planets, neither known nor observed by any one of the astronomers before my time, which have their orbits round a certain bright star, one of those previously known, like Venus and Mercury round the Sun, and are sometimes in front of it, sometimes behind it, though they never depart from it beyond certain limits. All which facts were discovered and observed a few days ago by the help of a telescope devised by me, through God's grace first enlightening my mind.

Perchance, other discoveries still more excellent will be made from time to time by me or by other observers, with the assistance of a similar instrument, so I will first briefly record its shape and preparation, as well as the occasion of its being devised, and then I will give an account of the observations made by me.

THE TELESCOPE. About ten months ago a report reached my ears that a Dutchman had constructed a telescope, by the aid of which visible objects, although at a great distance from the eye of the observer, were seen distinctly as if near; and some proofs of its most wonderful performances were reported, which some gave credence to, but others contradicted. A few days after, I received confirmation of the report in a letter written from Paris by a noble Frenchman, Jaques Badovere, which finally determined me to give myself up first to inquire into the principle of the telescope, and then to consider the means by which I might compass the invention of a similar instrument, which after a little while I succeeded in doing, through deep study of the theory of Refraction; and I prepared a tube, at first of lead, in the ends of which I fitted two glass lenses, both plane on one side, but on the other side one spherically convex, and the other concave. Then bringing my eye to the concave lens I saw objects satisfactorily large and near, for they appeared one-third of the distance off and nine times larger than when they are seen with the natural eye alone. I shortly afterwards constructed another telescope with more nicety, which magnified objects more than sixty times. At length, by sparing neither labour nor expense, I succeeded in constructing for myself an instrument so superior that objects seen through it appear magnified nearly a thousand times, and more than thirty times nearer than if viewed by the natural powers of sight alone.

FIRST TELESCOPIC OBSERVATIONS.   It would be altogether a waste of time to enumerate the number and importance of the benefits which this instrument may be expected to confer, when used by land or sea. But without paying attention to its use for terrestrial objects, I betook myself to observations of the heavenly bodies; and first of all, I viewed the Moon as near as if it was scarcely two semidiameters of the Earth distant. After the Moon, I frequently observed other heavenly bodies, both fixed stars and planets, with incredible delight; and, when I saw their very great number, I began to consider about a method by which I might be able to measure their distances apart, and at length I found one. And here it is fitting that all who intend to turn their attention to observations of this kind should receive certain cautions. For, in the first place, it is absolutely necessary for them to prepare a most perfect telescope, one which will show very bright objects distinct and free from any mistiness, and will magnify them at least 400 times, for then it will show them as if only one-twentieth of their distance off. For, unless the instrument be of such power, it will be in vain to attempt to view all the things which have been seen by me in the heavens, or which will be enumerated hereafter.

OBSERVATIONS OF LUNAR MOUNTAINS AND VALLEYS.   Let me first speak of the surface of the Moon, which is turned towards us. For the sake of being understood more easily, I distinguish two parts in it, which I call respectively the

brighter and the darker. The brighter part seems to sur-
round and pervade the whole hemisphere; but the darker
part, like a sort of cloud, discolours the Moon's surface and
makes it appear covered with spots. Now these spots, as
they are somewhat dark and of considerable size, are plain
to every one, and every age has seen them, wherefore I
shall call them *great* or *ancient* spots, to distinguish them
from other spots, smaller in size, but so thickly scattered
that they sprinkle the whole surface of the Moon, but especially the brighter portion of it. These spots have never been
observed by any one before me; and from my observations
of them, often repeated, I have been led to that opinion
which I have expressed, namely, that I feel sure that the
surface of the Moon is not perfectly smooth, free from inequalities and exactly spherical, as a large school of philosophers considers with regard to the Moon and the other
heavenly bodies, but that, on the contrary, it is full of inequalities, uneven, full of hollows and protuberances, just
like the surface of the Earth itself, which is varied everywhere by lofty mountains and deep valleys.

The appearances from which we may gather these conclusions are of the following nature: On the fourth or fifth
day after new-moon, when the Moon presents itself to us
with bright horns, the boundary which divides the part in
shadow from the enlightened part does not extend continuously in an ellipse, as would happen in the case of a perfectly spherical body, but it is marked out by an irregular,
uneven, and very wavy line. For several bright excrescences,
as they may be called, extend beyond the boundary of light
and shadow into the dark part, and on the other hand pieces
of shadow encroach upon the light—nay, even a great quantity of small blackish spots, altogether separated from the
dark part, sprinkle everywhere almost the whole space
which is at the time flooded with the Sun's light, with the
exception of that part alone which is occupied by the great
and ancient spots. I have noticed that the small spots just
mentioned have this common characteristic always and in
every case, that they have the dark part towards the Sun's
position, and on the side away from the Sun they have
brighter boundaries, as if they were crowned with shining

summits. Now we have an appearance quite similar on the
Earth about sunrise, when we behold the valleys, not yet
flooded with light, but the mountains surrounding them on
the side opposite to the Sun already ablaze with the splen-
dour of his beams; and just as the shadows in the hollows
of the Earth diminish in size as the Sun rises higher, so also
these spots on the Moon lose their blackness as the illuminated part grows larger and larger. Again, not only are the
boundaries of light and shadow in the Moon seen to be
uneven and sinuous, but—and this produces still greater
astonishment—there appear very many bright points within
the darkened portion of the Moon, altogether divided and
broken off from the illuminated tract, and separated from
it by no inconsiderable interval, which, after a little while,
gradually increase in size and brightness, and after an hour
or two become joined on to the rest of the main portion,
now become somewhat larger; but in the meantime others,
one here and another there, shooting up as if growing, are
lighted up within the shaded portion, increase in size, and
at last are linked on to the same luminous surface, now still
more extended. Now, is it not the case on the Earth before
sunrise, that while the level plain is still in shadow, the
peaks of the most lofty mountains are illuminated by the
Sun's rays? After a little while does not the light spread further, while the middle and larger parts of those mountains
are becoming illuminated; and at length, when the Sun has
risen, do not the illuminated parts of the plains and hills
join together? The grandeur, however, of such prominences
and depressions in the Moon seems to surpass both in magnitude and extent the ruggedness of the Earth's surface, as
I shall hereafter show.

APPEARANCES OF STARS IN THE TELESCOPE. Hitherto I
have spoken of the observations which I have made concerning the Moon's body; now I will briefly announce the
phenomena which have been, as yet, seen by me with reference to the Fixed Stars. And first of all the following fact is
worthy of consideration: The stars, fixed as well as erratic,
when seen with a telescope, by no means appear to be increased in magnitude in the same proportion as other ob-

jects, and the Moon herself, gain increase of size; but in the case of the stars such an increase appears much less, so that you may consider that a telescope, which (for the sake of illustration) is powerful enough to magnify other objects a hundred times, will scarcely render the stars magnified four or five times. But the reason of this is as follows: When stars are viewed with our natural eyesight they do not present themselves to us of their bare, real size, but beaming with a certain vividness, and fringed with sparkling rays, especially when the night is far advanced; and from this circumstance they appear much larger than they would if they were stripped of those adventitious fringes, for the angle which they subtend at the eye is determined not by the primary disc of the star, but by the brightness which so widely surrounds it. A telescope removes from the stars their adventitious and accidental splendours before it enlarges their true discs (if indeed they are of that shape), and so they seem less magnified than other objects, for a star of the fifth or sixth magnitude seen through a telescope is shown as of the first magnitude only.

The difference between the appearance of the planets and the fixed stars seems also deserving of notice. The planets present their discs perfectly round, just as if described with a pair of compasses, and appear as so many little moons, completely illuminated and of a globular shape; but the fixed stars do not look to the naked eye bounded by a circular circumference, but rather like blazes of light, shooting out beams on all sides and very sparkling, and with a telescope they appear of the same shape as when they are viewed by simply looking at them, but so much larger that a star of the fifth or sixth magnitude seems to equal Sirius, the largest of all the fixed stars.

THE INFINITE MULTITUDE OF TELESCOPIC STARS. But beyond the stars of the sixth magnitude you will behold through the telescope a host of other stars, which escape the unassisted sight, so numerous as to be almost beyond belief, for you may see more than six other differences of magnitude, and the largest of these, which I may call stars of the seventh magnitude, or of the first magnitude of invisible stars, appear with the aid of the telescope larger and brighter than stars of the second magnitude seen with the unassisted sight. But in order that you may see one or two proofs of the inconceivable manner in which they are crowded together, I have determined to make out a case against two star-clusters, that from them as a specimen you may decide about the rest.

As my first example, I had determined to depict the entire constellation of Orion, but I was overwhelmed by the vast quantity of stars and by want of time, and so I have deferred attempting this to another occasion, for there are adjacent to, or scattered among, the old stars more than five hundred new stars within the limits of one or two degrees. For this reason I have selected the three stars in Orion's Belt and the six in his Sword, which have been long well-known groups, and I have added eighty other stars recently discovered in their vicinity, and I have preserved as exactly as possible the intervals between them. The well-known or old stars, for the sake of distinction, I have depicted of larger size, and I have outlined them with a double line; the others, invisible to the naked eye, I have marked smaller and with one line only. I have also preserved the differences of magnitude as much as I could. As a second example, I have depicted the six stars of the constellation Taurus, called the Pleiades (I say *six* intentionally, since the seventh is scarcely ever visible), a group of stars which is enclosed in the heavens within very narrow precincts. Near these there lie more than forty others invisible to the naked eye, no one of which is more than half a degree off any of the aforesaid six.

TELESCOPIC APPEARANCE OF MILKY WAY. The next object which I have observed is the essence or substance of the Milky Way. By the aid of a telescope any one may behold this in a manner which so distinctly appeals to the senses that all the disputes which have tormented philosophers through so many ages are exploded at once by the irrefragable evidence of our eyes, and we are freed from wordy disputes upon this subject, for the Galaxy is nothing else but a mass of innumerable stars planted together in clusters. Upon whatever part of it you direct the telescope straightway a vast crowd of stars presents itself to view; many of them are tolerably large and extremely bright, but the number of small ones is quite beyond determination.

DISCOVERY OF JUPITER'S SATELLITES.   I have now finished my brief account of the observations which I have thus far made with regard to the Moon, the Fixed Stars, and the Galaxy. There remains the matter, which seems to me to deserve to be considered the most important in this work, namely, that I should disclose and publish to the world the occasion of discovering and observing four Planets, never seen from the very beginning of the world up to our own times, their positions, and the observations made during the last two months about their movements and their changes of magnitude; and I summon all astronomers to apply themselves to examine and determine their periodic times, which it has not been permitted me to achieve up to this day, owing to the restriction of my time. I give them warning, however, again, so that they may not approach such an inquiry to no purpose, that they will want a very accurate telescope, and such as I have described in the beginning of this account.

On the 7th day of January in the present year, 1610, in the first hour of the following night, when I was viewing the constellations of the heavens through a telescope, the planet Jupiter presented itself to my view, and as I had prepared for myself a very excellent instrument, I noticed a circumstance which I had never been able to notice before, owing to want of power in my other telescope, namely, that three little stars, small but very bright, were near the planet; and although I believed them to belong to the number of the fixed stars, yet they made me somewhat wonder, because they seemed to be arranged exactly in a straight line, parallel to the ecliptic, and to be brighter than the rest of the stars, equal to them in magnitude. The position of them with reference to one another and to Jupiter was as follows:

Ori.   *   *   O   *   Occ.

On the east side there were two stars, and a single one towards the west. The star which was furthest towards the east, and the western star, appeared rather larger than the third.

I scarcely troubled at all about the distance between them and Jupiter, for, as I have already said, at first I believed them to be fixed stars; but when on January 8th, led by some fatality, I turned again to look at the same part of the heavens, I found a very different state of things, for there were three little stars all west of Jupiter, and nearer together than on the previous night, and they were separated from one another by equal intervals, as the accompanying figure shows.

Ori.   O   *   *   *   *Occ.*

At this point, although I had not turned my thoughts at all upon the approximation of the stars to one another, yet my surprise began to be excited, how Jupiter could one day be found to the east of all the aforesaid fixed stars when the day before it had been west of two of them; and forthwith I became afraid lest the planet might have moved differently from the calculation of astronomers, and so had passed those stars by its own proper motion. I, therefore, waited for the next night with the most intense longing, but I was disappointed of my hope, for the sky was covered with clouds in every direction.

But on January 10th the stars appeared in the following position with regard to Jupiter, the third, as I thought, being

Ori.   *   *   O   *Occ.*

hidden by the planet. They were situated just as before, exactly in the same straight line with Jupiter, and along the Zodiac.

When I had seen these phenomena, as I knew that corresponding changes of position could not by any means belong to Jupiter, and as, moreover, I perceived that the stars which I saw had always been the same, for there were no others either in front or behind, within a great distance, along the Zodiac—at length, changing from doubt into surprise, I discovered that the interchange of position which I saw belonged not to Jupiter, but to the stars to which my attention had been drawn, and I thought therefore that they ought to be observed henceforward with more attention and precision.

Accordingly, on January 11th I saw an arrangement of the following kind:

Ori.   *   *   O   *Occ.*

namely, only two stars to the east of Jupiter, the nearer of which was distant from Jupiter three times as far as from the star further to the east; and the star furthest to the east was nearly twice as large as the other one; whereas on the previous night they had appeared nearly of equal magnitude. I, therefore, concluded, and decided unhesitatingly, that there are three stars in the heavens moving about Jupiter, as Venus and Mercury round the Sun; which at length was established as clear as daylight by numerous other subsequent observations. These observations also established that there are not only three, but four, erratic sidereal bodies performing their revolutions round Jupiter.

These are my observations upon the four Medicean planets, recently discovered for the first time by me; and although it is not yet permitted me to deduce by calculation from these observations the orbits of these bodies, yet I may be allowed to make some statements, based upon them, well worthy of attention.

In the next two articles, devoted to Tycho Brahe and Johannes Kepler, we are privileged to observe one of the most productive partnerships in the history of science. Moreover, this partnership illustrates the interrelationship between two factors in research—observation and the formulation of hypotheses. Today, the importance of precision in scientific observation and experiment is taken for granted. The most

exact and delicate measurements, the most sensitive instruments, capable of measuring millionths of an inch or
velocities of hundreds of thousands of miles a second, have
been developed. Tiny discrepancies, which have been revealed
by carrying such measurements "to the next decimal place,"
have led to great discoveries. This factor was virtually unrecognized in Tycho's day. His own observations were miracles
of accuracy. We have seen that Copernicus would have
been elated to be "correct to ten minutes of arc." Tycho's
observations, made without a telescope, could be trusted
almost to minutes. In 1893, Sir Oliver Lodge wrote that "for
certain purposes connected with the proper motion of stars
they are still appealed to." The conclusions Tycho drew from
his own observations were unsound; it remained for a greater
man to interpret them. Yet as Dingle points out, Kepler's
work would have been incomplete or impossible without that
of Tycho. Kepler was a theoretician, at times to the point
of absurdity. It was the direction provided by Tycho's facts
and the knowledge that he could rely on them implicitly
which led him, after many years of labor, to the conclusions
embodied in his laws of planetary motion.

Ivor B. Hart has written extensively on scientific subjects.
He is the author of The Great Engineers, James Watt, and
Makers of Science, from which the selection on Kepler is
taken. He was a group captain in the Royal Air Force during
World War II and later became deputy director of
educational services for the Air Ministry.

TYCHO BRAHE

HERBERT DINGLE

THE PERIOD known as the Renaissance was a critical
epoch in many departments of thought and knowledge, and
in none more so than in astronomy. The importance of this
fact is greater than appears at first, for astronomy was so
interwoven with the general texture of medieval thought

that its reformation entailed a new outlook on life and on the world as a whole. Fortunately its development at this time is easy to trace and understand, at least in its broad outlines, for it was mainly the work of four men. The essential change of viewpoint was introduced by Copernicus, but Copernicus did little to take advantage of the opportunity he had created. He took the medieval vision with him to the modern viewpoint and saw the celestial spheres and the Ptolemaic deferents and epicycles enveloping the sun instead of the earth. Kepler was the first to show what possibilities lay in the Copernican reform, and his laws of planetary motion, in which spheres and perfect circular motion were finally abandoned, contained in essence the solution of the whole problem of medieval astronomy. Kepler's work would have closed the study of astronomy, except for a few minor adjustments, had not Galileo with his new mechanics and "optic tube" given the subject a new life and opened up the limitless fields of inquiry which we are still exploring. But their work would have been essentially incomplete or impossible without that of a fourth. It is to Tycho Brahe that Kepler was indebted for the observations which enabled him to express the true planetary laws in Copernican terms, and this was not a mere accidental debt. The work of Tycho represented a new outlook, a change as radical in its way as that of Copernicus, for, surprising as it may seem now, the idea that before describing phenomena one should know as accurately as possible what those phenomena were, was almost unthought of in the sixteenth century. Tycho was thoroughly modern, and in his day almost unique, in realizing the value of precision in measurement, and Dreyer, his excellent modern biographer, opines that his accuracy "but for the invention of the telescope could hardly have been much exceeded by his successors." Certainly without Tycho's work there would have been no Kepler's laws, and possibly Newton would have been unable to formulate his law of gravitation.

Tycho Brahe (or Tyge Brahe, to give him his Danish name) was born at Knudstrup on 14th December, 1546. He was the second child and eldest son of Otto Brahe, a privy councillor and member of an ancient noble Danish

family, and his wife, Beate Bille. He was brought up by his
uncle, Jörgen Brahe, who, being childless, had, partly by
force and partly by persuasion, succeeded in obtaining
charge of him. After preliminary education under a tutor he
went, at the age of 12, to the University of Copenhagen,
and studied rhetorics and philosophy with a view to becoming a statesman. A partial eclipse of the sun on 21st August,
1560, however, profoundly impressed him, and he thought
it "as something divine that men could know the motions
of the stars so accurately that they could long before foretell their places and relative positions." He immediately
began to study the subject, and bought a volume of the
works of Ptolemy which seems to have absorbed his interest
during the remainder of his three years' study at Copenhagen. This aberration somewhat disturbed his uncle, who,
on sending him to a foreign university according to custom
(Leipzig was chosen for Tycho), sent with him as tutor a
young man, Anders Vedel, whose duty it was to see that his
studies were such as befitted a nobleman. Vedel—who subsequently attained distinction as a historian and remained a
lifelong friend of Tycho—tried conscientiously to fulfil his
obligations, and at first Tycho had to study astronomy and
mathematics while Vedel was asleep. After some remon-
strances, however, Vedel was forced to acknowledge that
Tycho was born for astronomy and for nothing else, and a
tacit working arrangement seems to have established itself.
When only 16 years of age, says Dreyer, "his eyes were
opened to the great fact, which seems to us so simple to
grasp, but which had escaped the attention of all European
astronomers before him, that only through a steadily pursued course of observations would it be possible to obtain a
better insight into the motions of the planets, and decide
which system of the world was the true one." His first observation was of an approaching conjunction of Jupiter
and Saturn, made with a pair of ordinary compasses on 17th
August, 1563, but he soon set about acquiring a better instrument. In the following year he secured a "radius"—two
graduated rods of which the longer bisected the shorter at
right angles and could move in its own direction so that,
sights being fixed at each end of the shorter rod and at one

end of the longer, a position could be found in which the
eye, placed at the last-named sight, could see through the
others two stars whose angular separation was to be learned.
This did not satisfy him, but, being unable to get money
from Vedel for a still better instrument, he made observational history by constructing a table of corrections to its
readings.

Tycho's uncle died shortly after his return to Denmark,
and, his relatives looking with disfavour on his odd interests, he soon left again for Wittenberg and later Rostock,
where, in a famous duel, he lost his nose and made for himself an artificial one of gold and silver. In the meantime,
however, his astronomical pursuits were not entirely dis-
countenanced at home, and on 14th May, 1568, King Frederick II of Denmark granted him the next vacant canonry
—a sinecure which would afford him means of continuing
his astronomical work in his native country. Nevertheless,
more than two years elapsed before he returned—years in
which at Augsburg he constructed, with his friends the
brothers Hainzel, a quadrant with a radius of 14 cubits
(about 19 ft.), a sextant, and a celestial globe 5 ft. in
diameter. For some reason he did not immediately continue
this work in Denmark but turned his attention to alchemy,
until, on leaving his laboratory on 11th November, 1572,
he noticed an extremely bright star in Cassiopeia where, as
he well knew, no such star was wont to appear. Doubting
his senses, he appealed to some neighbouring peasants for
confirmation, and when the reality of the star could no
longer be questioned he at once proceeded to measure its
position. From then onwards Tycho never allowed his
interest in astronomy to lapse. He constructed instruments, introduced devices to make them foolproof, determined their errors, and gave the limits of accuracy of the
results—a procedure in observation which was unique in
his day. Its importance in this case was that Tycho established beyond question that the parallax of the star was
too small for it to be as near as the planets, and it must
therefore belong to the sphere of the stars whose immutability had been a cardinal principle of astronomy from the
earliest days. Nothing but observations of which the degree

of exactitude was high and was known could have placed this momentous fact beyond question. Later, when a comet appeared in 1577, he was able to show by precise measurements that it must have passed through the material of the spheres, if these existed, and another ancient illusion was shattered.

After completing his work on the new star, Tycho travelled extensively in central Europe, finding in particular a kindred spirit in the Landgrave Wilhelm of Cassel, an astronomer of no mean ability. It was through the Landgrave that King Frederick realised fully what a remarkable subject he possessed, and when Tycho, during a short visit to his native land in 1576, was planning to settle permanently in Basle, the King made him such a munificent offer that he altered his plans and decided to remain. The chief part of the gift was the island of Hveen "with all our and the Crown's tenants and servants who thereon live, with all rent and duty which comes from that, and is given to us and to the Crown, to have, enjoy, use and hold, quit and free, without any rent, all the days of his life." There were also sums of money for building an observatory, and various sources of income involving little more than nominal duties. The offer was too good to be refused, and at the end of May Tycho began to build the observatory which was to be his home for more than twenty years and at which the greater part of his work was done.

The main building, known as Uraniborg, was nearly in the centre of the island and was built in the Gothic Renaissance style then becoming popular. It was at first the only astronomical building, but in 1584 a second observatory was erected to the south, known as Stierneborg. To this island astronomers from all over Europe came to work with Tycho, and the work done there is the basis of modern astronomy. Tycho's innovations consisted first in the great size of his instruments; secondly in his improved method of graduation—he was the first astronomer to use the method of *transversals* in which the main graduations were made alternately on each of a pair of parallel arcs, successive marks being joined diagonally so as to form a zigzag pattern; thirdly in a greatly improved method of constructing and arranging his "sights"; and, finally, in the practice already mentioned of determining as precisely as possible the errors of his instruments. His most outstanding contributions, in addition to the destructive ones already mentioned (to which may be added the final disproof of a long-maintained belief in a false movement of the stars known as *trepidation*), included far more accurate observations of the positions of the heavenly bodies than any previously made, the first observations of the effect of atmospheric refraction on apparent positions, and the discovery of the third and fourth inequalities (known respectively as the *variation* and *annual equation*) in the moon's motion as well as the fluctuation in the inclination of the moon's orbit to the ecliptic. Tycho differed from all his predecessors in making his observations in a systematic manner. Whereas it had been customary to make occasional observations of the positions of the planets, Tycho observed them regularly and systematically before and after opposition. This systematic observation, combined with the care and accuracy with which the observations were made, enabled Kepler to deduce his three laws of planetary motion and so to lay the foundation of celestial mechanics. These laws could never have been deduced from a few observations made near opposition.

In general, Tycho was less concerned with the interpretation of his observations than with their acquisition; it was left to Kepler to show what an abundance of knowledge they enshrined. He was anything but indifferent, however, to the great question of the day—the decision between the Ptolemaic and Copernican views of the universe—and it is possible that he thought more highly of his own solution of this problem than of any of his other achievements. This was a rather strange compromise between the two alternatives: the planets, excluding the earth, travelled round the sun in Copernican fashion, but the whole system, thus formed, itself moved round the stationary earth. So far as the solar system is concerned this is mathematically equivalent to the Copernican conception, but it fails to account for the aberration of light and the annual parallax of the stars. These phenomena, however, were not known to Tycho, and he accordingly believed that he had found the true answer to the central problem of astronomy; his last request to Kepler, in fact, was that he would interpret the observations according to the Tychonic and not the Copernican system. This is by no means a unique example of a creator proving himself an indifferent critic of his own achievements.

The great work at Uraniborg came to a melancholy end in 1597. On the death of King Frederick in 1588 his son Christian, then only 11 years of age, came largely under the control of certain nobles, some of whom were inimical to Tycho. This circumstance together, it must be admitted, with Tycho's somewhat arbitrary behaviour—led to an increasing degree of estrangement, which culminated in Tycho's position at Hveen finally becoming untenable. In March or April 1597 he left his historic observatory forever. The instruments were gradually dismantled and some of them sent to him in Bohemia, but their great work was done. They were all too jealously guarded after Tycho's death by Curtius, who would not allow even Kepler to use them, and ultimately all were destroyed by war or by fire. Of Uraniborg scarcely a trace remains. When Gassendi in 1647 visited Hveen in search of memorials of Tycho his findings were summed up in the simple phrase: "There is in the island a field where Uraniborg was."

On leaving Hveen Tycho, after some wandering, sought and obtained the patronage of the Emperor Rudolph. He was granted the Castle of Benatky, on the river Yser, about twenty-two miles north-east of Prague, and here, with reduced equipment, he resumed his observations. Little time was left, however, and the work in Bohemia is chiefly notable for the collaboration of Tycho and Kepler which produced such momentous results. Tycho's health gradually failed, and he died on 24th October, 1601.

As a man Tycho was not altogether lovable or admirable. He was overbearing, and failed to carry out the extremely light obligations which the generosity of the King had placed on him in return for his privileges. Of his utterly selfless devotion to astronomy, however, there is no doubt, and it must be recorded in his favour that in an unfortunate dispute with Kepler, in general a far more noble-minded man, it is Tycho who appears in the more favourable light. Also, while at Hveen it was his habit to give away medicines which, through his lifelong love of alchemy, he made a practice of preparing and in which he placed considerable trust. Tycho was fond of mystery and display, and his observatory at Uraniborg abounded in mechanical devices and imperceptible means of communication with which he liked to mystify his visitors. He wrote tolerable verses, some of which, as well as paintings, adorned the walls of his observatory. A typical example of the ornate character of the building was the ceiling and walls of the study at Stierneborg, which showed the Tychonic system of the world and the portraits of eight astronomers, ending with Tycho and "Tychonides," a successor yet unborn. In the inscriptions underneath, Tycho leaves his own work to the judgment of posterity, but the hope is expressed that Tychonides might be worthy of his great ancestor. Attached to the observatory was a dwarf called Jep, whom Tycho used to feed with an occasional morsel at table, like a dog. Jep was supposed to be clairvoyant and to have made some remarkable prophecies. Tycho was a firm believer in astrology and gave as rational a defence of the doctrine as was perhaps possible. In this, however, he was by no means abnormal, since astrology was a respectable university subject in his day, and only very exceptional men like Copernicus seem to have ignored it; open disbelief was almost out of the question. In short, Tycho was a typical child of the Renaissance—one of those strange mixtures of the medieval and the modern which are so baffling to us today.

Enough has been said, however, to indicate the indispensable part which Tycho's work played in the development of astronomy. In a sense he was more of an originator than most of the deeper thinkers of his time, for while the perception of the necessity for accurate and systematic observation called for a less powerful intellect than the rational organization of the universe, it was much less conformable with the spirit of the time.

JOHANNES KEPLER

IVOR B. HART

KEPLER's chief claim to memory lies in his enunciation of the laws of planetary motion. The record of this faithful follower of science is remarkable. The whole of his life is one long story of domestic trouble, ill-health, and financial worry. Yet through all he displayed a genius and an enthusiasm for mathematics and astronomy which led him to the highest pinnacles of scientific achievement. Kepler was denied the joy of astronomical observation. In his youth a serious illness had permanently injured his eyesight. Telescopes and other instruments of observation were for him "forbidden fruit". He conquered, but his victory was won in the battlefield of geometry and statistics with the aid of his calculations, his drawing instruments, and above all his wonderful perseverance in the face of repeated failure.

Johannes Kepler was born at Weil in the Duchy of Würtemberg on the 21st of December 1571. His father, though probably of good family, was idle and unreliable; his mother ignorant and of violent temper. Moreover, Johannes was a sickly child; and an attack of smallpox, which nearly killed him at the age of four, left him with an enfeebled constitution.

He went to a local school at a very early age, but it was not long before the first check to his studies appeared. It seems that his father had become surety for a friend who proved to be a defaulter. As a consequence he lost what little money he had and was obliged to keep a tavern. So we see the sorry spectacle of a future professor of astronomy withdrawn from school at the age of nine and employed as a pot-boy in his father's inn. For three years this state of affairs continued, but eventually owing to the kindly intervention of friends, young Johannes Kepler was enabled to attend a monastic school at Marlbronn. The ability which he displayed enabled him to be passed on, at the age of seventeen, to the University of Tübingen, where it was intended that he should prepare himself for the Church. Fortunately for the world, he here came under the influence of Michael Maestlin, then professor of mathematics at the university, who soon detected Kepler's genius.

Maestlin was an outspoken convert to the Copernican doctrine of the solar system, and in this doctrine Kepler may therefore be said to have been brought up. Its simplicity made a powerful appeal to his imagination, and he was its vigorous defender in lecture and debate. All this helped to build up for him a considerable reputation, so that when, in 1594, a professorship of mathematics fell vacant at the University of Graz, in Styria, it was immediately offered to Kepler, who accepted it with some hesitation. From the point of view of pay and prestige, astronomy was none too highly rated in the universities of those days, and the professors were expected to devote more time to the revelations of astrology than to anything else. It was because of this fact, and because of his bitter recollections of the acute poverty of his childhood that Kepler was so diffident in accepting the professorship, and he fully made up his mind that when anything better offered itself he would accept it.

In 1597, at the age of twenty-six, Johannes Kepler wooed and married a lady from Styria. It is not known whether he thought that, with her "dowry" she might have eased his financial position, for she had been twice married before. Be that as it may, it proved none too happy a union. There were three children of the marriage, and Kepler's financial cares were on the whole considerably increased in consequence.

At Graz, he busied himself with speculations as to the general scheme of the solar system. There were at the time six known planets—Mercury, Venus, Earth, Mars, Jupiter, and Saturn, and Kepler knew that these were at successively greater distances from the sun. Moreover he knew that the farther a planet was from the sun, the slower seemed its motion. It was Kepler's strong feeling that there was in all this some governing scheme. The unravelling of this problem he made his life work. His final efforts were indeed crowned with brilliant success, but his first theory, developed at Graz, was fantastic. He was a keen student of geometry, but his mathematics, in those days of astrology, were not unnaturally tinged with mysticism. Between six planets there are five spaces, and for some reason or other Kepler felt that this held the clue which he sought. The five spaces led him to think of the five symmetrical solid figures—the tetrahedron, the cube, the octahedron, the dodecahedron, and the icosahedron, with four, six, eight, twelve, and twenty faces respectively. Accordingly his scheme took the following form. Beginning with a sphere to represent the earth's orbit, he drew round it a dodecahedron, and round this another sphere to represent the orbit of Mars; about that a tetrahedron, and around that a larger sphere for Jupiter; about that a cube, and round that a final sphere for the orbit of Saturn. Again, returning to the sphere representing the earth's orbit, he drew within that an icosahedron, and inside that another sphere for Venus; inside that an octahedron, and finally inside that a sphere for the orbit of Mercury.

Kepler's delight is well worth recording. "The intense pleasure I have received from this discovery can never be told in words. I regretted no more the time wasted; I tired of no labour; I shunned no toil of reckoning, days and nights spent in calculation, until I could see whether my hypothesis would agree with the orbits of Copernicus or whether my joy was to vanish into air."

Kepler published his theory (as to the absurdity of which it will suffice for us to point out that we now know of eight large planets and a host of planetoids) in 1596 in a book called *Mysterium Cosmographicum,* and it brought him the enthusiastic applause of a wondering world. Of more immediate importance to Kepler, however, was a cordial invitation which he now received from a man at Prague who was destined to affect his whole future career. This man was the famous Tycho Brahe.

To Kepler, Tycho extended a cordial invitation to come

to Prague and test his fantastic theory with the observations in Tycho's possession. Tycho was not a follower of Copernicus but he nevertheless had sound advice to offer Kepler. "Do not build up abstract speculations concerning the system of the world," he advised, "but rather first lay a solid foundation in observations, and then by ascending from them, strive to come at the causes of things."

Kepler paid his visit, studied the records, and did not hesitate to abandon his theory when he realized it was not consistent with the accurate observations he knew himself to be handling. But he had earned the respect of his host, and when his professorship at Graz was rendered exceedingly uncomfortable owing to a religious change in the régime of the University, Kepler (who was a Protestant) gladly accepted in 1601 the offer of a post as imperial mathematician to King Rudolph II, his duty being to assist Tycho Brahe. This was a wonderful combination of talents. Tycho was a splendid observer, but a poor mathematician, Kepler was a splendid mathematician but a poor observer; both had unbounded enthusiasm for their work and admiration for each other. What might they not have achieved together had the alliance continued! But it was not to be. Tycho had never recovered from the disappointment of his dismissal from Uraniborg, and he died soon after Kepler joined him.

All this time, Kepler was in continuous financial straits, and periodically he was seized with illness. Tycho's generosity had tided him over his troubles, but at his colleague's death they broke out afresh. Bohemia was in a sorry state at that time; misgovernment and wars had brought the national exchequer to a low state and Kepler's salary was more often promised than paid. Yet he stuck to his post. A solemn duty had been entrusted to him by Tycho on his deathbed. Tycho, engrossed in the preparation of an elaborate set of planetary tables, had charged Kepler to complete them, and they were to be known as the Rudolphine Tables, in honour of his patron. They entailed enormous work and considerable expense. The latter consideration involved such delay that Kepler perforce had time to devote to other matters.

In 1604, he published a work called *Paralipomena in Vitellionem*,[1] in which the question of refraction came up in connexion with the theory of lenses. The telescope had but recently been invented, and Kepler clearly saw the necessity for such investigations. He tried to work out a relation between the angle of incidence and the angle of refraction. All schoolboys know of Snell's Law, which says that the ratio of the sine of the angle of incidence to the sine of the angle of refraction is a constant for any given pair of media. For glass, for example, this ratio, known as the refraction index, comes out somewhere about 1.5. Kepler did not discover this law, though there is no doubt but that his work inspired Snell to take up the subject so successfully. He did, however, discover a useful approximation to it.

It is convenient at this stage to do homage to Kepler's great influence on his contemporaries in the realms of mathematics, and particularly in geometry. This branch of mathematics had suffered some neglect at the expense of a great advance in algebra, the theory of equations, and trigonometry. The seventeenth-century revival in geometry was largely due to the influence of Kepler. In chapter 4 of his *Paralipomena*, for example, he introduced to the world of mathematics for the first time what has been called the *principle of continuity.*

Meanwhile Kepler's financial worries and domestic miseries were continual. His salary was always in arrears, and it was with difficulty that he could make both ends meet. His wife was suffering from long fits of despondency, and finally, in 1612, a series of misfortunes produced a crisis in his affairs. His patron, King Rudolph, died, and his salary now ceased. But worse was to come. Within a very short time, all his children fell ill, and smallpox carried off one of them. A few days later his wife also died. Yet when his fortune seemed at its lowest ebb, he was offered a professorship at the University of Linz, and without hesitation he accepted it, and off to Linz he went with his two remain-

1.   Vitello was a thirteenth-century Polish philosopher who commented on Alhazen and studied the subject of refraction.

ing children, leaving due to him a sum of 8,000 crowns in respect of arrears of salary.

There was little money in a professorship, and at Linz he had to supplement his income somehow. So he published a sort of Old Moore's Almanac, and told people's fortunes, and generally practised the arts of the astrologer in a way which in these days would have earned for him a prosecution, at any rate in England.

Having settled in Linz, Kepler did a somewhat bold thing in view of his unhappy experience of married life. He deliberately looked round him for a second wife, and he set about it very thoroughly and scientifically. There were, it seems, no less than eleven candidates for the privilege, and Kepler, statistician to his finger-tips, carefully set forth his estimate of the merits and demerits of each! That he was honest in all this, and free from any mercenary motives, is evidenced by the fact that he chose the poorest of them all —an orphan girl without dowry. Apparently it turned out a much more satisfactory marriage than his first one, though judging from the fact that his wife bore him seven children, his continuously scanty resources must have been taxed to the uttermost in his efforts to pay his way. Always something seemed to turn up to increase his difficulties. Thus, about this time, news reached him that his bad-tempered old mother had managed to get herself accused of sorcery at her home in Würtemberg. She was found guilty and was condemned to imprisonment and torture. Kepler hurried off to Würtemberg to intercede on her behalf, and although he failed to obtain her release, he at least saved her from torture. It took him another twelve months, however, before he could get her released from prison. She died shortly after, bellicose to the last.

At the same time Kepler was applying his mind to the problem of the solar system, and one by one, at long intervals, he gave to the world his three wonderful laws of planetary motion.

Nor did Kepler forget his promise to Tycho Brahe to complete the Rudolphine Tables of planetary motions. Year after year he worked at these, all the time puzzling as to how to raise the necessary funds for their publication. Time and again he applied to the court for assistance, but always without result.

Yet Kepler never abandoned his determination to publish his Rudolphine Tables, and at last, tired of further waiting, he determined to find the money himself. How he succeeded remains a mystery. It has been asserted that he had accumulated a secret hoard of money, the fruits of years of fortune-telling as an astrologer; but it is difficult to believe that he deliberately and unnecessarily subjected his wife and children to years of miserable proverty in the accumulation of such a hoard. Be that as it may, however, the Rudolphine Tables were published, and published handsomely too, in 1627. They were of the utmost importance. Their accuracy rendered them indispensable to the navigators of the seventeenth century, by whom they were used for practically the same purpose as is served today by the Nautical Almanac. Even had he produced nothing beyond this Kepler would deserve our lasting remembrance.

But the publication of the Tables left Kepler a broken man. The long strain of ill-health, poverty, worry, and constant study began to have its effect, and at last, in November 1630, in his sixtieth year, whilst on his return from a fruitless mission to Prague for the purpose of recovering the money so long due to him, he caught a chill and died. He was buried in St. Peter's Church at Ratisbon, and it is no credit to the country of his birth that so little was done to perpetuate his memory. "A century ago a proposal was made to erect a marble monument to his memory, but nothing was done. It matters little one way or the other whether Germany, having almost refused him bread during his life, should, a century and a half after his death, offer him a stone." [1] It matters little indeed. Kepler's true monument is not of stone. It stands in those brilliant laws of planetary motion which gave to the world for the first time a complete view of the cosmic scheme as far as it concerns the solar system of which our earthly home forms so integral a part.

We will conclude our study of Johannes Kepler by a con-

[1]. Sir O. Lodge, *Pioneers of Science.*

sideration of his three laws of planetary motions. He had
always felt that there was some profound law which controlled the motions of the planets round the sun. "There
were three things," he wrote, while still at Linz, "of which
I pertinaciously sought the causes why they are not other
than they are: the number, the size, and the motion of the
orbits." He fully realized the fundamental importance of his
self-imposed task, and in his book, *Treatise on the Motions
of the Planet Mars,* he took care to "warn off" the anti-
Copernicans: "If any one be too dull to comprehend the
science of astronomy, or too foolish to believe in Copernicus
without prejudice to his piety, my advice to him is, that he
should quit the astronomical school, and condemning, if he
will, any or all the theories of philosophers, look to his own
affairs, and leaving this worldly travail, go home and plough
his fields."

Kepler's materials were the invaluable records of Tycho
Brahe's observations, and his own knowledge of geometry.
His was essentially the method of trial and error. Every conceivable relationship between distance, the rate of motion,
and the path of the planets he tested in the light of Brahe's
results, only to reject them one after the other. Through all
he saw one ray of hope. "I was comforted," writes he,
"and my hopes of success were supported, as well by other
reasons which will presently follow, as by observing that

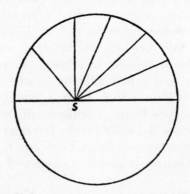

I-1. *Kepler's test of a circular orbit with the sun not at the
centre.*

the motions in every case seemed to be connected with the
distances, and that when there was a great gap between
the orbits, there was the same between the motions." Like
Copernicus, Kepler followed in particular the movements of
the planet Mars, these being sufficiently rapid to provide
adequate data for testing purposes. What was the correct
orbit of Mars? He soon convinced himself that if it were a
circle, then at any rate the sun could not be at its centre.
After much labour he got a step farther. He noticed that
when the planet's distance from the sun diminished, the
planet went faster, and when the distance increased, it went
slower, and this brought him to the idea that *the planet must
sweep out equal areas in equal intervals of time.* Suppose,
therefore, that he were to represent the orbit by a circle,
with the sun not at the centre (Figure I-1), would the planet
under such conditions sweep out equal areas in equal times?
He tested it for innumerable positions of the sun, but it never
quite fitted. He next tried an oval orbit, but this, too, never
quite fitted the facts. At last, however, he hit upon the right
solution. *Why not try an ellipse?* He tested it with Brahe's
observations, and it fitted beautifully. At last the long-sought
secret was his. *The path of the planet is that of an ellipse
with the sun at one focus, and the variations in speed are
such that in equal times the planet sweeps out equal areas.*
A reference to Figure I-2 will at once show the idea. S,
representing the sun, is at the focus of an ellipse *ABCD* &c.
This ellipse represents the orbit of any planet. Then obviously the distance of the planet will be a minimum at A

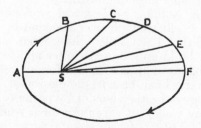

I-2.   *Illustrating Kepler's First Two Laws of Planetary Motion.*

and a maximum at F, and observation shows that the speed
of motion is, on the contrary, a maximum at A and a mimi-
mum at F, so that, if A, B, C, D, E, &c., be the positions
of the planet at equal intervals of time, and we join these
points to S, then the areas swept through by the planet will
be respectively ABS, BCS, CDS, DES, and EFS, and *these
areas are found to be exactly equal.*

Kepler was fully entitled to his triumph, but his work was
not yet complete. He had yet to unravel the relationship
which he felt existed between the distances of the different
planets and their average speeds round the sun. Why he felt
such a relationship to exist we can hardly say, but he had a
feeling that simple mathematical laws were traceable in all
natural phenomena. He had little to go on. It was part of his
genius that he felt intuitively that not only was there such a
relationship, but also that he would find it out sooner or
later. And find it out he did, though later rather than sooner.
Let him speak for himself:

What I prophesied two-and-twenty years ago, when I
discovered the five solids among the heavenly orbits—
what I firmly believed long before I had seen Ptolemy's
"Harmonies"—what I had promised my friends in the
title of this book, which I named before I was sure of my
discovery—what sixteen years ago, I urged as a thing to
be sought—that for which I joined with Tycho Brahe,
for which I settled in Prague, and for which I have devoted the best part of my life to astronomical contempla-
tions, this at length I have brought to light. It is not
eighteen months since the first glimpse of light reached
me, three months since the dawn, very few days since
the unveiled sun, most admirable to gaze upon, burst
out upon me. Nothing holds me; I will indulge in my
sacred fury; I will triumph over mankind by the honest
confession that I have stolen the golden vases of the
Egyptians to build up a tabernacle for my God, far away
from the confines of Egypt. If you forgive me, I rejoice;
if you are angry, I can bear it; the die is cast; the book is
written; to be read either now or by posterity, I care not
which; it may well wait a century for a reader, as God
has waited 6,000 years for an observer.

If you would know the precise moment, the idea first

came across me on the 8th of March of this year, 1618; but, chancing to make a mistake in the calculation, I then rejected it as false. I returned to it again with new force on the 15th of May; and it has dissipated the darkness of my mind, by such an agreement between this idea and my seventeen years' Labour on *Brahe's Observations*, that at first I thought I must be dreaming, and had taken my result for granted in my first assumptions. But the fact is certain, *that the proportion existing between the periodic times of any two planets is exactly the sesquiplicate proportion of the mean distances of the orbits.*

And now let us put this into simple language. Kepler's discovery was this: *that for all planets, the squares of the times of revolution round the sun are as the cubes of the mean distances.* Let us try it, for example, in the case of Mars.

The data are as follows, taking the Earth's distance as one unit, and the Earth's year (i.e. time of one complete revolution) also as unity:

Earth's Distance from Sun   .   .   1.000 units
Mars'   "   "   "   .   .   1.5237 "
Earth's Period of Revolution .   .   1.000 years

Required, the period of revolution for Mars. We have by Kepler's Third Law

$$\frac{(\text{Mars' Period})^2}{(\text{Mars' Distance})^3} = \frac{(\text{Earth's Period})^2}{(\text{Earth's Distance})^3}$$

Hence

$$\frac{(\text{Mars' Period})^2}{(1.5237)^3} = \frac{1^2}{1^3}$$

$$\text{Mars' Period of Revolution} = \sqrt{1.5237^3}$$
$$= 1.8808 \text{ years.}$$

which is true.

And so with all planets.

This then was Kepler's life work, and no more fitting tribute to his memory could be given than to conclude this chapter with a restatement of his laws:

Law 1. All the planets move round the sun with elliptic orbits with the sun at one focus.

Law 2. The radius vector, or line joining the planet to the sun, sweeps out equal areas in equal intervals of time.

Law 3. For all planets, the square of the time of one complete revolution (or year) is proportional to the cube of the mean distance from the sun.

"Newton was the greatest genius who ever lived and the most fortunate, for we cannot find more than once a system of the world to establish."

Any poll of those competent to judge would find almost universal agreement with this dictum of J. L. Lagrange, the French mathematician, much of whose life work was based on Newton's fundamental discoveries. Yet the statement is in an important sense incomplete. Newton's preeminence was based not alone on his discovery of a "system of the world." With his corpuscular hypothesis, and his discovery of the nature of white light, he became one of the founders of the science of optics. His three laws of motion, stated in the following article, carried Galileo's observations to their logical conclusion. His invention of the calculus, shared independently with Leibnitz, was one of the greatest in mathematics. As in the case of Galileo, such an important achievement as his construction of a reflecting telescope falls into relative insignificance. Taken as a whole, his life work justifies the magnificent epitaph inscribed on the Westminster tablet, "Let Men Rejoice that so great a glory of the human race has appeared."

Newton not only formulated the law of gravitation; he also pointed out many of its consequences—the movement of the tides, the precession of the equinoxes, the bulging of the earth at the equator. But the theory was so pregnant in its implications, that it has engaged the attention of astronomers and mathematicians for hundreds of years until the present day. Such giants as Laplace, Lagrange, Euler, Gauss, and Poincaré spent much of their careers applying it to the exploration of the heavens. As we shall see, Leverrier and Adams, through such application, discovered a body hitherto unknown, the planet Neptune. By applying the law to the rotation of double stars, we have what is today the most valuable method of determining star masses.

For all his greatness, Newton was a creature of his time. He was a believer in the pseudoscience of alchemy, the chemistry of his day. He himself apparently considered that his theological researches, which today must be dismissed as unimportant, were his greatest contribution to learning. The following article gives us a picture not only of Newton's achievements but also of Newton the man—cantankerous, secretive, interested not only in things of the mind but in worldly success. E. T. Bell was a well-known mathematician, born at Aberdeen, Scotland in 1883. Educated both in England and in the United States, he became professor of mathematics at the California Institute of Technology in 1926. He wrote numerous books on mathematics as well as works of science fiction, published under a pseudonym. He died in 1960.

ISAAC NEWTON

E. T. BELL

I DO NOT KNOW what I may appear to the world; but to myself I seem to have been only like a boy playing on the seashore, and diverting myself in now and then finding a smoother pebble or a prettier shell than ordinary, whilst the great ocean of truth lay all undiscovered before me.

Such was Isaac Newton's estimate of himself toward the close of his long life. Yet his successors capable of appreciating his work almost without exception have pointed to Newton as the supreme intellect that the human race has produced—"he who in genius surpassed the human kind."

Isaac Newton, born on Christmas Day ("old style" of

dating), 1642, the year of Galileo's death, came of a family of small but independent farmers, living in the manor house of the hamlet of Woolsthorpe, about eight miles south of Grantham in the county of Lincoln, England. His father, also named Isaac, died at the age of thirty seven before the birth of his son. Newton was a premature child. At birth he was so frail and puny that two women who had gone to a neighbor's to get "a tonic" for the infant expected to find him dead on their return. His mother said he was so undersized at birth that a quart mug could easily have contained all there was of him.

Not enough of Newton's ancestry is known to interest students of heredity. His father was described by neighbors as "a wild, extravagant, weak man;" his mother, Hannah Ayscough, was thrifty, industrious, and a capable manageress. After her husband's death Mrs. Newton was recommended as a prospective wife to an old bachelor as "an extraordinary good woman." The cautious bachelor, the Reverend Barnabas Smith, of the neighboring parish of North Witham, married the widow on this testimonial. Mrs. Smith left her three-year-old son to the care of his grandmother. By her second marriage she had three children, none of whom exhibited any remarkable ability.

As a child Newton was not robust and was forced to shun the rough games of boys his own age. Instead of amusing himself in the usual way, Newton invented his own diversions, in which his genius first showed up. It is sometimes said that Newton was not precocious. This may be true so far as mathematics is concerned, but if it is so in other respects a new definition of precocity is required. The unsurpassed experimental genius which Newton was to exhibit as an explorer in the mysteries of light is certainly evident in the ingenuity of his boyish amusements. Kites with lanterns to scare the credulous villagers at night, perfectly constructed mechanical toys which he made entirely by himself and which worked—waterwheels, a mill that ground wheat into snowy flour, with a greedy mouse (who devoured most of the profits) as both miller and motive power, workboxes and toys for his many little girl friends, drawings, sundials, and a wooden clock (that went) for himself—such were some of the things with which this "un-precocious" boy sought to divert the interests of his playmates into "more philosophical" channels. In addition to these more noticeable evidences of talent far above the ordinary, Newton read extensively and jotted down all manner of mysterious recipes and out-of-the-way observations in his notebook. To rate such a boy as merely the normal, wholesome lad he appeared to his village friends is to miss the obvious.

The earliest part of Newton's education was received in the common village schools of his vicinity. A maternal uncle, the Reverend William Ayscough, seems to have been the first to recognize that Newton was something unusual. A Cambridge graduate himself, Ayscough finally persuaded Newton's mother to send her son to Cambridge instead of keeping him at home, as she had planned, to help her manage the farm on her return to Woolsthorpe after her husband's death when Newton was fifteen.

Before this, however, Newton had crossed his Rubicon on his own initiative. On his uncle's advice he had been sent to the Grantham Grammar School. While there, in the lowest form but one, he was tormented by the school bully who one day kicked Newton in the stomach, causing him much physical pain and mental anguish. Encouraged by one of the schoolmasters, Newton challenged the bully to a fair fight, thrashed him, and, as a final mark of humiliation, rubbed his enemy's cowardly nose on the wall of the church. Up till this young Newton had shown no great interest in his lessons. He now set out to prove his head as good as his fists and quickly rose to the distinction of top boy in the school. The Headmaster and Uncle Ayscough agreed that Newton was good enough for Cambridge, but the decisive die was thrown when Ayscough caught his nephew reading under a hedge when he was supposed to be helping a farmhand to do the marketing.

While at the Grantham Grammar School, and subsequently while preparing for Cambridge, Newton lodged with a Mr. Clarke, the village apothecary. In the apothecary's attic Newton found a parcel of old books, which he devoured, and in the house generally, Clarke's stepdaughter,

Miss Storey, with whom he fell in love and to whom he became engaged before leaving Woolsthorpe for Cambridge in June, 1661, at the age of nineteen. But although Newton cherished a warm affection for his first and only sweetheart all her life, absence and growing absorption in his work thrust romance into the background, and Newton never married. Miss Storey became Mrs. Vincent.

To Newton is attributed the saying "If I have seen a little farther than others it is because I have stood on the shoulders of giants." He had. Among the tallest of these giants were Descartes, Kepler, and Galileo. From Descartes, Newton inherited analytic geometry, which he found difficult at first; from Kepler, three fundamental laws of planetary motion, discovered empirically after twenty two years of inhuman calculation; while from Galileo he acquired the first two of the three laws of motion which were to be the cornerstone of his own dynamics. But bricks do not make a building; Newton was the architect of dynamics and celestial mechanics.

Kepler's laws can be proved in a page or two by means of calculus applied to Newton's law of universal gravitation:

Any two particles of matter in the universe attract one another with a force which is directly proportional to the

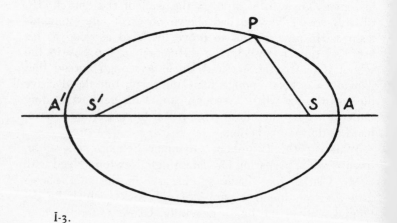

I-3.

product of their masses and inversely proportional to the
square of the distance between them. Thus, if *m*, *M* are the
masses of the two particles and *d* the distance between them
(all measured in appropriate units), the force of attraction
between them is $\dfrac{k \times m \times M}{d^2}$, where *k* is some constant
number (by suitably choosing the units of mass and distance
k may be taken equal to 1, so that the attraction is simply
$\dfrac{m \times M}{d^2}$).

For completeness we state Newton's three laws of motion.

I. *Every body will continue in its state of rest or of uni-*
form [unaccelerated] *motion in a straight line except in so*
far as it is compelled to change that state by impressed
force.

II. *Rate of change of momentum* ["mass times velocity,"
mass and velocity being measured in appropriate units] *is*
proportional to the impressed force and takes place in the
line in which the force acts.

III. *Action and reaction* [as in the collision on a friction-
less table of perfectly elastic billiard balls] *are equal and*
opposite [the momentum one ball loses is gained by the
other].

The most important thing for mathematics in all of this is
the phrase opening the statement of the second law of
motion, *rate of change.* What is a rate, and how shall it be
measured? Momentum, as noted, is "mass times velocity."
The masses which Newton discussed were assumed to remain constant during their motion—not like the electrons
and other particles of current physics whose masses increase
appreciably as their velocity approaches a measurable fraction of that of light. Thus, to investigate "rate of change of
momentum," it sufficed Newton to clarify *velocity,* which is
rate of change of position. His solution of this problem—
giving a workable mathematical method for investigating
the velocity of any particle moving in any continuous
manner, no matter how erratic—gave him the master key to

the whole mystery of rates and their measurement, namely, the *differential* calculus.

A similar problem growing out of rates put the *integral* calculus into his hands. How shall the total distance passed over in a given time by a moving particle whose velocity is varying continuously from instant to instant be calculated? Answering this or similar problems, some phrased geometrically, Newton came upon the integral calculus. Finally, pondering the two types of problem together, Newton made a capital discovery: he saw that the differential calculus and the integral calculus are intimately and reciprocally related by what is today called "the fundamental theorem of the calculus."

In June, 1661 Newton entered Trinity College, Cambridge, as a subsizar—a student who (in those days) earned his expenses by menial service.

In mathematics Newton's teacher was Dr. Isaac Barrow (1630-1677), a theologian and mathematician of whom it has been said that brilliant and original as he undoubtedly was in mathematics, he had the misfortune to be the morning star heralding Newton's sun. Barrow gladly recognized that a greater than himself had arrived, and when (1669) the strategic moment came he resigned the Lucasian Professorship of Mathematics (of which he was the first holder) in favor of his incomparable pupil.

The record of Newton's undergraduate life is disappointingly meager. He seems to have made no very great impression on his fellow students, nor do his brief, perfunctory letters home tell anything of interest. The first two years were spent mastering elementary mathematics. If there is any reliable account of Newton's sudden maturity as a discoverer, none of his modern biographers seems to have located it.

On the purely human side Newton was normal enough as an undergraduate to relax occasionally, and there is a record in his account book of several sessions at the tavern and two losses at cards. He took his B.A. degree in January, 1664.

The Great Plague (bubonic plague) of 1664-65, with its milder recurrence the following year, gave Newton his great if forced opportunity. The University was closed, and for the better part of two years Newton retired to meditate at Woolsthorpe. Up till then he had done nothing remarkable —except make himself ill by too assiduous observation of a comet and lunar halos—or, if he had, it was a secret. In these two years he invented the method of fluxions (the calculus), discovered the law of universal gravitation, and proved experimentally that white light is composed of light of all the colors. All this before he was twenty five.

A manuscript dated May 20, 1665, shows that Newton at the age of twenty three had sufficiently developed the principles of the calculus to be able to find the tangent and curvature at any point of any continuous curve. He called his method "fluxions"—from the idea of "flowing" or variable quantities and their rates of "flow" or "growth." His discovery of the binomial theorem, an essential step toward a fully developed calculus, preceded this.

The second of Newton's great inspirations which came to him as a youth of twenty two or three in 1666 at Woolsthorpe was his law of universal gravitation (already stated).

Most authorities agree that Newton made some rough calculations in 1666 (he was then twenty three) to see whether his law of universal gravitation would account for Kepler's laws. Many years later (in 1684) when Halley asked him what law of attraction would account for the elliptical orbits of the planets Newton replied at once the inverse square.

"How do you know?" Halley asked—he had been prompted by Sir Christopher Wren and others to put the question, as a great argument over the problem had been going on for some time in London.

"Why, I have calculated it," Newton replied. On attempting to restore his calculation (which he had mislaid) Newton made a slip, and believed he was in error. But presently he found his mistake and verified his original conclusion.

Much has been made of Newton's twenty years' delay in the publication of the law of universal gravitation as an undeserved setback due to inaccurate data. Of three explanations a less romantic but more mathematical one than either of the others is to be preferred here.

Newton's delay was rooted in his inability to solve a certain problem in the integral calculus which was crucial for the whole theory of universal gravitation as expressed in the Newtonian law. Before he could account for the motion of both the apple and the Moon Newton had to find the total attraction of a solid homogeneous sphere on any mass particle outside the sphere. For *every* particle of the sphere attracts the mass particle outside the sphere with a force varying directly as the product of the masses of the two particles and inversely as the square of the distance between them: how are all these separate attractions, infinite in number, to be compounded or added into one resultant attraction?

This evidently is a problem in the integral calculus. Today it is given in the textbooks as an example which young students dispose of in twenty minutes or less. Yet it held Newton up for twenty years. He finally solved it, of course: the attraction is the same as if the entire mass of the sphere were concentrated in a *single point* at its centre. The problem is thus reduced to finding the attraction between two mass particles at a given distance apart, and the immediate solution of this is as stated in Newton's law. If this is the correct explanation for the twenty years' delay, it may give us some idea of the enormous amount of labor which generations of mathematicians since Newton's day have expended on developing and simplifying the calculus to the point where very ordinary boys of sixteen can use it effectively.

On his return to Cambridge Newton was elected a Fellow of Trinity in 1667 and in 1669, at the age of twenty six, succeeded Barrow as Lucasian Professor of Mathematics. His first lectures were on optics. In these he expounded his own discoveries and sketched his corpuscular theory of light, according to which light consists in an emission of corpuscles and is not a wave phenomenon as Huygens and Hooke asserted. Although the two theories appear to be contradictory both are useful today in correlating the phenomena of light and are, in a purely mathematical sense, reconciled in the modern quantum theory. Thus it is not now correct to say, as it may have been a few years ago, that Newton was entirely wrong in his corpuscular theory.

The following year, 1668, Newton constructed a reflecting telescope with his own hands and used it to observe the satellites of Jupiter. His object doubtless was to see whether universal gravitation really was universal by observations on Jupiter's satellites. This year is also memorable in the history of the calculus. Mercator's calculation by means of infinite series of an area connected with a hyperbola was brought to Newton's attention. The method was practically identical with Newton's own, which he had not published, but which he now wrote out, gave to Dr. Barrow, and permitted to circulate among a few of the better mathematicians.

On his election to the Royal Society in 1672 Newton communicated his work on telescopes and his corpuscular theory of light. A commission of three, including the cantankerous Hooke, was appointed to report on the work on optics. Exceeding his authority as a referee Hooke seized the opportunity to propagandize for the undulatory theory and himself at Newton's expense. At first Newton was cool and scientific under criticism, but when the mathematician Lucas and the physician Linus, both of Liège, joined Hooke in adding suggestions and objections which quickly changed from the legitimate to the carping and the merely stupid, Newton gradually began to lose patience.

A reading of his correspondence in this first of his irritating controversies should convince anyone that Newton was not by nature secretive and jealous of his discoveries. The tone of his letters gradually changes from one of eager willingness to clear up the difficulties which others found, to one of bewilderment that scientific men should regard science as a battleground for personal quarrels. From bewilderment he quickly passes to cold anger and a hurt, somewhat childish resolution to play by himself in future. He simply could not suffer malicious fools gladly.

At last, in a letter of November 18, 1676, he says, "I see I have made myself a slave to philosophy, but if I get free of Mr. Lucas's business, I will resolutely bid adieu to it eternally, excepting what I do for my private satisfaction, or leave to come out after me; for I see a man must either resolve to put out nothing new, or become a slave to defend it." Almost identical sentiments were expressed by Gauss in connection with non-Euclidean geometry.

Newton's petulance under criticism and his exasperation at futile controversies broke out again after the publication of the *Principia*. Writing to Halley on June 20, 1688, he says, "Philosophy [science] is such an impertinently litigious Lady, that a man had as good be engaged to lawsuits, as to have to do with her. I found it so formerly, and now I am no sooner come near her again, but she gives me warning." Mathematics, dynamics, and celestial mechanics were in fact—we may as well admit it—secondary interests with Newton. His heart was in his alchemy, his researches in chronology, and his theological studies.

The years 1684-86 mark one of the great epochs in the history of all human thought. Skilfully coaxed by Halley, Newton at last consented to write up his astronomical and dynamical discoveries for publication. Probably no mortal has ever thought as hard and as continuously as Newton did in composing his *Philosophiae Naturalis Principia Mathematica* (Mathematical Principles of Natural Philosophy). Never careful of his bodily health, Newton seems to have forgotten that he had a body which required food and sleep when he gave himself up to the composition of his masterpiece. Meals were ignored or forgotten, and on arising from a snatch of sleep he would sit on the edge of the bed half-clothed for hours, threading the mazes of his mathematics. In 1686 the *Principia* was presented to the Royal Society, and in 1687 was printed at Halley's expense.

A description of the contents of the *Principia* is out of the question here, but a small handful of the inexhaustible treasures it contains may be briefly exhibited. The spirit animating the whole work is Newton's dynamics, his law of universal gravitation, and the application of both to the solar system—"the system of the world."

First, Newton deduced Kepler's empirical laws from his own law of gravitation, and he showed how the mass of the

Sun can be calculated, also how the mass of any planet having a satellite can be determined. Second, he initiated the extremely important theory of *perturbations:* the Moon, for example, is attracted not only by the Earth but by the Sun also; hence the orbit of the Moon will be perturbed by the pull of the Sun. In this manner Newton accounted for two ancient observations due to Hipparchus and Ptolemy. In addition to these ancient observations, seven other irregularities of the Moon's motion observed by Tycho Brahe (1546-1601), Flamsteed (1646-1719), and others, were deduced from the law of gravitation.

So much for lunar perturbations. The like applies also to the planets. Newton began the theory of planetary perturbations, which in the nineteenth century was to lead to the discovery of the planet Neptune and, in the twentieth, to that of Pluto.

The "lawless" comets—still warnings from an angered heaven to superstitious eyes—were brought under the universal law as harmless members of the Sun's family, with such precision that we now calculate and welcome their showy return (unless Jupiter or some other outsider perturbs them unduly), as we did in 1910 when Halley's beautiful comet returned promptly on schedule after an absence of seventy four years.

He began the vast and still incomplete study of planetary evolution by calculating (from his dynamics and the universal law) the flattening of the earth at its poles due to diurnal rotation, and he proved that the shape of a planet determines the length of its day, so that if we knew accurately how flat Venus is at the poles, we could say how long it takes her to turn completely once round the axis joining her poles. He calculated the variation of weight with latitude. He proved that a hollow shell, bounded by concentric spherical surfaces, and homogeneous, exerts no force on a small body anywhere inside it. The last has important consequences in electrostatics—also in the realm of fiction, where it has been used as the motif for amusing fantasies.

The precession of the equinoxes was beautifully accounted for by the pull of the Moon and the Sun on the equatorial bulge of the Earth causing our planet to wobble like a top.

The mysterious tides also fell naturally into the grand scheme—both the lunar and the solar tides were calculated, and from the observed heights of the spring and neap tides the mass of the Moon was deduced. The First Book laid down the principles of dynamics; the Second, the motion of bodies in resisting media, and fluid motion; the Third was the famous "System of the World."

Probably no other law of nature has so simply unified any such mass of natural phenomena as has Newton's law of universal gravitation in his *Principia*. It is to the credit of Newton's contemporaries that they recognized at least dimly the magnitude of what had been done, although but few of them could follow the reasoning by which the stupendous miracle of unification had been achieved, and made of the author of the *Principia* a demigod. Before many years had passed the Newtonian system was being taught at Cambridge (1699) and Oxford (1704). France slumbered on for half a century, still dizzy from the whirl of Descartes' angelic vortices. But presently mysticism gave way to reason and Newton found his greatest successor not in England but in France, where Laplace set himself the task of continuing and rounding out the *Principia*.

In 1696, at the age of fifty four, Newton became Warden of the Mint. His job was to reform the coinage. Having done so, he was promoted in 1699 to the dignity of Master. The only satisfaction mathematicians can take in this degradation of the supreme intellect of ages is the refutation which it afforded of the silly superstition that mathematicians have no practical sense. Newton was one of the best Masters the Mint ever had. He took his job seriously.

In 1701-2 Newton again represented Cambridge University in Parliament, and in 1703 was elected President of the Royal Society, an honorable office to which he was reëlected time after time till his death in 1727. In 1705 he was knighted by good Queen Anne. Probably this honor was in recognition of his services as a money-changer rather than in acknowledgment of his preëminence in the temple of wisdom.

Was Newton's mathematical genius dead? Most emphatically no. He was still the equal of Archimedes.

In 1696 Johann Bernoulli and Leibniz between them concocted two devilish challenges to the mathematicians of Europe. The first is still of importance; the second is not in the same class. Suppose two points to be fixed at random in a vertical plane. What is the shape of the curve down which a particle must slide (without friction) under the influence of gravity so as to pass from the upper point to the lower in the *least time?* This is the problem of the *brachistochrone* (="shortest time"). After the problem had baffled the mathematicians of Europe for six months, it was proposed again, and Newton heard of it for the first time on January 29, 1696, when a friend communicated it to him. He had just come home, tired out, from a long day at the Mint. After dinner he solved the problem (and the second as well), and the following day communicated his solutions to the Royal Society anonymously. But for all his caution he could not conceal his identity—while at the Mint Newton resented the efforts of mathematicians and scientists to entice him into discussions of scientific interest. On seeing the solution Bernoulli at once exclaimed, "Ah! I recognize the lion by his paw." (This is not an exact translation of B's Latin.) They all knew Newton when they saw him, even if he did have a moneybag over his head and did not announce his name.

A second proof of Newton's vitality was to come in 1716 when he was seventy four. Leibniz had rashly proposed what appeared to him a difficult problem as a challenge to the mathematicians of Europe and aimed at Newton in particular.* Newton received this at five o'clock one afternoon on returning exhausted from the blessed Mint. He solved it that evening. This time Leibniz somewhat optimistically thought he had trapped the Lion. In all the history of mathematics Newton has had no superior (and perhaps no equal) in the ability to concentrate all the forces of his intellect on a difficulty at an instant's notice.

The story of the honors that fall to a man's lot in his life-

* The problem was to find the orthogonal trajectories of any one-parameter family of curves (in modern language).

time makes but trivial reading to his successors. Newton got all that were worth having to a living man. On the whole Newton had as fortunate a life as any great man has ever had. His bodily health was excellent up to his last years; he never wore glasses and he lost only one tooth in all his life. His hair whitened at thirty but remained thick and soft till his death.

The record of his last days is more human and more touching. Even Newton could not escape suffering. His courage and endurance under almost constant pain during the last two or three years of his life add but another laurel to his crown as a human being. He bore the tortures of "the stone" without flinching, though the sweat rolled from him, and always with a word of sympathy for those who waited on him. At last, and mercifully, he was seriously weakened by "a persistent cough," and finally, after having been eased of pain for some days, died peacefully in his sleep between one and two o'clock on the morning of March 20, 1727, in his eighty-fifth year. He is buried in Westminster Abbey.

II. Tools and Techniques

II. Tools and Techniques

Until contemporary times, astronomy has been unique among the sciences in that, with the exception of certain meteorites that have fallen to earth, all its observations, experiments and theories have been entirely dependent on the properties of light. Physicists could smash atoms, chemists combine substances, botanists originate new breeds. All such methods were closed to the astronomers. In 1931–1932, a young engineer named Karl Jansky made a new kind of observation in which, in place of optical waves, those of a longer length were employed. He thus founded radio astronomy, adding a new dimension to the science. But the two methods have much in common. If one is "seeing," the other may be termed "listening," and both are dependent on observation of phenomena which are essentially similar in nature. Basically, the same limitations continue to prevail—there can be no direct contact with the objects to be examined. (In our generation, this limitation may also be partially voided—men may yet land on the moon.) Yet despite this handicap, the astronomer has succeeded, by using instruments which are sometimes incredibly complex, in building up an enormous body of knowledge. These instruments are basic to the science—without them it would largely cease to exist.

Before their invention, astronomers could make rough observations of the relative sizes and colors of the heavenly bodies. More important, they could observe their seeming movements and from them build theories about the universe and man's place in it. At first with the eye alone and then with such primitive instruments as the astrolabe—in essence a circular graduated disk for determining celestial altitudes—they charted the courses of stars and planets. We have seen how Tycho's observations served as a basis for Kepler's theories and how planetary movements were explained.

71

We have also seen how Galileo's telescope gave astronomy its most powerful weapon. Its function and that of its successors was to provide more light. And the cry of the astronomer from that day to this has been for "more light." In the inspired phrase of R. G. Aitken, the late Lick Observatory astronomer, he has been engaged in "driving back the dark." He has succeeded in doing this in part by building larger telescopes, and by developing auxiliary instruments such as optical or electronic image converters, bolometers, and photoelectric cells. But the telescope cannot analyze the light it captures. That function is reserved to other instruments, the most astonishing of which is the spectroscope. Incredible as it may appear to the layman, the spectroscope can obtain from a ray of light, no matter how distant its source, a staggering amount of information of the most diverse nature. By the light of some distant star can be determined its composition, motion, density, temperature, and magnetic field. It can in fact supply us with sufficient evidence to solve problems dealing with celestial objects at the very limits of the observable universe. The nature of this magical tool is discussed in the following article.

The photographic plate is another valuable adjunct to the telescope. It provides an accuracy of observation of which the human eye is incapable, and offers a permanent record for study and comparison. Sometimes a relatively simple and inexpensive improvement in photographic technique, such as a more sensitive photographic plate, has accomplished the same purpose as building a larger telescope.

Collecting, analyzing, and recording light is thus the function of the instruments described in the following article by Helen Wright. Born at Washington, D. C., Miss Wright received her B.A. and M.A. from Vassar College, and she has been associated with the Vassar College Astronomy Department, the U. S. Naval Observatory, the Mt. Wilson Observatory, and the Maria Mitchell Observatory. She is the author of Sweeper in the Sky, a biography of Maria Mitchell, Palomar, from which the following selection is taken, and a forthcoming biography of George Ellery Hale. She is also one of the general editors of the New York University Library of Science, of which this volume is a part.

TELESCOPE, SPECTROSCOPE, AND CAMERA

HELEN WRIGHT

NEARLY THREE AND ONE-HALF centuries have passed since Galileo made that first gigantic step which along a winding, often difficult way would lead to the 200-inch Hale telescope.

While Galileo was working in Padua, a German named Johannes Kepler heard of the new invention and of Galileo's startling results. Instead of a concave glass like Galileo's, he tried a convex lens in a new design which gave a larger field, had greater power, and proved so successful that the principle has been used almost unchanged ever since.

Kepler's telescope, like Galileo's, was of the refracting type, with a lens at one end of a tube and an eyepiece at the other. The light from the star enters the tube, is refracted or bent by the first lens, and passes through the tube to the observer looking through an eyepiece at the other end.

Yet with his more powerful instrument Kepler soon had trouble, a trouble that was to plague astronomers for nearly two hundred years. He found that the higher the power of his telescope, the greater the effects of spherical and chromatic aberration; that is, the images, instead of shining as

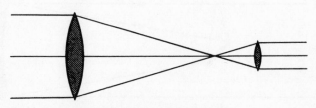

II-1. *Principle of the Refracting Telescope.*

73

clear points of light, appeared diffuse, surrounded by colored halos.

In the next two hundred years many solutions were proposed by many men. Some lessened the blurring of detail and improved the images by building longer telescopes. None could overcome the effect completely. One of the earliest and greatest of these was Christian Huygens, son of a Dutch poet. With fine tools of his own design, he ground and polished lenses far better than Galileo's, mounted them in telescopes which started at twelve feet and finally reached the incredible and quite unwieldy length of 210 feet.

The answer was finally suggested by a lawyer of the Inner Temple in London—Chester Moor Hall. It was perfected by an English weaver, John Dollond, who saw that the difficulty came from use of a single lens. He decided, therefore, to combine lenses of two different types, crown and flint. The result was the achromatic telescope we use today in which the rays of different colors are brought to a common focus.

Meanwhile, however, one of the greatest men of all time, born on Christmas Day in the year of Galileo's death, decided it was impossible to overcome the difficulty, and turned to a telescope of an entirely different sort, suggested first by a Scotsman, James Gregory. Instead of a lens to refract the light, he used a mirror to reflect it. With a cardboard tube, a speculum mirror, and an eyepiece he made the little instrument now in the Royal Society in London, forerunner of the 200-inch telescope completed just three hundred years after his birth. This man's name was, of course, Isaac Newton. He describes the instrument in his *Optics:*

"Seeing therefore the improvement of telescopes of given

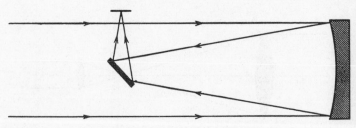

II-2. *Principle of the Newtonian Telescope.*

length by Refractions is desperate; I contrived heretofor a perspective by Reflexion, using instead of an Object Glass a concave metal. The diameter of the Sphere to which the Metal was ground concave was about twenty five English inches, and by consequence the length of the instrument about six inches and a quarter. The Eye-glass was plano convex, and the Diameter of the Sphere to which the convex side was ground was about 1/5 of an inch, or a little less, and by consequence it magnified between 30 and 40 times."

While Newton was experimenting in England, Guillaume Cassegrain, a French sculptor at the court of Louis XIV, designed another form of reflecting telescope. Like Newton, he used a mirror instead of a lens at the base of a tube. They differed, however, in their way of reflecting light from the mirror to the observer.

In Newton's telescope the light strikes the mirror, is reflected back, and by means of a small secondary mirror is reflected to the observer looking through an eyepiece at the side of the tube.

In the Cassegrain telescope a convex mirror is used inside the main focus to reflect light back to the observer who looks through a hole at the base of the telescope.

Yet, if these telescopes were good in principle, in practice their mirrors were too poor to be of any astronomical value. Fifty years passed before John Hadley succeeded in making a good parabolic mirror and for the first time saw the stars clearly through his telescope.

Some years after this, William Herschel, an organist at Bath, England, became fascinated by astronomy and set to

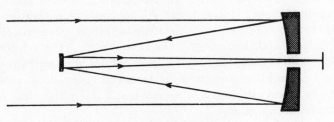

II-3. *Principle of the Cassegrain Telescope.*

work to make his own telescope. After two hundred unsuc-
cessful tries, he cast his first successful mirror. With a seven-
foot telescope, he discovered the planet Uranus. By that
discovery he doubled the known diameter of the solar system
and gained a place in his king's favor unequaled before or
since by any astronomer. He discovered that the stars, instead of being "fixed," as everyone had always thought, are
all moving in different directions, at different rates. Instead of
being at the same distance from the earth in a bowl-like sky,
they lie at different distances, some relatively near, others
fantastically far away. Herschel, working with his new and
better mirrors, laid plans for a systematic study of the entire
heavens. He looked far beyond the solar system, through the
canopy of "fixed stars" to observe thousands of nebulae and
suggest the existence of countless other "island universes"
like our own disk-shaped galaxy.

Herschel died in 1822. Twenty years later an Irish amateur
astronomer, William Parsons, Earl of Rosse, built a huge telescope, its mirror six feet in diameter, its focal length fifty-
three feet. (The focal length is the distance from the center
of the mirror to the point at which the light rays meet.) He
swung this giant on chains between two walls. The observer,
perched precariously in the air, looked down into the telescope from a platform high above the ground. To see anything through such a telescope was amazing; to make
valuable discoveries was extraordinary. Yet, when in 1845
Lord Rosse looked at the nebula called Messier 51 in the
constellation of Canes Venatici, he observed it had a spiral
form. Soon afterward he noted that other nebulae had similar
"convolutions."

These observations were made under the hazards described—in a treacherous climate. Lord Rosse, conscious of
his limitations, looked hopefully to further observation of
these strange objects by the "distinguished astronomers at
Poulkova and Cambridge in the United Sates." This reference
to the observatory at Cambridge is notable. It is perhaps the
first favorable reference to an American observatory. It was
made when astronomy in America, still in embryo, was just
beginning to grow.

Meanwhile the solution to the problem of making good

optical glass, which had long troubled astronomers and pre-
vented the making of lenses of any size, came from a Swiss
bellmaker, Louis Guinand, who lived in the town of Chaux-
de-Fonds in the canton of Neuchâtel. In 1799, after repeated
and discouraging failure, he succeeded in producing beautiful flint disks.

Six years later he left Switzerland and, in Munich, built
the shop which was destined to become the seed of the
German optical industry. There, he helped to train the young
Bavarian orphan, Joseph von Fraunhofer, who, at the age of
fourteen, had been rescued by the Elector Maximilian Joseph
from a burning house in which his parents had died. Fraunhofer, who developed even greater skill than his master,
made the first precise achromatic objectives and was soon
making some of the largest European refractors. His telescopes were mounted in observatories in Germany, Austria,
and Prussia, with the greatest, a 9½-inch refractor, at
Dorpat.

At Harvard, William and George Bond, father and son,
obtained a 15-inch refracting telescope from Germany. It
was mounted in 1847, and as America's first "great" telescope, it created intense excitement. With it George Bond
discovered the dark ring of Saturn and on the night of July
16, 1850, made the first daguerreotype of a star. In 1857 he
made the first real photograph of a star taken with wet plates.
The image was poor, but in that result he foresaw possibilities of photography which would revolutionize astronomy.

"On a fine night," he wrote to William Mitchell in Nan-
tucket, "the amount of work which can be accomplished with
entire exemption from the trouble, vexation and fatigue that
seldom fail to attend upon ordinary observations, is astonishing. The plates, once secured, can be laid by for future
study by daylight and at leisure. The record, is there, with
no room for doubt or mistake as to its fidelity."

The results still did not approach the possibilities. He had
photographed stars of the sixth magnitude—a star brightness
equal to the faintest star visible to the naked eye. He saw the
need for faster, more sensitive plates, then, as now, one of
the astronomer's greatest needs. He predicted that on a
lofty mountain, in a purer atmosphere, fainter stars might

be photographed. In a significant postscript he suggested a method for the accurate measurement of the light of stars by study of the intensity and size of a star image with length of exposure. Years later this method, developed by E. C. Pickering at Harvard, was to lead to extensive photometric work and intensive analysis of star magnitudes and their relation to other stellar characteristics, such as color, temperature, and mass.

Over a hundred years have passed since the Bonds worked at Harvard. With increased expansion over the earth's surface and faster communication, our earth has narrowed its bounds, decreased its apparent size. In the same hundred years the bounds of our universe have expanded beyond man's wildest dreams. A hundred years ago astronomers estimated that the universe contained, at most, ten million stars. Today this number stands conservatively at one hundred billion stars in our own galaxy, one of hundreds of millions of other galaxies scattered sparsely through a volume of space so vast that Sir James Jeans has graphically compared it to St. Paul's Cathedral with six lonely flies flying about at different points inside.

This change in outlook has been brought about by development of the astronomer's tools. The first was the telescope. The second was the photographic plate. The third was the spectroscope, which, by its ability to analyze and sort starlight, opened an entirely new field of observation.

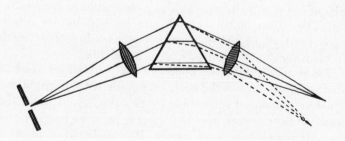

II-4.   *Principle of the Spectroscope.*

Perhaps the question most often asked of astronomers and physicists is this: What is a spectrum, anyway? What do you do with it? The idea appears puzzling. Yet the answer is simple. We have all seen rainbows—giant spectra—in the sky. We have watched the brilliant band of color made by sunlight falling on water drops in a garden spray. By wiggling a radio dial we know we can find a station broadcasting on a certain wave length; by centering on that band we can get clear reception.

In the same way the astronomer turns his spectroscope on sun and stars, sees the colored spectrum crossed by thousands of lines, each "broadcasting" on a different wave length, each telling the story of the physical composition of an individual star. When white light is passed through the triangular block of glass called a prism, it is spread out into its component colors. When that light is also passed through a slit, the astronomer sees the spectrum crossed by lines often dark, more rarely bright. Each of these lines, he has learned, is characteristic of a given element. When he studies the light from a star in his spectroscope, he finds that each star has its characteristic spectrum. When he compares the lines in the stars with lines of various elements in his laboratory, he finds he can identify iron, cobalt, magnesium and, above all, hydrogen in great abundance in the sun and other stars. In this way astronomers found helium in the sun before it was found on earth.

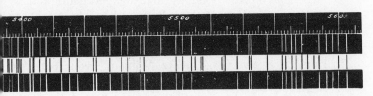

II-5.

Today astronomers accept unquestioningly the astrophysical character of the greater part of modern astronomy. A hundred years ago this was emphatically not the case. Astronomers, still concerned with the positions, motions, and distances of the stars, had no interest in their physical composition. When, in 1850, C. H. Davis stated that astronomers not only were not, but never would be concerned with the physical nature of the planets, he reflected the prevailing attitude. In the face of indifference, often of downright opposition, a small band of pioneers followed in the path broken by Isaac Newton, persisted in their study of the composition of light, and prepared the way to discovery of the universe we know today.

It was the year 1666 when Newton cut a hole in his landlady's window shade and watched the sun's light come through that hole, enter a prism, and spread itself in the beautiful rainbow of color we call the spectrum. White light, he concluded, is made up of many colors, ranging from red at one end of the spectrum to violet at the other.

Nearly 140 years were to pass before the next great step was taken. In 1815, about the time of Napoleon's defeat at Waterloo, the "great telescope maker" Joseph von Fraunhofer began his observation of the solar spectrum that would earn him the greater name of the Father of Astrophysics.

One day he happened to pass a narrow beam of sunlight through his telescope onto a large prism. To his amazement, instead of the usual continuous spectrum, he saw the sun's spectrum crossed by "an almost countless number of strong and weak vertical lines." In succeeding weeks he charted those lines, lettered them carefully, and concluded:

"I have convinced myself by many experiments and by varying the methods, that these lines and bands are due to the nature of sunlight and do not arise from diffraction or illusion."

In England twelve years before, William Hyde Wollaston had passed the sun's light through a slit, had observed seven of these lines, but had supposed them mere boundaries to the various colors in the spectrum. Now Fraunhofer, ignorant of Wollaston's early work, decided to compare them with lines in other stars. He looked first at the bright star Sirius, and saw lines in different positions from those he had seen in the sun. He looked at other stars, found other lines, and concluded that "all these stars, with respect to these bands, seem to differ among themselves." He looked at Venus and the moon and found those lines he had first observed in the sun, weaker, but still there.

How, he asked, would these spectra compare with the spectra of flames or of heated elements in the laboratory? To answer his question he studied the spectrum of a flame in his laboratory. Again he found lines he had seen in the sun; but instead of appearing dark, as in the sun, they appeared bright. The brilliant yellow flame (first seen in firelight by the Scot Thomas Melvill long before) shone out as two bright lines. They matched exactly the two dark lines he had marked *D* in the solar spectrum.

Here, evidently, was the clue to the sun's composition. But Fraunhofer failed to solve his own puzzle. He died without realizing the connection between the elements existing in the sun and the earth which this experiment now indicates so clearly.

Thirty years passed, in which physicists in Germany and England tried unsuccessfully to answer Fraunhofer's riddle. The answer finally came from two German physicists, Robert Bunsen and Gustav Kirchhoff, working in Heidelberg in the mid-nineteenth century. They made, as they said, "some observations which disclose an unexpected explanation of the origin of Fraunhofer's lines, and authorize conclusions therefrom respecting the material constitution of the atmosphere of the sun, and perhaps also of the brighter fixed stars."

In their laboratory they set up a Bunsen gas burner, which produces a nonluminous and very hot flame. Into that burner they put some sodium and looked at its spectrum. They saw the two bright lines in the place marked *D* in the solar spectrum. They asked why these lines should be bright in the laboratory but dark in the sun. Next they tried sodium vapor, and passed sunlight through it. The dark *D* lines, intensified by the vapor, widened. In the same way, when they passed the light of a flame through the sodium vapor in their laboratory, the ordinary bright lines in that flame turned dark like those in the sun.

"The phenomenon in question is easily explained," said Kirchhoff, "upon the supposition that the sodium flame absorbs rays of the same degree of refrangibility as those it emits, whilst it is perfectly transparent for all other rays."

The sodium vapor, they realized, absorbed the light coming from the incandescent body of the sun. In place of the absorbed rays dark lines appeared. They repeated the experiment with other elements in the laboratory—calcium, potassium, strontium, and barium. In each case the characteristic dark lines appeared. The substances in the sun, they concluded, must be like those found on earth. Any variation in the character of the lines must show the state of that substance in the sun and, as they saw later, in other stars also.

Now, a star could be brought into the laboratory to be tested as surely as any earthly substance. Here, in 1859, year of publication of the *Origin of Species,* was a discovery equally far-reaching in its influence on the development of astronomy, physics, and chemistry.

Here was the beginning of an age in which astronomers with spectroscopes joined to telescopes would attempt to fathom the mystery of everything that shines in the sky— sun, stars, comets, meteors, nebulae; in which astronomers would count increasingly on the help of physicists and chemists; and in which conversely, study of conditions in "cosmic crucibles" would illuminate atomic studies on earth.

One of the first to analyze the spectra of stars and nebulae in his observatory founded on the new principle was the English astronomer Sir William Huggins.

"Then it was," he wrote, "that an astronomical observatory began, for the first time, to take on the appearance of a laboratory. Primary batteries, giving forth noxious gases, were arranged outside one of the windows; a large induction coil mounted on a stand on wheels so as to follow the positions of the eye end of the telescope, together with a battery of several Leyden jars; shelves with Bunsen burners, vacuum tubes, and bottles of chemicals, especially of specimens of pure metals, lined its walls.

"The observatory became a meeting place where terrestrial chemistry was brought into direct touch with celestial chemistry. The characteristic light rays from earthly hydrogen shone side by side with the corresponding radiations from starry hydrogen, the dark lines due to the absorption of hydrogen in Sirius or in Vega. Iron from our mines was line matched, light for dark with stellar iron from opposite parts of the celestial sphere. Sodium which upon the earth is always present with us was found to be widely diffused through the celestial spaces.

"The time was indeed one of strained expectation and of scientific exaltation for the astronomer almost without parallel; for nearly every observation revealed a new fact, and almost every night's work was red-lettered by some discovery."

In 1863 Sir William, with spectroscope and collodion plate joined to his eight-inch telescope, made the first "spectrogram" of a star. The image was foggy and blurred and quite useless; but it foreshadowed a time when, with invention of the faster, more sensitive dry or gelatine plate, thousands of stars and nebulae would record their spectra.

The following year Sir William turned his telescope on those "mysterious bodies," the nebulae, whose nature was still an "unread riddle." As telescopes had increased in size, more and more of the nebulae had been resolved into stars. Astronomers believed that, in time, all of them would be so resolved and that all evidence of nebulosity would disappear. To find the answer, Huggins directed his telescope to the planetary nebula in Draco:

"The reader may now be able to picture to himself to some extent the feeling of excited suspense, mingled with a degree of awe, with which, after a few moments of hesitation, I put my eye to the spectroscope. Was I not about to look into a secret place of creation?

"I looked into the spectroscope. No spectrum such as I expected! A single bright line only. . . . The riddle of the nebula was solved. The answer which had come to us in the light itself, read: Not an aggregation of stars, but a luminous gas. . . ."

Sir William Herschel had regarded the nebulae as regions of fiery mist, out of which the stars have been formed. Now Huggins with his spectroscope had apparently proved it. He had discovered the first and strongest of the nebular lines produced by a gas which he called "nebulium." But while he could give it a name he had no idea what this gas really was.

It remained a mystery until Ira S. Bowen, working at the California Institute of Technology sixty years later, discovered its true character. He showed that many of these mysterious lines in the nebulae are actually due to jumps of electrons from one energy level to another in atoms of oxygen and nitrogen.

Four years later Huggins made another discovery which, as he said, "could not fail in future to have a powerful influence on the progress of astronomy." This was his observation of "motion in the line of sight," or the radial velocity of a star, as we now call it.

We are all familiar with the variation in pitch of a train whistle as it goes away, stands still, or approaches us. This principle was discovered by Christian Doppler, who soon found that the same principle applies to light. He saw that, as positions of observer and light source change, the color of the light will shift. Huggins now took Doppler's observation and applied it to the spectrum of a star. If the wave length or position of any line in the spectrum of a star is known, he reasoned, then any change in the star's distance relative to the earth should show up in a shift of that line in the star's spectrum. This is exactly what he found when he compared the spectra of certain stars with spectra taken in the laboratory. The shifts were small and difficult to measure, but they were quite real and, in accord with the Doppler principle, gave the exact velocity of approach or recession.

This discovery became the basis for thousands of observations of "radial velocities." It led to important studies of double stars and their motions. It pointed to observation of the now famous "red shift" in the spectra of spiral nebulae, first observed by V. M. Slipher about 1914.

By the end of the nineteenth century, astronomers and physicists had learned a great deal about the behavior of spectral lines. They knew little or nothing of the origin of those lines. They could not explain the cause of the radiation. Atoms were still "the permanent bricks" of the universe— indestructible, unchangeable. The shattering of this simple picture, the breaking up of the atom, was augured by J. J. Thomson's discovery of the electron in 1897; but its implications for the study of the spectrum were not yet clear. Astronomers did not then know that a spectrum line is characteristic of a given atom in a certain energy state in the element under observation. They could not foresee that from a study of these lines in sun and stars we would learn a great deal about the behavior of atoms in the high temperature states observable only in "cosmic laboratories." From studies of electronic transitions in atoms and the release of energy in sun and stars knowledge of the constitution of matter of enormous value to physicists has been gained. These studies have also opened the way to further understanding of the evolution of stars and the origin of the universe.

Pioneering contributions to this still changing astrophysical picture include the efforts of Angelo Secchi, the Italian, to classify the stars into four definite groups according to spectral type, with the white stars like Sirius and Vega at one end of the scale, the red stars at the other, and the yellow and orange stars in between; the extension of this classification in the Henry Draper Catalogue of the Harvard Observatory, in which the gradual change from one type to the next is shown; and the experiments in which Sir Norman Lockyer showed that by changing the temperature of a single element, its spectrum can be changed—an epoch-making idea at a time when the spectrum of an element was still believed to be unchangeable and the atom indestructible.

More recently, astronomers, returning to this early result, have explained unknown lines in the spectrum, the weakening of some, the strengthening of others, by such changes in temperature, as well as, to a lesser degree, by differences in pressure and density.

We shall now return to the beginning of the modern era of telescope building. By the 1860's and 1870's both refracting and reflecting telescopes had advanced far. Both had definite merits. Both had strong advocates. English astronomers usually favored large reflectors. In America, astronomers tended increasingly to build large refractors. This tendency was strengthened when in the 1860's Lewis M. Rutherfurd, at Columbia University, developed a telescope corrected for photography and took with it some of the most remarkable photographs of the moon ever made.

Meanwhile, Karl August von Steinheil in Germany and

Léon Foucault in France developed independently a new method of depositing silver on glass. The advantages over the old speculum mirrors used by Herschel and Lord Rosse were great. In England astronomers were enthusiastic. The first to use one was William Lassell; the first to manufacture it was Sir Howard Grubb. In 1874, when Sir Howard read of the gift of the eccentric James Lick for a telescope "more powerful than any yet made," he concluded that such a telescope would be a reflector. Instead, the Lick trustees, advised by the majority of American astronomers, decided on a refractor. In 1888 the 36-inch refractor was mounted in "the greatest observatory in the world," on Mount Hamilton above San José, in northern California.

Already, however, a group of wealthy men in southern California, jealous of the superiority of the north, ordered two 40-inch disks from Paris, and planned to set the telescope up on a Mount Wilson peak above the newborn community of Pasadena. These plans sprung from the vast real-estate boom which swept southern California in the 1880's. Unfortunately, by 1892 the land bubble burst, their plans swiftly deflated, and dreams of a great telescope vanished.

In 1892 a twenty-four-year-old astronomer from Chicago, George Ellery Hale, was attending the meeting of the American Association for the Advancement of Science in Rochester. There he happened to hear of the disks cast in Paris, which were still unpaid for. Here was a remarkable opportunity to get a great telescope for the new University of Chicago. He convinced the streetcar magnate Charles T. Yerkes to donate the money—on condition that it would be the "largest telescope in the world."

In this way the Yerkes Observatory was born, an observatory different from any previously built. In it, for the first time, an observatory and a physical laboratory were combined:

"One of the principal aims of the Observatory," said Hale, "will be to bring together the physical and astronomical sides of the work. Therefore the building will be provided with laboratories for optical, spectroscopic and chemical work, concave grating room, large dark rooms, developing, emulsion and enlarging rooms, a galvanometer room and the large heliostat room."

He commented significantly: "The Observatory will be in reality a large physical laboratory as well as an astronomical establishment. You know it is not altogether absurd to regard a telescope as simply a large lens used to form an image of a celestial source of light on the slit of a spectroscope. In this sense the whole institution may be regarded as a physical laboratory."

Today such a concept of an observatory seems natural. Then it was revolutionary. To most people a telescope is still an instrument to look through, to observe familiar objects like the stars, moon, and planets enormously magnified. The actual picture, as the result of the historical developments just traced, is quite different. While a part of the modern astronomer's work is done at the telescope, the greater part is done in the office or laboratory. While he follows a star with his eye to help in guiding the telescope, practically all of the actual recording is done on a photographic plate which provides a permanent image for future study. While a part of his time is spent in the photographing of stars, planets, and nebulae, a still larger part is spent in the recording of their spectra which, when studied afterward, will reveal their composition, distance, temperature, velocity.

The 40-inch refractor, with a light-gathering power 35,000 times that of the human eye, was mounted in 1897. With it Hale and the members of his staff obtained important results in lunar photography, in the survey of the Milky Way, in the study of parallaxes, in the spectroscopic examination of certain classes of stars.

Yet, from the beginning, Hale knew the limit of the refracting telescope had probably been reached. For spectroscopic work, moreover, he knew that a reflector would be far more effective. To penetrate invisible regions, to separate the closely packed lines in the spectrum, he needed wider dispersion. To observe distant stars and nebulae he wanted greater light-gathering power.

Even before Yerkes was finished, therefore, he ordered a 24-inch block of glass from Paris. The disk was ground by George Willis Ritchey, who soon after the opening of the observatory took the most beautiful photographs of nebulae ever taken up to that time.

Already, however, Hale had made plans for a much larger, 60-inch disk, had persuaded his father to give him the money for such a disk, and had ordered another block of glass from France. The 60-inch disk was successfully cast in Paris. It arrived at Yerkes, and preliminary grinding was begun by Ritchey. But Hale could not persuade anyone to provide for its mounting. Many years were to pass before the 60-inch, thanks to Andrew Carnegie's generosity, would be mounted on Mount Wilson.

Meanwhile, James Keeler, appointed Director of the Lick Observatory in 1898, redesigned the 36-inch reflector originally made by the English optician Calver, and mounted by Andrew A. Common. With it he discovered hundreds of nebulae and estimated the number still undiscovered, but observable with that telescope, at 120,000. Most of them, he found to his surprise, had a spiral or elliptical form, a fact significant, he said, in "many, if not all questions concerning cosmogony."

Keeler died in 1900, when the modern era of astrophysics was really opening. The period from 1850 to 1900 had been one of preparation for the great advance to come in the next fifty years. The way to that advance was opened in 1902, when Andrew Carnegie founded the Carnegie Institution of Washington and provided $10,000,000, "To encourage in the broadest and most liberal manner, investigation, research and discovery, and the application of knowledge to the improvement of mankind."

Out of this gift the Mount Wilson Observatory was born in 1904. From the beginning it was directed by George Hale. Four years later, the 60-inch disk, brought from Yerkes as a part of the Carnegie scheme for an independent observatory, was mounted. Yet even before the 60-inch went to work, Hale had begun to think of a still larger telescope. In 1906, John D. Hooker, a Los Angeles businessman, agreed to give the mirror if someone else would mount it.

After great difficulty the 100-inch mirror was finally cast at Saint-Gobain in France. It was mounted in 1917, and began regular work in 1919. While the 60-inch had been able to gather as much light as 57,600 human eyes—an amazing advance over Herschel's 37,000—the 100-inch could gather 160,000 times as much. While the human eye can see stars of the sixth magnitude, or a candle at a distance of six miles, the 100-inch could see stars as faint as the nineteenth magnitude, or a candle at a distance of 2,400 miles. With the photographic plate this phenomenal distance was extended still more. Stars of the twenty-first magnitude could be seen; a candle at a distance of 9,600 miles could be photographed.

The 100-inch found thousands of additional nebulae and extended the known universe a millionfold. By 1924 Edwin Hubble, member of the Mount Wilson staff who had joined the group in 1919, began to get spectacular results with the new telescope. By means of the Cepheid variables, which provide a key to stellar distance, he found the distance to the Andromeda Nebula.

By 1929 observations had accumulated through which he could show a definite relation between the velocities and distances of these remote nebulae. The distances, he discovered, varied proportionally with the velocities. In other words, the farther away the nebula is from us, the greater its velocity. Milton Humason extended these observations still farther. The red shifts, it appeared, increased with distance at a rate of about 100 miles per second for each million light years of distance. Unless some other explanation could be found for these extraordinary shifts, the natural conclusion was that our universe must be expanding at a tremendous rate.

Other important results were obtained with the 100-inch. By 1936, with the help of more sensitive photographic plates, Mount Wilson astronomers reached out 600 million light years into space—a distance in miles of about 36 followed by 20 zeros. They could therefore look back in time to an age long, long before Man appeared on the earth, long even before the dinosaurs walked there.

Yet already Hale and his associates had foreseen the need of a still larger telescope, which could penetrate ever farther into space, and farther back in time.

In 1917 the 100-inch first went into action. By 1923 Hale was writing on the "Possibilities of Instrumental Development." "Looking ahead and speculating on the possibilities of future instruments it may be mentioned that comparative tests of the 60 inch and 100 inch promise well for larger apertures."

Three years later this article was followed by an article in the *Publications of the Astronomical Society of the Pacific*. The article was by F. G. Pease, who had designed a 300-inch telescope. He wrote, "The question has often been asked, 'How large a telescope can be built today?'" In answer he declared somewhat rashly, "My reply would be that anything up to a hundred feet in aperture can be built provided one wants to pay for it."

Hale was more cautious. From long and hard experience he knew that it is one thing to dream on paper, quite another to convince a millionaire to part with his money for something so abstract as a telescope. He was therefore cautious about prediction, hesitant about future plans until he had something more concrete to build on.

Yet, unexpectedly in 1926, the fertile seed was planted, not in the heart of a millionaire, but in the representative of a great foundation.

On the first of October, 1926, H. J. Thorkelson of the General Education Board of the Rockefeller Foundation arrived in Pasadena. He visited Hale in his Solar Laboratory on Holladay Road. There, through the spectroheliograph which Hale had invented thirty-seven years before, he watched in amazement the flaming solar prominences rising hundreds of thousands of miles above the sun's surface. Later he went over to the laboratories of the California Institute of Technology. In the afternoon he visited the Mount Wilson laboratories on Santa Barbara Street.

But the most eventful part of his visit came the following day, when Walter S. Adams, Director of Mount Wilson, took him up the mountain. Thorkelson described the visit in his diary afterward. He tells there of his meeting with Pease, of his astonishment when Pease asked, "Would you like to see one of our pipe dreams?" and his excitement when Pease brought out the blueprints for his proposed 300-inch telescope. This proposal, he notes, was so striking "that I think the astronomers detected my excitement and also my dismay at the probable cost."

Immediately Thorkelson reported the incident to Wickliffe Rose, who replied enthusiastically, "This is very interesting," then commented, "we should watch closely for any possible developments."

In this unexpected way an interest was born which would have results more far-reaching than anyone then anticipated. In later years the incident was almost completely forgotten. In 1928 Hale wrote an article for *Harper's Magazine* which has been given complete credit for rousing interest in the telescope. "Rarely," said Spencer Jones, Astronomer Royal of England, "can a magazine article have been so productive of result." Undeniably it stimulated interest, but it was not the original impetus.

Two years later, early in March, 1928, Hale in New York called on Rose, told him in detail of his dream. When he had finished, Rose questioned him closely. How much would such a telescope cost? What were the chances of success? Hale emphasized the possibilities, yet did not deny the chance of failure. This was why he had asked for a grant for the mirror, the most difficult, the most fundamental problem in the building of any telescope. Suddenly Rose asked, "Do you want a 200- or a 300-inch telescope?" This, of course, was not a new question to Hale. While Pease and Ritchey strongly advocated a 300-inch, he had long thought the jump from 100 to 300 inches too great. It would be safer, he felt, to attempt the 200-inch first.

On the 16th of April, in a long letter requested by Rose, Hale summed up the reasons for wanting a 200-inch telescope. Again he spoke of the accomplishments with the 100-inch, its advantages over the 60-inch, and the need for greater light-gathering power in the attack on still more important problems. Again he listed the outstanding questions to be solved with a greater telescope. In this list he included the following "outstanding" questions, vital now, as they were then:

"*a.*) The structure of the universe, calling for a more intensive study of the Galaxy, of which our solar system is a minute part, and especially of the vast region of spiral nebulae ('island universes') beyond the Milky Way, where the 100" telescope has fixed the distance of the two nearest spiral nebulae at about one million light years and disclosed their true nature by partially resolving them into stars. It has also revealed hundreds of thousands of more remote spirals, many of which could be analyzed and measured with a larger instrument.

"*b.*) The evolution of spiral nebulae, partially suggested by our recent studies.

"*c.*) The evolution of stars, showing their origin, sequence, and physical and chemical development throughout their life history.

"*d.*) The constitution of matter, since the enormously greater range in mass, temperature, pressure and density of the heavenly bodies presents opportunities for discovery far beyond the possibilities of laboratory experiment.

"Scores of other problems calling for a larger telescope might be mentioned if space permitted," he added, as he gave further argument for a 200-inch telescope. "No method of advancing science is so productive as the development of new and more powerful instruments and methods of research. A larger telescope would not only furnish the necessary gain in light, space-penetration, and photographic resolving power, but permit the application of ideas and devices derived chiefly from the recent fundamental advances in physics and chemistry. These advances which have suddenly transformed spectroscopy from an empirical into an exact and rational science would undoubtedly render possible many new discoveries with such an instrument."

That fall, after endless, often frustrating negotiation, the Rockefeller Foundation voted $6,000,000 "for the erection of a great telescope of the reflector type with a mirror 200″ in diameter."

The results achieved with it, have surpassed Hale's hopes. Already, by 1951, it had carried man 50 percent farther out into space than he had ever been before.

The Astronomer at Work

When we first see the great telescope at Palomar, it is difficult, perhaps, to realize how or where the astronomer works. It even takes a while to adjust to the idea of a reflecting telescope in which the light from a star comes down through a latticed tube to a mirror and back to the observer, instead of coming directly from the star through a system of lenses to the observer looking through an eyepiece at the end of the traditional closed tube.

In this telescope, the huge 200-inch mirror is placed at the bottom of the telescope. When the astronomer wants to observe at the "prime focus" at the opposite end of the telescope, he enters the elevator which climbs the side of the slit of the curving dome. This elevator or observing platform moves up and down so that he can step into his observing cage at the top of the telescope and can then go anywhere the telescope goes. With his back to the sky, he looks down at the mirror which will reflect light back to his photographic plate.

This method of observation in the cage at the prime focus is not, however, the only method the astronomer uses. Many members of the Mount Wilson-Palomar staff are more inter-

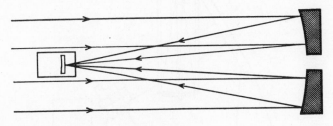

II-6.   *Telescope at Prime Focus.*

ested in an inch-long spectrum than in any number of photographs of nebulae. Here again the advantage of the 200-inch telescope is its greater light-gathering power.

For such work the astronomer needs additional mirrors. These may be combined in two different ways—the Cassegrain and the coudé. In both cases the astronomer must

change his position and move to the other end of the telescope. The change of mirrors is easily made by means of the
electric controls and mechanisms which move the mirrors
automatically, swinging them out of one position and into
another swiftly and smoothly.

In the first position, the Cassegrain, named for the French
sculptor at the court of Louis XIV, a convex mirror is set in
the convergent beam of light below the prime-focus cage.
This reverses the beam of light and sends it back along a
path through the 40-inch hole in the center of the 200-inch
mirror. Here, at the base of the telescope, the observer
records the star's image or its spectrum—a spectrum much
larger than he would receive in the cage at the other end, as
he is able to use here a longer spectrograph which will give
a larger scale. In this position, too, he may photograph the
moon and planets, also larger because of the greater focal

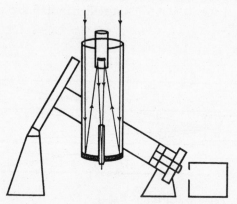

II-7.   *Cassegrain Telescope.*

length. In this combination the telescope has an equivalent
focal length of 267 feet.

At the coudé focus the astronomer works in a miniature
laboratory in an air-conditioned constant-temperature room
beyond and below the telescope mirror south of the telescope. Here he can use large accessory instruments—power-

ful long-focus spectrographs, bolometers, radiometers. Here the light, by use of additional mirrors, is brought to a fixed stationary focal point. The first of these is a convex mirror, similar to the Cassegrainian but of different curvature. The second is an oval coudé diagonal flat which deflects the converging light from the first mirror along the hollow south polar axis to the coudé spectrograph. In this position the telescope will have a focal length of 500 feet.

Drive and Control System

In any of these positions, by means of the remarkable system of controls, which surpasses anything ever applied to a telescope before, the astronomer can tell where he is, what time it is, where the star is, and where he, with the telescope, is going. At any time he can read the zenith angle of the telescope, the rates of motion, the focus position, the sidereal time, the Pacific Standard Time. To move to another position he calls through the "intercom" system to his night assistant at the control board below. The assistant presses a button and the telescope moves automatically. The astronomer does not even have to worry, like the astronomer of old, about the position of dome and slit. As the telescope moves, the dome automatically rotates, and the slit moves to follow the star in the field.

But the 200-inch is not the only telescope mounted on Palomar Mountain. Here two other remarkable telescopes have achieved extraordinary results. These two telescopes are named after the strange German genius Bernhard Schmidt, who invented the principle in 1929 and built his first instrument in 1930.

Twenty years ago, on October 5, 1931, Hale received a note from J. A. Anderson which interested him greatly.

"It is said," Anderson wrote, "there is nothing new under the sun, but Dr. Baade has brought with him from Germany an idea which comes pretty near being new."

"The idea," he continued, "was evolved by one Schmidt, and is a reflecting telescope having an aperture ratio of, say, F/2 and a huge increase in field. The trick is to use a

spherical mirror. In a plane roughly parallel to the mirror
surface, but passing through the *center of curvature,* is
placed a thin sheet of glass—really a very weak negative
lens so figured that it distorts the incoming parallel light just
enough to correct the spherical aberration of the mirror."

He went on enthusiastically: "The capital fact is that if it
does this for rays parallel to the axis, it will also do it for rays
making an angle of several degrees with the axis, depending
somewhat on the thickness of the glass plate. A little consideration of the geometry of the thing makes this quite
obvious. The thin sheet of glass will, of course, bend somewhat, due to its own weight, but this is more or less im-
material."

He concluded, "If you have not already heard of this, I
feel sure it will interest you."

Hale was so interested in this new telescope, which has
been called the first radical innovation in telescope making
since Newton's reflector in 1671, that plans were soon started
to build one in connection with the 200-inch. In the meantime Theodore Dunham applied the principle to a spectrograph used with the 100-inch telescope. The first Schmidt
telescope, now in the smallest of the domes on Palomar, had
an 18-inch correcting plate and a 26-inch mirror. By 1936

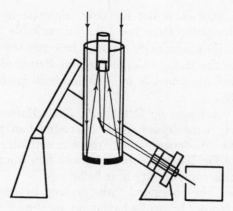

II-8.   *Telescope at the Coudé Focus.*

Walter Baade, Schmidt's friend who was with him when he thought of the idea, was working with the new telescope. The results were indeed remarkable. The star images were sharp all the way out to the edge. Aberrations which had disturbed astronomers since the time of Kepler did not exist in this telescope in which distortion was eliminated by use of the thin correcting plate in combination with a spherical mirror. But this new instrument had other powers even more amazing. It could photograph an extraordinarily wide field. At the same time it saw far deeper into space than any telescope of similar size had ever been able to go.

Soon other astronomers, entranced by the results obtained by Baade and his associate from the California Institute, Fritz Zwicky, began to think of owning a Schmidt telescope also. Soon telescopes were ordered by Harvard and by the Warner and Swasey Observatory in Cleveland. Soon, too, not only astronomers, but doctors, and eventually even television men realized the possibilities of the remarkable correcting lens which could at the same time clarify and enlarge the area of a photograph. Today the Schmidt principle is being used increasingly for X-ray work in hospitals as well as in navigation, aerial mapping, and many other fields.

Today, also, the pioneer instrument on Palomar has been joined by the much larger 48-inch Schmidt, which acts as a scouting instrument for the 200-inch. The new Schmidt has completed a survey of the sky down to stars of the twentieth magnitude. With its power of seeing wide as well as deep, it has done in four years what it would take five thousand for the 200-inch to do. This program was sponsored jointly with

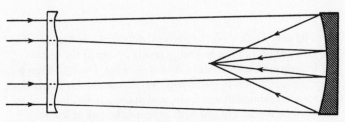

II-9.   *Principle of the Schmidt Telescope.*

the National Geographic Society. This society, which has usually encouraged expeditions on the earth, now realizing that there are greater realms than dreamed of on earth, is spreading its frontiers far beyond the earth's narrow confines, in this exploration of the sky.

On June 3, 1948, when the 200-inch was dedicated, it was named for the founder, George Ellery Hale, "whose vision and leadership made it a reality."

In the years since that dedication, the Hale telescope has vastly extended the known limits of the universe, and expanded our knowledge of the processes of evolution in distant galaxies. With its aid, astronomers have been able to reach out more than two billion light years on the new distance scale. They have observed that the Andromeda nebula may be nearly three million light years away from us and about 2.5 times as large as originally estimated. Spectroscopic observations with the Hale telescope indicate that the most distant measurable galaxies are receding at a speed of about 75,000 miles per second, thus offering further support for the theory of an expanding universe.

From Galileo to Hale: we have come a long way. Step by step, by means of larger and larger telescopes, we have penetrated deeper and deeper into space. If Galileo could return today, he would be amazed at the transformation in his narrow world. Yet, in some ways, this transformation is not as great as the revolution wrought when he removed Man from his self-arrogated place at the center of the universe and put him on a minor planet moving around a central sun.

The new window on the universe discovered by Karl Jansky is the subject of the following article by one of the world's leading radio astronomers. As Lovell states, Jansky's discovery, like many others in astronomy, was accidental. He was looking for something different from, and not nearly as important as, what he found. He had been assigned the task of learning the cause of static which was interfering with transoceanic

radio communication. He discovered a hitherto unsuspected
aspect of the universe.

Since the days of Jansky and his successor Reber, radio
astronomy has become a science of great complexity, through
which numerous avenues of research have opened. Various
types of radio telescopes, designed for specialized functions,
have been built. The "big dish" type, of which the Jodrell
Bank instrument is the outstanding example, is the best known.
There are also systems involving arrays of antennae, in which
the principle of interference is used to intensify radio signals.
Instruments are designed for observation of specific wave
lengths or of particular areas of the sky. Theoretically, an inter-
ferometer with antennae on two revolving earth satellites
could be built. Its construction no doubt remains for
the distant future.

It is not to be supposed that the radio telescope supersedes
the optical variety. With increasing frequency, the two types
work hand in hand. The radio telescope scans a wide range
but provides little resolving power. (It has been calculated
that under certain circumstances, an aperture roughly the radius
of the earth would be required to equal the resolving power
of the 200-inch.) Thus the radio telescope may discern an
area of unusual celestial activity. With the 200-inch it may be
photographed and analyzed.

A. C. B. Lovell is the director of the Jodrell Bank Observatory at Manchester, England. Born in Gloucestershire in
1913, he studied at the University of Bristol and became an
assistant lecturer in physics at the University of Manchester in
1936 and senior lecturer in 1945. He was appointed professor of astronomy there in 1951. He has become recognized
as an authority on his subject and is the author of a number
of successful books, including The Exploration of Outer Space,
from which the following selection is taken.

RADIO TELESCOPES

A. C. B. LOVELL

FOR MANY YEARS it seemed that man's only hope of obtaining information about the stars and the galaxies was by the use of big optical telescopes. He has evolved with eyes which are sensitive to that part of the spectrum in the visible region between the ultra-violet and infra-red, and it is over this region of the spectrum that a transparency, or window, exists in the earth's atmosphere. If man had evolved with eyes which were sensitive only in the infra-red or ultra-violet then he would have had very little knowledge indeed of outer space until the present day, when it has become possible to move beyond the obscuring region of the atmosphere with satellites and space probes.

Because the earth's atmosphere almost completely obscures any radiation which lies outside the familiar colours of the rainbow it seemed impossible that any useful knowledge of outer space would ever be accumulated in parts of the spectrum other than in this visible gap. This is in spite of the fact that the early researches with radio waves in the 1920s had led to the realization that there was another transparency or gap in the earth's atmosphere at much longer wavelengths in the radio wave region. Whereas the wavelengths of visible light are measured in millionths of a centimetre, the radio wave region, in which there is this other transparency in the atmosphere, extends from a fraction of a centimetre to many meters in wavelength. In the middle of this radio wave band the ordinary broadcasting and television transmissions are made on earth.

Although the existence of this transparency was known, it seemed unlikely that any use could be made of it for astronomical purposes. After all, the stars and the sun are very hot bodies and the fundamental laws of physics indicate that the maximum output of energy from such hot bodies with surface temperatures of many thousands of degrees is in the visible and near visible regions of the spectrum. It was therefore with some incredulity that astronomers received the news in 1931 and 1932 that an electrical engineer, Karl Jansky, who was working at the Bell Telephone Laboratories in America, had detected some radiations or signals in this part of the spectrum which he was convinced had their origin from regions of space outside the solar system. Jansky's apparatus worked on rather a long wavelength between 14 and 20 metres and the aerial consisted of an array of rods which could be rotated on a brick foundation. Jansky was investigating the static which was interfering with and limiting the usefulness of radio communications around the world. He discovered that even when there was no obvious form of atmospherics such as a thunderstorm, nevertheless there was a residual disturbance in his receiving apparatus and he noticed that this residual noise in his equipment had a diurnal variation; that is it varied in strength throughout the day. Furthermore he made the classic observation that the maximum in this signal did not come exactly every day at the same time but that it was four minutes earlier each day. This led Jansky to conclude, quite correctly, that the only

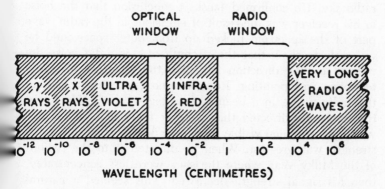

II-10. *The complete electromagnetic spectrum showing the regions of transparency of the Earth's atmosphere and ionosphere.*

possibility of explaining this residual noise must be that it
was a result of radio waves generated somewhere in regions
of space outside the solar system which were being picked
up in his aerial system (the reason being that the period of
maximum of 23 hours 56 minutes represents the sidereal day,
that is the period of rotation of the earth with respect to the
stars, and not the solar day of 24 hours). This perfectly
simple and straightforward observation of Jansky led to the
correct conclusion that the source of this radio noise had its
origin not merely in extraterrestrial space but in extrasolar
space, and that it originated either on the stars or in the
space between the stars. Astronomers took little notice of
Jansky's discovery and the further development of this subject in the years before the second world war was left to an
amateur, Grote Reber, who built the prototype of the
modern radio telescope in the garden of his home in Illinois.
This radio telescope was a bowl, 30 feet in diameter, in the
form of a paraboloid, mounted so that it could be directed to
any part of the sky. This telescope of Reber's has been
re-erected recently as a museum piece at the entrance to the
United States National Radio Astronomy Observatory at
Greenbank, West Virginia.

With this instrument Reber was able to explore with a
reasonable degree of precision the radio waves from the
Milky Way, and, indeed, he made the first real map of the
radio sky. He confirmed Jansky's conclusion that the noise
in his receiver was the result of emissions in the radio wave
part of the spectrum picked up from outer space, and he
was able to show that the strength of this radio noise depended on the direction in which the beam of his radio
telescope was pointing. Reber's radio telescope picked up
the radio waves in a beam a few degrees wide. He found
that when he directed this beam at the region of the sky
where the common visible stars were densest, then his signal
strength was greatest. When he directed it to the regions
of the Milky Way where the stars were less concentrated,
then his signal strength decreased. This seemed a natural
result leading to the conclusion that the stars which we see
with our eyes in the visible part of the spectrum also emit
radio waves. But this picture proved too simple, for when

Reber hopefully directed his telescope at some of the bright and nearer stars in the sky such as Sirius and Capella, expecting to be able to find quite strong radio emissions from them, he discovered to his surprise that there were no emissions at all. Thereby he established a paradox which is still not completely resolved, namely that the Milky Way system with its hundred thousand million stars appears to emit radio waves, as well as the light waves by which we see the stars. Although the radio waves are most intense in the regions where there are the most stars, the individual star members do not seem to be radio emitters.

Apart from one or two doubtful and unusual cases this remains the situation today—that nobody has succeeded in detecting radio waves from the individual or common stars which we see by eye in the Milky Way. The sun is an exception; although, for reasons presumably associated with the long period cycle of sunspots, Reber was unable to find any radio emissions from the sun, which itself appears to be an extremely powerful source of radio emission. Indeed, under some conditions, the solar radio waves are so intense that they hinder the investigation of the remote parts of the cosmos. This situation is analogous to the optical case where sunlight makes it impossible to see the faint light of the stars by day. Even if all the stars in the Milky Way system were to emit with the same intensity as the sun, they are so distant and the dilution factor is so great, that there would be no significant contribution to the strength of the signal from the regions of space outside the solar system picked up in a radio telescope. The solution of this paradox seemed to Reber to lie in the following argument. The stars were obviously not emitting radio waves which made a significant contribution to his records but, since there was this close relationship between intensity of the visible light and the strength of the radio emission, the source of the radio waves must be the interstellar hydrogen gas. Since Reber reached that conclusion in the period 1934 to 1938 there have been many changes of opinion about the origin of these radio waves, and now it does seem that Reber was partially correct. First there was a violent swing against this view and it was believed that the interstellar gas did not contribute at all. Now the situation, although extremely complex, involves an explanation in which the radio waves generated in the interstellar hydrogen gas represent a significant component of the extraterrestrial radio emission.

There was a long hiatus in the development of these discoveries by Jansky and Reber because of the war, but it was the excellence of the techniques and our new ideas about radio and radar which evolved under the stress of military requirements which led to a vigorous resurgence of these studies immediately after the war. It soon became obvious in the early stages of this development that the problem of the radio astronomer was analogous to that of the optical astronomer, namely that large radio telescopes were needed for the same kind of reason that the optical astronomer required large optical instruments. The optical instrument needs a large mirror in order to collect as much light as possible to penetrate further into space, and also to obtain good definition. A similar situation exists with the radio telescope, where it is necessary to collect the radio waves over a big area in order to improve the signal strength of the faint emissions which are generated at great distances in the cosmos, and also because the definition or the resolution of the beam of such a telescope depends directly, for a given wavelength, on the size of the telescope.

Reber's radio telescope was a parabolic bowl 30 feet in diameter. The largest contemporary version of this form of radio telescope is the instrument at Jodrell Bank in which a parabolic bowl 250 feet in diameter is mounted so that it can be directed with precision to any part of the sky. Incoming radiation is reflected from the steel bowl on to the primary feed which is mounted on a mast at the focus 62½ feet from the apex of the paraboloid. Then the signals are transformed by electronic apparatus and recorded. It is possible to direct this bowl to any part of the sky, and for a given wavelength the telescope has something like 8 times the definition and 64 times greater gain than the instrument originally used by Reber. The paraboloidal steel bowl of the radio telescope is formed of 80 tons of steel sheet. This is mounted on a cradle which itself weighs 800 tons and the whole cradle is suspended on trunnion bearings 180 feet above the ground. The elevation drive, or tilt of the bowl, is obtained by electric motors driving through large gun racks, originally part of the *Royal Sovereign* battleship. The 180-ft. towers which support the elevation bearings and motors are connected at ground level by a diametral girder, pivoted at its centre point. The two towers are each carried on six bogies which move on a double railway track 320 feet in diameter so that the instrument can be given rotation or movement in azimuth. The whole superstructure, which moves on the railway track, weighs over 2,000 tons.

On the reverse side of the steel bowl a small hanging laboratory is suspended so that it always remains in the upright position whatever the tilt of the bowl. This is approached by catwalks when the bowl is in the zenith and contains receiving equipment and, if necessary, the observer. Sometimes in order to avoid losses in cables it is necessary to mount the receiving equipment close to the primary feed at the focus. On the top of the aerial tower which rises 62½ ft. from the apex a box about 6-ft. cube is fixed and access to this is obtained by a hydraulic platform from the base of the bowl. This box contains some of the receiving equipment and for some work at high frequencies the aerial itself in the form of a horn feed, as distinct from the common rod dipole, emerges directly from this box.

The control room of the telescope is 200 yards from the superstructure and from a main control desk the controller can command the instrument to perform any motion which the experiment requires. It can be driven separately in azimuth and elevation or a sidereal motion can be obtained by driving through a computer in right ascension and declination. Under those conditions the computer works out the position to which the telescope has to be directed and it will then automatically follow a given star from rising to setting, or a planet, or the sun, depending on the needs of the research programme.

The Jodrell Bank telescope is still the biggest steerable

radio telescope, but several specialized instruments have been built which have a better definition and cover a bigger area of ground. These are not generally in this paraboloidal form and they are usually built so that they work in a restricted wavelength range; whereas the great adaptability of the Jodrell Bank instrument and the fact that it can be used as a transmitter as well as a receiver over a very wide range of wavelengths has turned out to be of considerable importance.

Partly because of their association with space probes, radio telescopes have become rather popular instruments. There are now many completely steerable parabolic radio telescopes of sizes between 50 ft. and 100 ft. in operation, but still very few of larger diameter. The nearest competitor to the Jodrell Bank telescope is the 210-ft. diameter instrument opened in the autumn of 1961 as part of the equipment of the radio astronomy division of the Council for Scientific and Industrial Research Organization in Australia. The Russians appear to be operating a steerable telescope with an effective aperture of 140 ft. in their deep-space tracking network.

The optical telescope produces its records on a photographic plate, either of the stars or nebulae themselves, or in the form of spectrographs. The records of the output of the radio telescope generally appear as an ink trace on a paper chart recording the strength of the signal in relation to the time and position of the beam of the telescope. Even for the investigation of a single object such as the M31 nebula in Andromeda it may be necessary to obtain hundreds of these records with the telescope scanning over different parts of the nebula. So one obtains a mosaic from which can be built up a system of isophotes which give the radio picture of the nebula. Nowadays these final processes of treatment of the individual scans are increasingly the subject for computers and other machines which save hundreds of hours of time in the reduction of the basic records.

Experiments of this type with a radio telescope on the Andromeda nebula reveals a very interesting situation which seems to epitomize many of the investigations with radio telescopes, in that they reveal the same kind of paradox as that found in the early work of Reber. Here the radio contours on the whole show a good concentration in the region of the stars which make up the Andromeda nebula, but they also show a considerable intensity of emission at distances which are far removed from anything which the photographic plate records. In fact there appears to be nothing but empty space in regions surrounding the nebula of stars where there is still an intense radio output. We know that both in the M31 nebula and in many of the other extragalactic nebulae which are within the range of our radio observations, the visible stars are surrounded by a corona, or halo, of radio emission which stretches for great distances outside the regions where any matter can be seen in the ordinary photographs. The probable explanation of this emission was suggested by Shklovsky the Russian scientist many years ago. He suggested the galaxies are surrounded by magnetic fields and the radio emission is generated by electrons moving at high speeds in this magnetic field.

It is strange that the radio telescopes which were developed to study the radio emissions from space should have become such an essential part of the work of the earth satellite and the space probe. Indeed it is altogether remarkable that, after hundreds of years of the development of the optical telescope as the primary astronomical instrument, man has achieved within the space of a few years two completely new techniques for the exploration of space in the form of the radio telescope and the space probe. The importance of both space probe and earth satellite is that they enable us to take our instruments away from the obscuring layers of the earth's atmosphere into regions outside where we can study the incoming radiation and particles in the planetary system before they are absorbed or distorted by the earth's own atmosphere. The developments in this field since the Russians launched Sputnik I on 4 October 1957 have been tremendous.

The association of the radio telescope with the satellite or space probe arises because the payload can carry only a small amount of weight in spite of the hundreds of tons which have to be lifted from earth by the launching rockets. Thus the transmitter which has to send back to earth the record of the scientific data collected by the instruments in the probe has to be low-powered. The situation is much the same as in the case of the emissions generated naturally in space. There we need a big radio telescope to detect the faint signals and similarly large radio telescopes are required to track the low-powered signals emanating from the probe. The conjunction of the Jodrell Bank telescope with the American space probe Pioneer V enabled the probe to be tracked for four months after it was launched from earth to a distance of nearly 23 million miles. Then some trouble developed in the power supply, the batteries appear to have sprung a leak, and the signals were lost at that stage.

The scientific results with the earth satellites and space probes have revolutionized our ideas about the conditions in the outer regions of the earth's atmosphere and about our immediate environment in space. Perhaps the most remarkable and unexpected of these discoveries was made by the Americans who were behind the Russians in 1957 and whose difficulties were increased by the failure of the early Vanguard launchings in the autumn and winter of 1957. However, in the early hours of the 1st of February, 1958, when the Russians had already launched Sputnik I and Sputnik II, the Americans had their first success with Explorer I. This satellite was launched into an elliptical orbit around the earth with a period of 115 minutes. At its closest approach, the satellite was about 370 kilometres distant whilst its apogee was about 2,500 kilometres away. Amongst the equipment in the satellite Dr. van Allen, of Iowa University, placed a geiger counter which was designed to study the radiations entering the earth's atmosphere from space. At one stage in the early part of this flight records of the telemetry which was being picked up on earth from Explorer I seemed to indicate that this geiger-counter system had failed because it had apparently stopped counting. However, after a time the system recovered and started counting again, sending back to earth records of the number of particles which were incident on the satellite. This process of apparent failure and recovery was repeated and soon it was realized that this was not a fault in the apparatus but that a real effect was occurring. In fact, when the device stopped counting the satellite was passing through a region at a distance of 1,000 kilometres or so from the earth and the cessation of the counting was due to the fact that the radiation on it was so intense that the instrument was blocked. When the satellite was below 1,000 kilometres the system behaved normally and the geiger counter responded in the manner which had been anticipated. It was encased in the steel hull of the satellite and van Allen concluded that the radiation causing the blockage of his equipment must be due to corpuscular radiation of quite unforeseen intensity.

Subsequently this radiation was the subject of intense study by the American earth satellites and deep-space probes and by the Russian Luniks. It seems that as we move out from the earth through the concentration of electrons

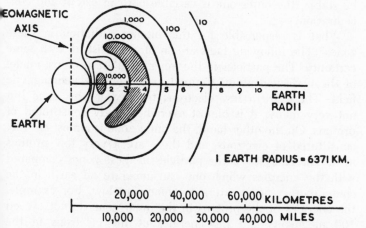

II-11. A cross-section of a three-dimensional figure of revolution around the Earth's geomagnetic axis, showing the intensity of the trapped radiation around the Earth. The numbers on the contours are the counts/second recorded by the radiation counter and indicate the relative intensity of radiation in the zones.

(After Professor J. A. van Allen)

in the ionized regions which extend to about 400 kilometres, we do not pass into the emptiness of interplanetary space but into regions densely packed with ionized particles. There appear to be two zones surrounding the earth in which ionized particles are trapped by the earth's magnetic field—now commonly known as the van Allen radiation belts or zones. The inner zone is the one first discovered by van Allen, and then the Lunik II and the Pioneer series of space probes found that at a greater distance from earth there was another distinct zone of trapped charged particles with a different constitution. As a probe moves out from the earth it passes through the electron concentrations at a few hundred kilometres, then on into the first zone of trapped radiation at a few thousand kilometres. The intensity then decreases, but soon rises again to a much greater strength at a distance 20,000 to 30,000 kilometres from the earth. The exact situation is complicated; for example, it is probable that this outer zone has more than one maximum in it, and whereas the inner zone seems to be stable, the outer one is variable both in extent and concentration.

What is responsible for this intense radiation in these zones? The following facts are so far established with some certainty. The particles in the inner zone are protons, nuclei of the hydrogen atom, trapped in the earth's geomagnetic field. There are a few electrons trapped in this zone but not very many; it is almost overwhelmingly constituted of protons. On the other hand, the outer zone is almost entirely constituted of electrons, and there are a very few protons in it. The energies of the particles in these zones compared with the energies which one can generate on earth in the contemporary accelerating machines are low. For example, the energies of the protons in the inner zone do not exceed 100 megavolts and the energies of the electrons in the outer zone are less than 100 kilovolts. On the other hand the number of particles is enormous. In the inner zone the flux of protons is about $2 \times 10^4 / \text{cm.}^2 / \text{sec.}$, and the flux of electrons in the outer zone is something like 10^{11} electrons/cm.^{2}/sec. These numbers have to be compared with the flux of cosmic ray particles from space—about two protons and heavy nuclei/cm.^{2}/sec., representing the extent of the radiation to be anticipated in these regions. It is the quantity rather than the energy which gives the radiation zones this special importance and, indeed, danger to living organisms. In terms of common radiation dosage, cosmic rays represent about 0.01 roentgen/hour, compared with the permissible human dosage of 0.3 roentgen/week. In the heart of the outer radiation zone, the dose is about 10 roentgen/hour—5,000 times greater than a human being could stand.

The origin of the particles in these radiation zones is not yet finally resolved. The inner zone of protons is stable and constant. This zone seems to contain the same kind of energetic particles and about the same quantity whenever it has been investigated. It is believed that the protons in this zone arise from the decay of neutrons which are moving out of the atmosphere of the earth, and that the neutrons responsible are some of the products of nuclear disintegrations produced in the earth's atmosphere by cosmic ray bombardment. In contrast to the stability of the inner zone, the outer zone of electrons is extremely unstable and is influenced in some detail by events on the sun. Solar flares and magnetic storms appear to have a controlling influence on this zone of electrons. For example, it has been found that a big magnetic storm on the earth drains the electrons from this zone. After a few days the zone recovers, presumably repopulated with electrons from the sun. Cause and effect are not yet distinguished, but it is clear that this outer radiation zone is closely linked with the major geophysical effects observed on earth, such as magnetic storms and the aurora polaris. It seems that this outer zone acts in the role of a reservoir of charged particles with the sun as the source and the earth as the sink.

It seems likely that the regions of space containing the outer limits of the radiation zones, 50,000 kilometres from the earth, are the regions where outer space can really be said to begin. This is where the solar wind, consisting of streams of electrons continuously blown out from the solar atmosphere (with particular intensity during solar eruptions), reach a compromise with the earth's own geophysical environment. Only a few years ago we would have talked about outer space beginning just above the ionospheric regions—only 400 or 500 kilometres above the earth's surface. Now we must think in terms of outer space beginning in the region of 60,000 or 70,000 kilometres from the earth. Moreover, we begin to visualize the earth and planets as bodies enveloped in the solar atmosphere, closely under solar control, in the environmental as well as the gravitational sense.

One aspect of the astronomer's struggle to obtain "more light" has been his efforts to eliminate those factors which shield it from his observing instruments. The dust and particles of interstellar space are beyond his optical control. The sea of atmosphere has been scarcely less amenable. It may be obscured by clouds or distorted by turbulence or filled with the reflected light of great cities. British astronomers are plagued by their notoriously bad climate. The seeing in the Eastern half of the United States is almost equally uncertain. To escape the handicaps of an observatory in the city of Chicago, George Ellery Hale built the Yerkes Observatory on a Wisconsin lake. From there, in search of better seeing, he traveled to Mt. Wilson and Palomar in California. Moreover, the atmosphere presents another obstacle to observation. A star radiates not only visible light but gamma rays, X rays, ultraviolet waves, infrared waves and radio waves. In varying degrees, they are shielded from instruments on the earth's surface.

The latest step in the struggle to escape the atmosphere is here discussed by a foremost authority on balloon astronomy. Written in 1959, it describes one of the pioneer attempts to lift a telescope above the sources of bad seeing. Since then, Dr. Schwarzschild has succeeded in sending aloft a 36-inch telescope, weighing a number of tons, for the observation of Mars.

There are such obvious possibilities in this new technique that it may supersede earthbound telescopes for certain purposes. Optical observations of the planets, for example, can be done more effectively from outside the atmosphere. It should be noted also that carriers other than balloons have recently come into being. In 1946, the ultraviolet radiation from the sun was photographed from a V-2 rocket at a height of about 100 kilometers. Astronomical instruments are now frequently being lifted in rockets and carried around the earth in satellites. The Russians have photographed the far side of the moon. On July 31, 1964, Ranger 7 transmitted television photographs of the moon's surface which are calculated to have as much as 2000 times the resolving power of the best optical photographs. The clarity of detail is shown in the photograph which appears in the section of illustrations.

Related to such techniques is the possibility of establishing observational platforms in space. Although the idea may seem to partake of the elements of science fiction it is under serious consideration. How far can such programs go? The method is in its infancy and any prophecy must be subject to constant modification.

Martin Schwarzschild was born at Potsdam, Germany in 1912 and received his Ph.D. at the University of Göttingen in 1935. He came to the United States in 1937 and became associated with the Harvard College Observatory. He became assistant professor of astronomy at Columbia in 1940, and Higgins Professor of Astronomy at Princeton in 1950. His wife, and co-author of this article, is also an astronomer.

BALLOON ASTRONOMY

MARTIN AND BARBARA SCHWARZSCHILD

ON A QUIET September morning in 1957 a huge, transparent balloon, brilliantly lighted by the sun, floated across the sky 15 miles above the fields of Minnesota. Following its course in automobiles on the ground a group of anxious astronomers wondered whether the telescope and camera they had hung beneath the bright bubble were working. Like all astronomers, they were used to the fact that the objects they were studying were hopelessly out of reach. But to have their viewing equipment also inaccessible was a new experience. Fortunately this time their fears were unnecessary; the instruments did quite nicely on their own, obtaining pictures of the sun's surface sharper than any made previously.

Soon there will be other and more elaborate balloon experiments. Telescopes will be mounted on satellites revolving hundreds of miles above the earth's surface. Why this effort to get a mere few miles closer to celestial objects? The answer is of course that this short distance takes us above the earth's atmosphere, which hangs like a distorting and dimming veil between our telescopes and the stars. The air is heated unevenly, particularly near the ground and in the region at about 40,000 feet called the tropopause. The resulting turbulence distorts light rays passing through the air, smearing points of light into irregularly varying spots. Anyone who has seen the stars twinkle has observed this effect, which astronomers call "bad seeing." Making each point of light look bigger than it actually is, the effect limits our ability to distinguish separate stars when they are close together, and to make out fine detail on a larger object like the sun.

To help overcome the effects of bad seeing, many observatories are located on carefully selected mountaintops, where the lower air is quietest. But even on mountaintops there is still much local turbulence, and the problem of the tropopause is completely unsolved. In 1956 a telescope was taken aloft in a manned balloon by D. E. Blackwell and D. W. Dewhirst of the University of Cambridge and A. Dollfus of the Meudon Observatory in France; however, the ceiling of their flight was below the tropopause, so they eliminated only one of the two sources of bad seeing.

In addition to causing bad seeing, the atmosphere handicaps astronomers in another way: it absorbs all the ultraviolet and much of the infrared radiation of the sun and stars. Balloon altitudes may suffice to overcome the infrared absorption. But for investigations in the ultraviolet—potentially extremely important—the much higher altitudes of rockets and satellites are needed. Indeed, rockets have already carried ultraviolet spectrographs up 40 miles or more. However, there are many astronomical problems affected by bad seeing but not by absorption; for them stratospheric balloons are a very effective tool.

At the Princeton University Observatory we have long been interested in off-the-ground astronomy, largely because of the enthusiasm of Lyman Spitzer, Jr., director of the Observatory. For the first venture into the field our group chose a comparatively easy yet important problem: a study of the sun. Because of its nearness and brightness the sun is often a good starting point in astronomical research. It is the only star that appears to us as anything more than a point of light. By studying its visible features we can learn not only about conditions of its surface, but also something about its interior. This information helps illuminate many other problems, such as how the stars evolve.

The bright surface of the sun, known as the photosphere, has a finely mottled appearance when it is viewed through a telescope. On it there are bright spots, or "granules," separated by darker regions. The bright spots are columns of hot gas rising from the interior, while the dark areas are cooler gas that is sinking back again. The whole surface of the sun is covered by this ever shifting convective pattern. From the details of the pattern—the size, brightness and duration of the individual granules—we get information about the mechanism by which heat is transported outward from the depths of the star.

Through the years astronomers have taken innumerable photographs of the sun's granulation. For more than half a century—such is the importance of seeing—the prize plate remained one that was made at an unusually favorable moment in 1885 by the French astronomer Jules Janssen. In recent years techniques have improved; photographs of high resolution have been obtained not only during the 1956 manned-balloon flight but also from the ground by Jurgen Rösch of the Pic du Midi Observatory in France, Robert B.

Leighton of the California Institute of Technology and G. Thiessen of the Bergedorf Observatory in Germany. However, an accumulation of indirect evidence indicated that there must be finer details in the granulation pattern than were revealed on any of the plates.

To see these details there seemed no alternative but to get a telescope above the tropopause. When James A. Van Allen of Iowa State University encouraged us to use balloons, our group at Princeton began planning. We turned for advice to several experts: John W. Evans of the Sacramento Peak Observatory in New Mexico, the Navy balloonist Malcolm Ross and cosmic-ray physicists at the University of Minnesota. The resulting plans received financial support from the Office of Naval Research, from the Air Force Geophysical Directorate and more recently from the National Science Foundation.

For the 1957 flights the telescope was designed and constructed by the Perkin-Elmer Corporation; the pointing control, by the Research Service Laboratories of the University of Colorado. The balloons were made and the flights conducted by General Mills, Inc. The capability, enthusiasm and spirit of cooperation of these firms have played a decisive role throughout the project.

A good deal of ingenuity went into building a system that would operate automatically in the lonely reaches of the stratosphere. Perhaps the best way to get an idea of the difficulties involved is to look briefly at the apparatus designed to overcome them.

The telescope itself has an eight-foot tube, at one end of which is a parabolic quartz mirror 12 inches in diameter. At the other end of the tube are a plane mirror and a prism that reflect the light gathered by the parabolic mirror back along the path above the tube of the telescope into a 35-millimeter motion-picture camera. A lens in the light path enlarges the image presented by the primary mirror to the size of an image that would be produced by a 200-foot telescope. At this magnification each frame of the 35-millimeter film covers a rectangle about 50,000 by 35,000 miles on the surface of the sun. Exposures are made at the rate of one per second, each lasting a thousandth of a second.

To find the sun, and to remain pointed at it, the telescope must be free to turn both horizontally and vertically. It is mounted in a metal frame in which it can swing vertically,

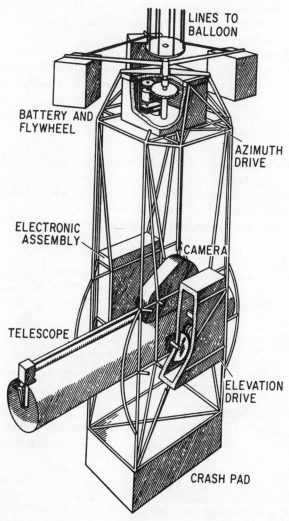

LINES TO BALLOON

BATTERY AND FLYWHEEL

AZIMUTH DRIVE

ELECTRONIC ASSEMBLY

CAMERA

TELESCOPE

ELEVATION DRIVE

CRASH PAD

II-12.   *Mounting of the telescope is depicted in this simplified drawing. The telescope is shown in its observing position. As it is borne aloft it is stowed within the mounting.*

and the frame itself turns in the horizontal plane. A pair of motors, guided by light-sensitive semiconductor "eyes," drives the apparatus in the two directions. This guiding mechanism must hold the telescope very steadily centered on the sun; during exposures the rate of motion cannot exceed one rotation of the telescope per hour. The system did its duty well, as we confirmed in advance by ground tests. We suspended the assembly and allowed it to follow the sun; it pointed at the sun's center accurately and steadily. If someone tried to push the telescope away from its proper position, it would push sturdily back, uttering a low growl. During a preliminary test flight the pointing mechanism passed its final examination.

In flight the apparatus is hung from a parachute that is in turn attached to the balloon. After the film is exhausted a preset timer stows the telescope vertically within the frame and cuts the parachute away from the balloon. In addition to serving as a mounting, the frame protects the telescope

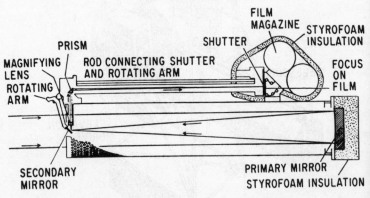

II-13. *Optical system of the telescope is shown in cross section. The arm on which the secondary mirror is mounted is rotated once a second to prevent the mirror from overheating. The magnifying lens increases the size of the image and projects it on the film.*

when it hits the ground. A Styrofoam crash pad on the bottom cushions the fall, and a large wheel at the top, which carries the batteries that drive the motors, takes up the impact when the frame topples over on its side.

Aside from the fundamental questions of optical design and guidance, the major problems that had to be faced concerned heating. Starting at a temperature of say, 60 degrees Fahrenheit on the ground, the telescope was exposed to air at about 70 below zero in the stratosphere while being simultaneously subjected to the full heat of the sun. To minimize distortions the quartz primary mirror was heavily insulated at the back and sides so that practically all the heat was absorbed and radiated at the front face. While the arrangement could not prevent changes in the focal length of the mirror, it did enable the mirror to maintain a nearly perfect surface.

Since the focus of the mirror would necessarily vary, and by an unknown amount, the focal image could not always be expected to fall sharply on the film. We therefore adopted the stratagem of moving the magnifying lens between the mirror and the camera, driving it steadily back and forth over the full range of anticipated variation every 20 seconds. Thus 19 out of every 20 pictures would be blurred, but one was sure to be in focus.

The flat secondary mirror also presented a heating problem, located as it is at the hot primary image of the sun. To ensure its proper functioning it was mounted on an arm that rotated once a second, placing the mirror in the light beam for only a 30th of a second on each cycle. The shutter of the camera was of course synchronized with the motion of the mirror.

By September 16, 1957, all the apparatus had been assembled and tested at an airport near Minneapolis, the headquarters of General Mills. From there it was to be launched. But though we were ready, the stratosphere was not. Overhead was the jet stream, blowing violently toward the north woods. Eight days passed before the winds became favorable. Then we were alerted for a flight at dawn.

Starting at 1:30 a.m. we completed the final check-out, and the launching crew went into action. Using a fork-lift truck, they moved the delicate, top-heavy equipment from the tent where it was stored to the launching truck, hanging it from a pair of hooks on a tall rack. The parachute shrouds were attached to the top of the frame and stretched over the launching truck to the canopy of the parachute, which was laid out in a line. The top of the parachute was attached to the bottom of the balloon, which had been unrolled from its box. The balloon, made of polyethylene two thousandths of an inch thick and reinforced with Fiberglas tapes, would be 130 feet in diameter when it was fully inflated. Now about two thirds of it lay stretched in a thin line beyond the parachute. At the two-thirds point it was held under a roller on a small auxiliary truck. The remaining third was inflated from the top with helium.

As we all tensely awaited sunrise, the quietest time for launching, the inflated portion of the balloon towered above us. It caught the first light of day on its smooth and shining sides, and as the sun brightened it gleamed with a rosy sheen. At last the launching chief gave the signal. The roller holding down the balloon was released and the small truck was driven quickly out of the way. The whole bag rose free, with loud snapping noises, pulling downwind and drawing the parachute up after it. As soon as the shrouds were taut, the launching truck started forward. At the instant it came directly under the balloon a powder squib was fired, cutting a cord that tied the parachute to the truck and allowing the balloon to lift the load. After all the bustle and excitement, the quiet calm as the telescope floated noiselessly away came as a striking contrast.

It was just 7:15 a.m. when the launching was completed and the chase began. The posse included a small plane and a truck (both equipped to receive radio signals from the balloon and thus to track it in case of clouds), a van for carrying back the equipment, and several personnel cars.

By nine o'clock the balloon had reached altitude (about 82,000 feet, or above 96 per cent of the atmosphere), and the master timer turned on the electronic equipment. At 9:15 the pointing motors centered the telescope on the sun. An hour later, when the temperature had settled down, the camera was turned on. A thousand feet of film, containing 8,000 frames, was fully exposed by 12:30. At 12:45 the timer gave the signal to restow the telescope in its vertical position. A little later a powder squib cut the parachute free. Those of us who were watching through binoculars saw the balloon shatter into a thousand pieces, and the red- and white-striped parachute open, its load swinging wildly underneath. The shreds of balloon spread out and followed like the silvery tail of a comet.

The parachute landed its cargo in a field about 150 miles east of Minneapolis. Guided by the plane we arrived at the site 15 minutes after impact. We examined the equipment, which had suffered little damage, stowed it in the van after removing the camera with the exposed film and left for home. Arriving at midnight, we had 24 hours of astronomi- cal ballooning behind us. We were so tired we had to go to bed leaving unanswered the burning question of whether the experiment had been successful.

Next morning, when we had rested enough to do reliable work in the darkroom, we started to develop the film. The first 100 feet proved that it was not blank, as we had seen it in our nightmares. The apparatus had functioned well, and we had some photographs of unprecedented quality.

A second flight a short time later gave us another 1,000 feet of photographs. All told about 10 frames turned out to have the superior resolution for which we had hoped. These 10 frames exceeded the minimum goal of the entire under- taking, and contained a wealth of new information. Many other frames contained excellent portions. That there were not more of top quality was the fault of vibration from the motors and other rotating parts. There was no evidence at all that bad seeing interfered in any of the frames.

Three main characteristics stand out on the photographs. First, the granules come in widely assorted sizes. Many of them are only 180 miles in diameter, far too small to have been recognized on photographs taken from the ground. From this size they range up to diameters of about 1,000 miles. Second, most of the granules have the complicated shapes of irregular polygons. Third, the dark areas differ sharply from the bright ones; they tend to form a connected net of narrow lanes separating the more substantial bright spots.

This pattern came as a complete surprise. It represents one of the types of motion that may be set up when a fluid is heated evenly from below, as the gas in the sun is. But it is not the type we expected to see.

The behavior of such a fluid depends on its depth and on the rate at which it is heated. If it is shallow and the heating is gentle, the rising columns of gas or liquid form a series of neatly defined polygons of uniform size. This condition is known as stationary convection. Increasing the depth or the rate of heating causes the stationary cells to break up into a shifting array of irregular polygons of varying sizes. The surface now presents an ever changing appearance, from which comes the term nonstationary convection.

The sun's outer layer is exceedingly deep, and heat flows through it at an enormous rate. Because of these extreme conditions we had expected the granulation pattern to be still more chaotic than for nonstationary convection. Instead the new photographs show unmistakably that the pattern of the solar granulation is that of nonstationary convection. This unexpected result corrects our picture of conditions in the solar atmosphere. It contributes to our knowledge of how the heat produced at the center is carried outwards. It therefore provides new information about conditions in the interior of the sun, and is bound to help us in understanding the evolution of stars in general.

Readers who would like to get a vivid picture of conditions on the sun's surface can do so in the following home experiment: Pour molten paraffin to a depth of about an eighth of an inch into a flat-bottomed Pyrex dish at least six inches across. Add a little powdered aluminum and lampblack to make the convection patterns visible. Place the dish on an electric plate and heat it evenly over the entire bottom just enough to keep the paraffin liquid. Soon the surface will divide into uniform, well-defined polygons: the pattern of stationary convection. Now add enough paraffin to bring the depth to half an inch. The stationary cells will break up into the typical nonstationary pattern—irregular polygons of assorted sizes separated by lanes, just as in the solar granulation.

Although granulation studies were the primary aim of the first balloon experiment, the sharp pictures that were obtained throw new light on several other problems. One of them concerns certain small, dark spots known as pores. Photographs taken from the ground were rarely sharp enough to show up the pores clearly, so it was impossible to follow their development. An analysis by J. D. Bahng of the balloon pictures has now demonstrated that the pores have much longer lifetimes than the granules. This substantiates the earlier hypothesis that granules are nothing but small sunspots. In another investigation John B. Rogerson is using the new photographs to measure the sharpness of the edge of the sun. This will give information on the temperature in the outer layers of the solar atmosphere.

Now that it is under way, high-altitude astronomy will develop rapidly. At Princeton our Flying Telescope Project, headed by Lyman Spitzer, is planning both balloon and satellite experiments. In our next venture with the stratoscope (as the balloon telescope has been named) we shall attempt to point and focus the instrument by remote control.

A new television system being developed by V. K. Zworykin's section at the Radio Corporation of America Laboratories will present to ground observers the same picture that is falling on the photographic film. As they watch the television screen, they will adjust the focus of the telescope by radio and keep it sharp. Thus practically every frame should be in focus, rather than every 20th one. A major effort is also being made to eliminate from the system the mechanical vibrations that gave the chief trouble in 1957.

In the coming flights we plan to observe the granules continuously over an extended period to see how they develop and how long they persist. We also aim to study sunspots and the granulation at their periphery. Here the gas is subject to strong magnetic fields. Do the fields stabilize it sufficiently to set up stationary convection in these areas? This is one of the fascinating questions in the field of plasma physics, a field growing in importance for thermonuclear reactors and astrophysics alike.

Beyond these solar investigations are much broader opportunities for balloon astronomy. The very best night pictures taken from the ground have a resolution of about a third of a second of arc, which is the theoretical resolving power of a 12-inch mirror. With a 36-inch mirror the theoretical limit is a 10th of a second of arc, and above the atmosphere one might attain it. Planning for a 36-inch stratoscope has already begun, but the requirements are formidable. The mirror must be ground to unprecedented accuracy. The telescope must be guided steadily within a 10th of a second of arc for minutes at a time; in the first flights guiding to a third of a second of arc during a thousandth of a second sufficed. However great the difficulties, the potential rewards for solving them are dazzling.

Better resolution is the only answer to many basic astronomical problems. With the help of the 36-inch stratoscope we should be able to understand better the changes in the atmospheres of Venus and Jupiter, analyze the division in Saturn's rings and measure the diameter of Pluto. Farther out in space we could study the Great Nebula in Orion, where new stars seem to be forming in dense interstellar clouds. At the other end of the evolutionary scale we could investigate in detail whether the gigantic shells of gas known as planetary nebulae represent the dying phases of stars. Then there are the galaxies outside our own, whose mysterious dense nuclei may contain clues to their past history.

All these problems and many more can be tackled when a 36-inch telescope is put into the black and unwavering heights of the stratosphere. And at the same time invaluable experience can be gained for the next phase of astronomy with telescopes on artificial satellites.

III. The Solar System

III. The Solar System

The mechanics of the solar system and how it affects the apparent movement of the heavens around the earth form the substance of the following paper. It was originally written by one of the greatest mathematical astronomers of the nineteenth century. The present version is a revision prepared by a well-known American professor of astronomy. Nowadays, astronomers are predominantly interested in the examination of the solar system from the astrophysical rather than the mechanical viewpoint. Nevertheless, the facts Newcomb presents remain of fundamental importance.

Newcomb's treatment points up the importance of mathematics in astronomical research. Many of the workings of the solar system can be described in the relatively simple terms of spherical trigonometry. Others are more complex. The motions of the moon are determined by numerous separate forces. They have been investigated by divers mathematical means. As a later article describes, the discovery of Neptune resulted from the solution of a complex mathematical problem. Similarly modern theoretical astronomy depends in large measure on the use of advanced mathematics. Eddington, for example, in his classic exposition of the internal constitution of the stars, arrived at his conclusions by mathematical methods which have served as a model for contemporary theoretical astronomers. Until recently, the tools of this branch of astronomy were pencil and paper. Nowadays laborious calculations like those posed by Newcomb are performed by electronic computers. At the Naval Observatory in Washington, where the motions of the stars and planets are calculated by "electronic brains," staff members have been released for other research.

Simon Newcomb was born in Nova Scotia in 1835 and died at Washington in 1909. He won an international reputation by his investigation of the orbits of asteroids. At the United

States Naval Observatory, he made calculations of celestial
motions which have served as the basis for exact navigational
methods. His study of the theory of the moon's motion is
considered a classic. Professor Baker is a distinguished
astronomer in his own right and the author of standard
texts on astronomy.

THE HEAVENS AND THE EARTH

SIMON NEWCOMB

Revised by Robert H. Baker

Aspects of the Heavens

THE IMMENSITY of the distances which separate us from
the heavenly bodies makes it impossible for us to form
a distinct conception of the true scale of the universe, and
very difficult to conceive of the heavenly bodies in their
actual relations to us. If, on looking at a body in the sky,
there were any way of estimating its distance, and if our
eyes were so keen that we could see the minutest features
on the surface of the planets and stars, the true structure
of the universe would have been obvious from the time
that men began to study the heavens. A little reflection will
make it obvious that if we could mount above the earth to
a distance of, say, ten thousand times its diameter, so that
it would no longer have any perceptible size, it would look
to us, in the light of the sun, like a star in the sky. The ancients had no conception of distances like this, and so supposed that the heavenly bodies were, as they appeared, of a
constitution totally different from that of the earth. We ourselves, looking at the heavens, are unable to conceive of the
stars being millions of times farther than the planets. All
look as if spread out on one sky at the same distance. We

have to learn their actual arrangement and distances by reason.

It is from the impossibility of conceiving these enormous differences in the distances of objects on the earth and the heavens, that the real difficulty of forming a mental picture of them in their true relation arises. I shall ask the reader's careful attention in an attempt to present these relations in the simplest way, so as to connect things as they are with things as we see them.

Let us suppose the earth taken away from under our feet, leaving us hanging in mid space. We should then see the heavenly bodies—sun, moon, planets, and stars—surrounding us in every direction, up and down, east and west, north and south. The eye would rest on nothing else. As we have just explained, all these objects would seem to us to be at the same distance.

A great collection of points scattered in every direction at an equal distance from one central point must all lie upon the inner surface of a hollow sphere. It follows that, in the case supposed, the heavenly bodies will appear to us as if set in a sphere in the center of which we appear to be placed. Since one of the final objects of astronomy is to learn the directions of the heavenly bodies from us, this apparent sphere is talked about in astronomy as if it were a reality. It is called the *celestial sphere*. In the case we have supposed, with the earth out of the way, all the heavenly bodies on this sphere would at any moment seem at rest. The stars would remain apparently at rest day after day and week after week. It is true that, by watching the planets, we should in a few days or weeks, as the case might be, see their slow motion around the sun, but this would not be perceptible at once. Our first impression would be that the sphere was made of some solid, crystalline substance, and that the heavenly bodies were fastened to its inner surface. The ancients had this notion, which they brought yet nearer the truth by fancying a number of these spheres fitting inside of each other to represent the different distances of the heavenly bodies.

With this conception well in mind, let us bring the earth back under our feet. Now we have to make a draft upon

the reader's power of conception. Considered in its relation to the magnitude of the heavens, the earth is a mere
point; yet, when we bring it into place, its surface cuts
off one half of the universe from our view, just as an apple
would cut off the view of one side of a room from an insect
crawling upon it. That half of the celestial sphere which,
being above the horizon, remains visible is called the *visible
hemisphere;* the half below, the view of which is cut off
by the earth, is called the *invisible hemisphere.* Of course
we could see the latter by traveling around the earth.

Having this state of things well in mind, we must make
another draft on the reader's attention. We know that the
earth is not at rest, but rotates unceasingly around an axis
passing through its center. The natural result of this is an
apparent rotation of the celestial sphere in the opposite
direction. The earth rotates from west toward east; hence
the sphere seems to rotate from east toward west. This real
rotation of the earth, with the apparent revolution of the
stars which it causes, is called the *diurnal motion,* because
it is completed in a day.

Our next problem is to show the connection between the
very simple conception of the rotation of the earth and
the more complicated appearance presented by the apparent
diurnal motion of the heavenly bodies which it brings about.
The latter varies with the latitude of the observer upon the
earth's surface. Let us begin with its appearance in our
middle northern latitudes.

For this purpose we may in imagination build a hollow
globe representing the celestial sphere. We may make it as
large as we please, but one of thirty or forty feet in diameter
would answer our purpose. Let Figure III-1 be an inside
view of this globe, mounted on two pivots, P and Q, so that it
can turn round on them diagonally. In the middle, at O, we
have a horizontal platform, NS, on which we sit. The constellations are marked on the inside of the globe, covering
the whole surface, but those on the lower half are hidden
from view by the platform. This platform, as is evident,
represents the horizon.

The globe is now made to turn on its pivots. What will

happen? We shall see the stars near the pivot P revolving around the latter as the globe turns. The stars on a certain circle KN will graze the edges of the platform, as they pass below P. Those yet farther from P will dip below the platform to a greater or less extent, according to their distance from P. Stars near the circle EF, halfway between P and Q, will perform half their course above and half below the platform. Finally, stars within the circle ST will never rise above the level of the platform at all, and will remain invisible to us.

To our eyes the celestial sphere is such a globe as this, of infinite dimensions. It seems to us to be continually revolving round a certain point in the sky as a pivot, making one revolution in nearly a day, and carrying the sun, moon, and stars with it. The stars preserve their relative positions as if fastened to the revolving celestial sphere. That is to say, if we take a photograph of them at any hour of the night, the same photograph will show their appearance at any other hour, if we only hold it in the right position.

The pivot corresponding to P is called the *north celestial pole*. To dwellers in middle northern latitudes, where most of us live, it is in the northern sky, nearly midway between the zenith and the northern horizon. The farther south we live, the nearer it is to the horizon, its altitude above the latter being equal to the latitude of the place where the observer stands. Quite near it is the pole star, which we

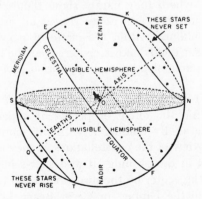

III-1. *The celestial sphere as it appears to us.*

shall hereafter show how to locate. To ordinary observation, the pole star seems never to move from its position. In our time it is little more than a degree from the pole, a quantity with which we need not now concern ourselves.

Opposite the north celestial pole, and therefore as far below our horizon as the north one is above, lies the *south celestial pole*.

An obvious fact is that the diurnal motion as we see it in our latitude is oblique. When the sun rises in the east it does not seem to go straight up from the horizon, but moves over toward the south at a more or less acute angle with the horizon. So when it sets, its motion relative to the horizon is again oblique.

Now, imagine that we take a pair of compasses long enough to reach the sky. We put one point on the sky at the north celestial pole, and the other point far enough from it to touch the horizon below the pole. Keeping the first point at the pole, we draw a complete circle on the celestial sphere with the other point. This circle just touches the north horizon at its lowest points and, in our northern latitudes, extends to near the zenith at its highest point. The stars within this circle never set, but only seem to perform a daily course around the pole. For this reason this circle is called the *circle of perpetual apparition*.

The stars farther south rise and set, but perform less and less of their daily course above our horizon, till we reach its south point, where they barely show themselves.

Stars yet farther south never rise at all in our latitudes. They are contained within the *circle of perpetual occultation*, which surrounds and is centered on the south celestial pole, as the circle of perpetual apparition is centered on the north one.

Figure III-2 shows the principal stars of the northern heavens within the circle of perpetual apparition for the Northern States. By holding it with the month on top we shall have a view of the constellations as they are seen about eight o'clock in the evening. It also shows how to find the pole star in the center by the direction of the two outer stars or pointers in the Dipper, or Great Bear.

Now let us change our latitude and see what occurs. If we

journey toward the equator, the direction of our horizon changes, and during our voyage we see the pole star constantly sinking lower and lower. As we approach the equator, it approaches the horizon, reaching it when we reach the equator. It is plain enough that the circle of perpetual apparition grows smaller until, at the equator, it ceases to exist, each pole being in our horizon. There the diurnal motion seems to us quite different from what it is here. The sun, moon, and stars, when they rise, commence their motion directly upwards. If one of them rises exactly in the east, it will pass through the zenith; one rising south of the east will pass south of the zenith; one rising north of the east, north of the zenith.

Continuing our course into the southern hemisphere, we find that the sun, while still rising in the east, generally passes the meridian to the north of the zenith. The main point of difference between the two hemispheres is that, as the sun now culminates in the north, its apparent motion is not in the direction of the hands of a watch, as with us, but in the opposite direction. In middle southern latitudes, the northern constellations, so familiar to us, are always below the horizon, but we see new ones in the south. Some of these are noted for their beauty, the Southern Cross, for example. Indeed, it has often been thought that the southern heavens are more brilliant and contain more stars than the

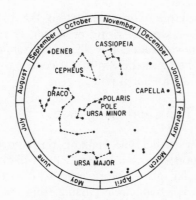

III-2. *The northern sky and the pole star.*

northern ones. But this view is now found to be incorrect. Careful study and counts of the stars show the number to be about the same in one hemisphere as in the other. Probably the impression we have mentioned arose from the superior clearness of the sky in the southern regions. For some reason, perhaps because of the drier climate, the air is less filled with smoke and haze in the southern portions of the African and American continents than it is in our northern regions.

What we have said of the diurnal motion of the northern stars round and round the pole applies to the stars in the southern heavens. But there is no southern pole star, and therefore nothing to distinguish the position of the southern celestial pole. The latter has a number of small stars around it, but they are no thicker than in any other region of the sky. Of course, the southern hemisphere has its circle of perpetual apparition, which is larger the farther south we travel. That is to say, the stars in a certain circle around the south celestial pole never set, but simply revolve around it, apparently in an opposite direction from what they do in the north. So, also, there is a circle of perpetual occultation containing those stars around the north pole which, in our latitudes, never set. After we go beyond 20° south latitude we can no longer see any part of the constellation Ursa Minor. Still farther south the Great Bear will only occasionally show itself to a greater or less extent above the horizon.

Could we continue our journey to the south pole we should no longer see any rising or setting of the stars. The latter would move around the sky in horizontal circles, the center or pole being at the zenith. Of course, the same thing would be true at the north pole.

Relation of Time and Longitude

We all know that a line running through any place on the earth in a north and south direction is called the meridian of that particular place. More exactly, a meridian of the earth's surface is a semicircle passing from the north to the south pole. Such semicircles pass in every direction from the north pole, and one may be drawn so as to pass through any place. The meridian of the Royal Observatory at Greenwich is now adopted by most nations, our own included, as the one from which longitudes are measured, and by which in the United States and a considerable part of Europe the clocks are set.

Corresponding to the terrestrial meridian of a place is a celestial meridian which passes from the north celestial pole through the zenith, intersects the horizons at its south point, and continues to the south pole. As the earth revolves on its axis it carries the celestial as well as the terrestrial meridian with it, so that the former, in the course of a day, sweeps over the whole celestial sphere. The appearance to us is that every point of the celestial sphere crosses the meridian in the course of a day.

Noon is the moment at which the sun passes the meridian. Before the introduction of railways, people used to set their clocks by the sun. But owing to the obliquity of the ecliptic and the eccentricity of the earth's orbit around the sun, the intervals between successive passages of the sun are not exactly equal. The consequence is that, if a clock keeps exact time, the sun will sometimes pass the meridian before and sometimes after twelve by the clock. When this was understood, a distinction was made between apparent and mean time. Apparent time is the unequal time determined by the sun; mean time is that given by a clock keeping perfect time month after month. The difference between these two is called the equation of time. Its greatest amounts are reached every year about the first of November and the middle of February. At the former time, the sun passes the meridian sixteen minutes before the clock shows twelve; in February, fourteen or fifteen minutes after twelve.

To define mean time astronomers imagine a mean sun which always moves along the celestial equator so as to pass the meridian at exactly equal intervals of time, and which is sometimes ahead of the real sun and sometimes behind it. This imaginary or mean sun determines the time of day. The subject will perhaps be a little easier if we describe things as they appear, imagining the earth to be at rest while the mean sun revolves around it, crossing the meridian of every place in succession. We thus imagine noon to be constantly traveling around the world. In our latitudes, its speed is not far from a thousand feet per second; that is to say, if it is noon at a certain place where we stand, it will one second afterward be noon about one thousand feet farther west, in another second a thousand feet yet farther west, and so on through the twenty-four hours, until noon will once more get back to where we are. The obvious result of this is that it is never the same time of day at the same moment at two places east or west of each other. As we travel west, we shall continually find our watches to be too fast for the places which we reach, while in traveling east they will be too slow. This varying time is called *local time*.

Formerly the use of local time caused great inconvenience to travelers. Every railway had its own meridian which it ran its trains by; and the traveler was frequently liable to miss his train by not knowing the relation between his watch or a clock and the railway time. So in 1883, our present system of standard time was introduced. Under this system, standard meridians are adopted fifteen degrees apart, this being the space over which the sun passes in one hour. The time at which noon passes a standard meridian is then used throughout a zone extending seven or eight degrees on each side. This is called *standard time*. The longitudes which mark the zones are reckoned from Greenwich. It happens that Philadelphia is about seventy-five degrees in longitude, or five hours in time from Greenwich. More exactly, it is about one minute of time more than this. Thus the standard meridian which we use for the Eastern States passes a little east of Philadelphia. When mean noon reaches this meridian it is considered as twelve o'clock as far west as Ohio. An hour later, it is considered twelve o'clock in the Mississippi Valley. An hour later, it is twelve o'clock for the region of the Rocky Mountains. In yet another hour, it is twelve o'clock on the Pacific coast. Thus we use four different kinds of time, Eastern time, Central time, Mountain time, and Pacific time, differing from each other by entire hours. Using this time, the traveler has only to set his watch forward or back one hour at a time, as he travels between the Pacific and the Atlantic coast, and he will always find it correct for the region in which he is at the time.

It is by this difference of time that the longitudes of places are determined. Imagine that an observer in New York makes a tap with a telegraph key at the exact moment when a certain star crosses his meridian, and that this moment is recorded at Chicago as well as New York. When the star reaches the meridian of Chicago, the observer taps the time of its crossing over his meridian in the same way. The interval between the two taps shows the difference of longitude between the two cities.

Another method of getting the same result is for each observer to telegraph his local time to the other. The difference of the two times gives the longitude.

In this connection, it must be remembered that the heavenly bodies rise and set by local, not standard, time. Hence the time of rising and setting of the sun, given in the almanacs, will not answer to set our watches by for standard time unless we are on one of the standard meridians. One difference between these two kinds of time is that local time varies continuously as we travel east or west, while standard time varies only by jumps of one hour when we cross the boundaries of any of the four zones just described.

Midnight, like noon, is continually traveling round the earth, crossing all the meridians in succession. At every crossing it inaugurates the beginning of another day on that meridian. If it is Monday at any crossing, it will be Tuesday when it gets back again. So there must be some meridian where Monday changes to Tuesday, and where every day changes into the day following. This dividing meridian, called the "date line," is determined only by custom and convenience. As colonization extended toward the east and the west men carried their count of days with them. The result was that whenever it extended so far that those going east met those going west they found their time differing by one day. What for the westward traveler was Monday was

Tuesday for the eastern one. This was the case when we acquired Alaska. The Russians having reached that region by traveling east, it was found that, when we took possession by going west, our Saturday was their Sunday. This gave rise to the question whether the inhabitants, in celebrating the festivals of the Greek Church, should follow the old or the new reckoning of days. The subject was referred to the head of the church at St. Petersburg, and finally to Struve, the director of the Pulkova Observatory, the national astronomical institution of the empire. Struve made a report in favor of the American reckoning, and the change to it was duly carried out.

At the present time custom prescribes for the date line the meridian opposite that of Greenwich. This passes through the Pacific Ocean, and in its course crosses very little land—only the northeastern corner of Asia and, perhaps, some of the Fiji Islands. This fortunate circumstance prevents a serious inconvenience which might arise if the date line passed through the interior of a country. In this case the people of one city might have their time a day different from those of a neighboring city across the line. It is even conceivable that residents on two sides of the same street would have different days for Sunday. But being in the ocean, no such inconvenience follows. The date line is not necessarily a meridian of the earth, but may deviate from one side to the other in order to prevent the inconvenience we have described. Thus the inhabitants of Chatham Island have the same time as that of the neighboring island of New Zealand, although the meridian of 180° from Greenwich runs between them.

How the Position of a Heavenly Body is Defined

In this chapter I have to use and explain some technical terms. The ideas conveyed by them are necessary to a complete understanding of the celestial motions, and of the positions of the stars at any hour when we may wish to observe them. Turning back to our first figure, we see ourselves concerned with the relation of two spheres. One of these is the real globe of the earth, on the surface of which we dwell, and which is continually carrying us around by its daily rotation. The other is the apparent sphere of the heavens, which surrounds our globe on all sides at an enormous distance, and which, although it has no reality, we are obliged to imagine in order to know where to look for the heavenly bodies. Notice that we see this sphere from its center, so that everything we see upon it appears upon its inside surface, while we see the surface of the earth from the outside.

There is a correspondence between points and circles on these two spheres. We have already shown how the axis of the earth, which marks our north and south poles, being continued in both directions through space, marks the north and south poles of the celestial sphere.

We know that the earth's equator passes around it at an equal distance from the two poles. In the same way we have an equator on the celestial sphere which passes around it at a distance of ninety degrees from either celestial pole. If it could be painted on the sky we should always see it, by day or night, in one fixed position. We can imagine exactly how it would look. It intersects the horizon in the east and west points, and is in fact the line which the sun seems to mark out in the sky by its diurnal course during the twelve hours that it is above the horizon at the equinoxes, in March or September. In our northernmost States it passes about halfway between the zenith and the south horizon, but passes nearer the zenith the farther south we are.

As we have circles of latitude parallel to the equator passing around the earth both north and south of the equator, so we have on the celestial sphere circles parallel to the celestial equator, and therefore having one or the other of the celestial poles as a center. As the parallels of latitude on the earth grow smaller and smaller toward the pole, so do these celestial circles grow smaller toward the celestial poles.

We know that longitude on the earth is measured by the position of a meridian passing from the north to the south pole through the place where position is to be defined. The angle which this meridian makes with that through the Greenwich Observatory is the longitude of the place.

We have the same system in the heavens. Circles are

imagined to pass from one celestial pole to the other in every direction, but all intersecting the equator at right angles, as shown in Figure III-3. These are called *hour circles.* One of them is called the equinoctial colure, and is so marked in the figure; it passes through the vernal equinox. This circle plays a part in the sky corresponding to the meridian of Greenwich on the earth's surface.

The position of a star on the celestial sphere is defined in the same way that the position of a city on the earth is defined, by its longitude and latitude. But different terms are used. In astronomy, the measure which corresponds to longitude is called *right ascension;* that which corresponds to latitude is called *declination.* We thus have the following definitions, which I must ask the reader to remember carefully.

The declination of a star is its apparent distance from the celestial equator north or south. In the figure the star is in declination 25° north.

The right ascension of a star is the angle which the hour circle passing through it makes with the equinoctial colure which passes through the vernal equinox. In the figure the star is in three hours right ascension.

The right ascension of a star is, in astronomical usage, generally expressed as so many hours, minutes, and seconds, in the way shown on Figure III-3. But it may equally well be expressed in degrees, as we express the longitude of a

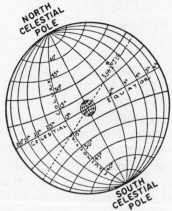

III-3.   *Circles of the celestial sphere.*

place on the earth. The right ascension expressed in hours may be changed into degrees by the simple process of multiplication by 15. This is because the earth revolves 15° in an hour. Figure III-3 also shows us that, while the degrees of latitude are nearly of the same length all over the earth, those of longitude continually diminish, slowly at first and more rapidly afterwards, from the equator toward the poles. At the equator the degree of longitude is about 69½ statute miles, but at the latitude of 45° it is only about 42 miles. At 60° it is less than 35 miles, at the pole it comes down to nothing, because there the meridians meet.

We may see that the speed of the rotation of the earth follows the same law of diminution. At the equator, 15° is about 1,000 miles. There the rotation is at the rate of 1,000 miles an hour. This is about 1,500 feet per second. But in latitude 45° the speed is diminished to little more than 1,000 feet per second. At 60° north, it is only half that at the equator; at the poles it goes down to nothing.

In applying this system the only trouble arises from the earth's rotation. As long as we do not travel, we remain on the same circle of longitude on the earth. But by the rotation of the earth, the right ascension of any point in the sky which seems to us fixed, is continually changing. The only difference between the celestial meridian and an hour circle is that the former travels round with the earth, while the latter is fixed on the celestial sphere.

There is a strict resemblance in almost every point between the earth and the celestial sphere. As the former rotates on its axis from west to east, the latter seems to rotate from east to west. If we imagine the earth centered inside the celestial sphere with a common axis passing through them, as shown in the figure, we shall have a clear idea of the relations we wish to set forth.

If the sun, like the stars, seemed fixed on the celestial sphere from year to year, the problem of finding a star when we knew its right ascension and declination would be easier than it actually is. Owing to the annual revolution of the earth round the sun there is a continual change in the apparent position of the sphere at a given hour of the night. We must next point out the effect of this revolution.

The Annual Motion of the Earth and Its Results

It is well known that the earth not only turns on its axis, but makes an annual revolution round the sun. The result of this motion—in fact, the phenomenon by which it is shown —is that the sun appears to make an annual revolution around the celestial sphere among the stars. We have only to imagine ourselves moving round the sun and therefore seeing the latter in different directions, to see that it must appear to us to move among the stars, which are farther than it is. It is true that the motion is not at once evident because the stars are invisible in the daytime. But the fact of the motion will be made very clear if, day after day, we watch some particular fixed star in the west. We shall find that it sets earlier and earlier every day; in other words, it is getting continually nearer and nearer the sun. More exactly, since the real direction of the star is unchanged, the sun appears to be approaching the star.

If we could see the stars in the daytime, all round the sun, the case would be yet clearer. We should see that if the sun and a star rose together in the morning the sun would, during the day, gradually work past the star in an easterly direction. Between the rising and setting it would move nearly its own diameter relative to the star. Next morning we

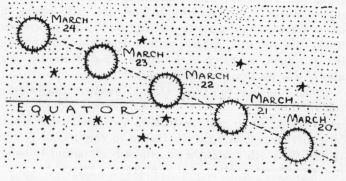

III-4.   *The sun crossing the equator about March* 21.

should see that it had gotten quite away from the star, being nearly two diameters distant from it. The figure shows how this would go on at the time of the spring equinox, after March 21. This motion would continue month after month. At the end of the year the sun would have made a complete circuit of the heavens relative to the star, and we should see the two once more together.

The Sun's Apparent Path

How the above effect is produced will be seen by Figure III-5, which represents the earth's orbit round the sun, with the stars in the vast distance. When the earth is at A, we see the sun in the line AM, as if it were among the stars at M. As we carried on the earth from A to B, the sun seems to move from M to N, and so on through the year. This apparent motion of the sun in one year around the celestial sphere was noticed by the ancients, who seem to have taken much trouble to map it out. They imagined a line passing around the celestial sphere which the sun always follows in its annual course, and which they called the *ecliptic*. They noticed that the planets follow nearly but not exactly the same general course as the sun among the stars. A belt extending around on each side of the ecliptic, and broad enough to contain all the known planets, as well as the sun,

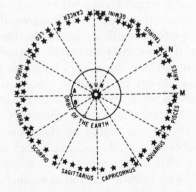

III-5. *The orbit of the earth, and the zodiac.*

was called the *zodiac*. It was divided into twelve signs, each marked by a constellation. The sun goes through each sign in the course of a month and through all twelve signs in a year. Thus arose the familiar signs of the zodiac, which bore the same names as the constellations among which they were situated. This is not the case at present, owing to the slow motion of precession soon to be described.

It will be seen that the two great circles we have described spanning the entire celestial sphere are fixed in entirely different ways. The equator is determined by the direction in which the axis of the earth points, and spans the sphere midway between the two celestial poles. The ecliptic is determined by the earth's motion around the sun.

These two circles do not coincide, but intersect each other at two opposite points, at an angle of 23½°, or nearly one quarter of a right angle. This angle is called the *obliquity of the ecliptic*. To understand exactly how it arises we must mention a fact about the celestial poles; from what we have said of them it will be seen that they are not determined by anything in the heavens, but by the direction of the earth's axis only; they are nothing but the two opposite points in the heavens which lie exactly in the line of the earth's axis. The celestial equator, being the great circle halfway between the poles, is also fixed by the direction of the earth's axis and by nothing else.

Let us now suppose that the earth's orbit around the sun is horizontal. We may in imagination represent it by the circumference of a round level platform with the sun in its center. We suppose the earth to move around the circumference of the platform with its center on the level of the platform; then, if the earth's axis were vertical, its equator would be horizontal and on a level with the platform and therefore would always be directed toward the sun in its center, as the earth made its annual course around the platform. Then, on the celestial sphere, the ecliptic determined by the course of the sun would be the same circle as the equator. The obliquity of the ecliptic arises from the fact that the earth's orbit is not vertical, as just supposed, but is inclined 23½°. The ecliptic has the same inclination to the plane of the platform; thus the obliquity is the result of the inclination of the earth's axis. An important fact connected with the subject is that, as the earth makes its revolutions around the sun, the direction of its axis remains unchanged in space; hence its north pole is tipped away from the sun or toward it, according to its position in the orbit. This is shown in Figure III-6, which represents the platform we have supposed, with the earth's axis tipped toward the right hand. The north pole will always be tipped in this direction, whether the earth is east, west, north, or south from the sun.

To see the effect of the inclination upon the ecliptic suppose that, at noon on some twenty-first day of March, the earth should suddenly stop turning on its axis, but continue its course around the sun. What we should then see during the next three months is represented in Figure III-7, in which we are supposed to be looking at the southern sky. We see the sun on the meridian, where it will at first seem to remain immovable. The figure shows the celestial equator passing through the east and west points of the horizon as already described and also the ecliptic, intersecting it at the equinox. Watching the result for a time equal to three of our months we should see the sun slowly make its way along the ecliptic to the point marked "summer solstice," its farthest northern point, which it would reach about June 22.

Figure III-8 enables us to follow its course for three

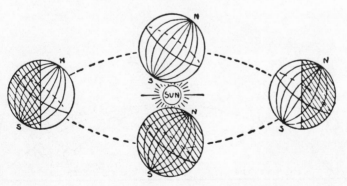

III-6.   How the obliquity of the ecliptic produces the changes of seasons.

months longer. After passing the summer solstice, its course gradually carries it once more to the equator, which it again crosses about September 22. Its course during the rest of the year is the counterpart of that during the first six months. It is farthest south of the equator on December 22, and again crosses it on March 21. The dates vary a little from year to year owing to the plan of leap years.

We see that there are four cardinal points in this apparent annual course of the sun: (1) Where we have commenced our watch is the vernal equinox. (2) The point where the sun, having reached its northern limit, begins to again approach the equator. This is called the summer solstice. (3) Opposite the vernal equinox is the autumnal equinox, which the sun passes about September 22. (4) Opposite the summer solstice is the point where the sun is farthest south. This is called the winter solstice.

The hour circles which pass from one celestial pole to the other through these points at right angles to the equator are called *colures*. That which passes through the vernal equinox is the equinoctial colure, from which right ascensions are counted as already described. The one at right angles to it is called the solstitial colure.

Let us now show the relation of the constellations to the seasons and the time of day. Suppose that today the sun and a star passed the meridian at the same moment; tomorrow

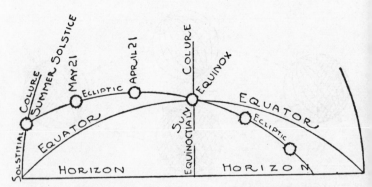

III-7. *Apparent motion of the sun along the ecliptic in spring and summer.*

the sun will be nearly a degree to the east of the star, which shows that the star will pass the meridian nearly four minutes sooner than the sun will. This will continue day after day throughout the entire year until the two will again pass the meridian at about the same moment. Thus the star will have passed once oftener than the sun. That is to say: In the course of a common year, while the sun has passed the meridian 365 times, a star has passed it 366 times. Of course, if we take a star in the south, it will have risen and set the same number of times.

Astronomers keep the reckoning of this different rising and setting of the stars by using a sidereal day, or star day, equal to the interval between two passages of a star, or of the vernal equinox, across the meridian. They divide this day into twenty-four sidereal hours, and these into minutes and seconds, according to the usual plan. They also use sidereal clocks which gain about three minutes and fifty-six seconds per day on the ordinary clocks and thus show sidereal time. Sidereal noon is the moment at which the vernal equinox crosses the meridian of the place. The clock is then set at 0 hours, 0 minutes, and 0 seconds. Thus set and regulated, the sidereal clock keeps time with the apparent rotation of the celestial sphere, so that the astronomer has only to look at his clock to see, by day or by night, what stars are on the meridian and what the positions of the constellations are.

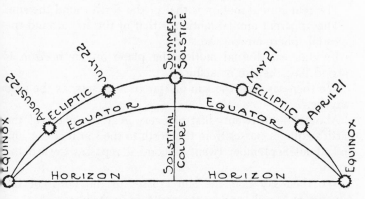

III-8. *Apparent motion of the sun from March till September.*

If the earth's axis were perpendicular to the plane of the ecliptic, the latter would coincide with the equator, and we should have no difference of seasons the year round. The sun would always rise in the exact east and set in the exact west. There would be only a very slight change in the temperature arising from the fact that the earth is a little nearer the sun in January than in July. Owing to the obliquity of the ecliptic it follows that, while the sun is north of the equator, which is the case from March to September, the sun shines upon the northern hemisphere during a greater time of each day, and at a greater angle, than on the southern hemisphere. In the southern hemisphere the opposite is the case. The sun shines longer from September till March than it does on the northern hemisphere. Thus we have winter in the northern hemisphere when it is summer in the southern, and vice versa.

Before going farther let us recapitulate the phenomena we have described from the two points of view: one, that of the real motions of the earth; the other, that of the apparent motions of the heavens, to which the real motions give rise.

The real diurnal motion is the turning of the earth on its axis.

The apparent diurnal motion is that which the stars appear to have in consequence of the earth's rotation.

The real annual motion is that of the earth round the sun.

The apparent annual motion is that of the sun around the celestial sphere among the stars.

By the real diurnal motion the plane of our horizon is carried past the sun or a star.

We then say that the sun or star rises or sets, as the case may be.

About March twenty-first of every year the plane of the earth's equator passes from the north to the south of the sun, and about September twenty-second it repasses toward the north.

We then say that the sun crosses to the north of the equator in March, and to the south in September.

In June of every year the plane of the earth's equator is

at the greatest distance south of the sun, and in December at the greatest distance north.

We say in the first case that the sun is at the northern solstice, and in the second that it is at the southern solstice.

The earth's axis is tipped twenty-three and a half degrees from the perpendicular to the earth's orbit.

The apparent result is that the ecliptic is inclined twenty-three and a half degrees to the celestial equator.

During June and the other summer months the northern hemisphere of the earth is tipped toward the sun. Places in north latitude, as they are carried round by the turning of the earth, are then in sunlight during more than half their course; those in south latitude less.

The result as it appears to us is that the sun is more than half the time above the horizon, and that we have the hot weather of summer, while in the southern hemisphere the days are short, and the season is winter.

During our winter months the case is reversed. The southern hemisphere is then tipped toward the sun, and the northern hemisphere away from it. Consequently, summer and long days are the order in the southern and the reverse in the northern hemisphere.

We most naturally define the year as the interval of time in which the earth revolves around the sun. From what we have said, there are two ways of ascertaining its length. One is to find the interval between two passages of the sun past the same star. The other is to find the interval between two passages of the sun past the same equinox, that is, across the equator. If the latter were fixed among the stars the two intervals would be equal. But it was found by the ancient astronomers, from observations extending through several centuries, that these two methods do not give the same length of year. It takes the sun about eleven minutes longer to make the circuit of the stars than to make the circuit of the equinoxes. This shows that the equinoxes steadily shift their position among the stars from year to year. This shift is called the precession of the equinoxes. It does not arise from anything going on in the heavens, but only from a slow change in the direction of the earth's axis from year to year as it moves around the sun.

If we should suppose the platform in Figure III-6 to last for six or seven thousand years, and the earth to make its six or seven thousand revolutions around it, we should find that, at the end of this time, the north end of the axis of the earth, instead of being tipped toward our right hand, as shown in the figure, would be tipped directly toward us. At the end of another six or seven thousand years it would be tipped toward our left; at the end of a third such period it would be tipped away from us, and at the end of a fourth, or about twenty-six thousand years in all, it would have gotten back to its original direction.

Since the celestial poles are determined by the direction of the earth's axis, this change in the direction of the axis makes them slowly go around a circle in the heavens, having a radius of about twenty-three and a half degrees. At the present time the pole star is a little more than a degree from the pole. But the pole is gradually approaching it and will pass by it in about two hundred years. In twelve thousand years from now the pole will be in the constellation Lyra, about five degrees from the bright star Vega of that constellation. In the time of the ancient Greeks their navigators did not recognize any pole star at all, because what is now such was then ten or twelve degrees from the pole, the latter having been between it and the constellation of the Great Bear. It was the latter which they steered by.

It follows from all this that, since the celestial equator is the circle midway between the two poles, there must be a corresponding shift in its position among the stars. The effect of this shift during the past two thousand years is shown in Figure III-9. Since the equinoxes are the points of crossing of the ecliptic and the equator, they also change in consequence of this motion. It is thus that the precession of the equinoxes arises.

The two kinds of year we have described are called *tropical* and *sidereal*. The tropical year is the interval between two returns of the sun to the equinox. Its length is 365 days 5 hours 48 minutes 46 seconds.

Since the seasons depend upon the sun's being north or

south of the equator, the tropical year is that used in the reckoning of time. The ancient astronomers found that its length was about three hundred and sixty-five and one quarter days. As far back as the time of Ptolemy the length of the year was known even more exactly than this, and found to be a few minutes less than three hundred and sixty-five and one quarter days. The Gregorian Calendar, which nearly all civilized nations now use, is based upon a close approximation to this length of the year.

The sidereal year is the interval between two passages of the sun past the same star. Its length is three hundred and sixty-five days six hours and nine minutes.

According to the Julian calendar, which was in use in Christendom until 1582, the year was considered to be exactly 365¼ days. This, it will be seen, was 11 minutes 14 seconds more than the true length of the tropical year. Consequently, the seasons were slowly changing in the course of centuries. In order to obviate this, and have a year whose average length was as nearly as possible correct, a decree was passed by Pope Gregory XIII by which, in three centuries out of four, a day was dropped from the Julian calendar. According to the latter, the closing year of every century would be a leap year. In the Gregorian calendar 1600 was still to remain a leap year, but 1500, 1700, 1800, and 1900 were all common years.

The Gregorian calendar was adopted immediately by all Catholic countries, and from time to time by Protestant countries also, so that for the past 150 years it has been universal in both.

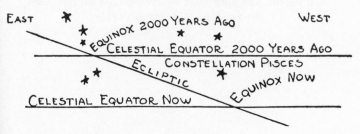

III-9. *Precession of the equinoxes.*

It has been stated that much of early astronomy dealt with the motions of the planets. Until Herschel, prevailing opinion held that the stars were in fixed positions in the heavens and thus that their study was less rewarding than that of the "wanderers." The fact that the planets moved in relation to their background was obvious even to early observers. The "morning star" and "evening star" worshipped by primitive man were of course planets. As planetary orbits were more accurately plotted, it became apparent that they did not conform to simple circular paths. Attempts to explain these asymmetries resulted in turn in the Ptolemaic, the Tychonian and finally the Keplerian hypotheses. Later, with the aid of the telescope, attempts were made to determine the compositions of planets. In the late nineteenth and early twentieth centuries, Camille Flammarion and Percival Lowell announced that they had discovered life on Mars. The possibility of intelligent beings on other planets inflamed the world's imagination. Works of what would now be described as science fiction, like H. G. Wells' War of the Worlds, appeared. Even decades later, when such theories had apparently been exploded, a radio broadcast of the Wells novel by Orson Welles created a panic. Today, with new methods and tools such as the balloons and satellites discussed in the previous section, the question of life on other worlds is again under investigation. This is the subject of the final article in this book.

Forest Ray Moulton was born at Le Roy, Michigan in 1872, obtained his Ph.D. in astronomy at the University of Chicago in 1899, became a member of the staff and was made professor of astronomy in 1912. He was the author of numerous books on astronomy, including "Consider the Heavens" from which the following article is taken. With T. C. Chamberlin, he suggested the planetesimal hypothesis of the origin of the solar system, which was once widely held and has now been revived in a different form. He died in 1952.

THE SOLAR FAMILY

FOREST RAY MOULTON

LET US SUPPOSE we are standing on a lofty mountain top, with all the earth beneath cut off from our view by low-lying mist. We see far below, just above the vaporous blanket that hides land and sea, a luminous spherical body, the sun in the model of our solar system. How enormous it is, a full mile in diameter, a hundred thousand times greater in volume than the largest balloon ever constructed! How dazzlingly brilliant is the light it radiates! How terrifying the eruptions shot up a full thousand feet from its storm-torn surface! How self-sufficient it appears to be, lying unsupported and alone in an ocean of empty space!

But wait! Let us examine all the vast region with telescopic aid. Perhaps some smaller body, some minor attendant of the resplendent sun has escaped our attention. Yes! There it is, a dull little speck in the distance, so far away that in the sunlight we did not see it with our unaided eyes. An astronomical friend accurately determines its direction from two points on our mountain top, and after making a few calculations he informs us that it is 41.6 miles away. After making careful measurements of its angular diameter and carrying out some logarithmic computations, he informs us that it is only 19 feet in diameter. He informs us that the little body is dark except where it is lighted on the side toward the sun. No wonder we did not see it, so distant, so small, and so dim it is. We name it Mercury.

Again we search with our telescope the wide spaces above the sea of fog, both near the sun and beyond tiny Mercury. Again our efforts are rewarded, for at a distance of 77.7 miles is another nonluminous little mass, this time 46 feet in diameter. We call it Venus and resume the quest. Next, at a distance of 108 miles comes Earth, 48 feet in diameter. Noth-

153

ing in particular distinguishes it from the other little bodies
which we have found. As we see it through our telescope, it
resembles Uriel's description of it to Satan, according to
Milton's account in *Paradise Lost*.

> *Look downward on that globe whose hither side*
> *With light from hence, though but reflected shines;*
> *That place is earth the seat of man, that light*
> *His day, which else as th'other hemisphere*
> *Night would invade.*

Beyond the earth in order we find little Mars, only 26 feet
in diameter, at a distance of 164 miles; then Jupiter, a larger
body 530 feet in diameter, at a distance of 559 miles; then
Saturn, 443 feet in diameter, 1030 miles away; then Uranus,
189 feet in diameter, at a distance of 2060 miles; and, finally,
Neptune, 201 feet in diameter, as far away (3230 miles) as
the distance across the continent. We should have long ago
abandoned the search for these relatively insignificant bodies
if the curiosity of the scientist had not been urging us on.
After many years of further search (in 1930), we eventually
discover Pluto at a distance of 4260 miles from the sun of our
model. This little body is so far away that we cannot measure
its diameter even with out greatest telescope, but we infer
from its faintness that it is not larger than the earth.

What a remarkable model we have constructed! It is not
like a mighty Everest with lesser mountains around it; nor is
it even like an isolated peak with its surrounding foothills.
It is more like a huge arc light around which at great distances tiny insects fly. Our central sun is a mile in diameter;
the planets are small bodies scattered out to a distance of
several thousand miles, so small and so far from the central
sun and our mountain top above it that we can see them only
with telescopic aid.

The actual solar system is on an enormously greater scale;
indeed, nearly a million times greater than that of our model.
Although the numbers which define its actual dimensions are
so great that they cannot be grasped by our imaginations,
we give them for reference in the table on page 166.

Now let us return to our mountain top and examine the
members of our model, for we can comprehend their dis-

tances and diameters. We find by a little computation that the volume of the central sun is 585 times greater than that of all the other bodies combined. If all these lesser bodies were rolled together and added to the sun, its diameter would be increased only one sixth of one per cent. If they were blotted out of existence, we should discover the fact from our mountain top only by a searching examination. If we were disembodied spirits capable of exploring the universe by traveling through the celestial spaces on the wings of light, we should probably entirely neglect the relatively insignificant planets. But that little body, that particle of dust in the distance which we call the Earth, is our home. When we see it near at hand, we find that it is inexhaustibly rich in variety and amazing properties. It is the abode of teeming life, a dwelling place for intelligent beings. So we refrain for a time from more ambitious explorations and consider further the family of relatively little objects to which the earth belongs.

Exclusive of remote and recently discovered Pluto, the planets form two distinct groups of four each. The first four in order from the sun—Mercury, Venus, Earth, and Mars—are called the terrestrial planets, because in size and density and mass and in several other respects they are similar to the earth. The next four planets—Jupiter, Saturn, Uranus, and Neptune—are called the Jovian planets because in size and density and mass they are comparable to Jupiter. The ter-

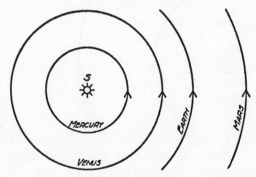

III-10. *Orbits of the four terrestrial planets—Mercury, Venus, Earth, Mars—to the same scale.*

restrial planets are solid bodies from 3000 to 8000 miles in diameter; the Jovian planets are gaseous to great depths and range from 30,000 to 86,000 miles in diameter. In volume, the terrestrial planets average only a thousandth as great as the Jovian planets, and the volume of the giant Jupiter is only one thousandth that of the sun.

When we examine our model of the solar system from our mountain top, we find that although the terrestrial planets are at great distances from the sun and from one another, yet these great distances are small in comparison with the corresponding ones for the Jovian planets. For example, in our model the distance from the sun to the farthest terrestrial planet, Mars is 164 miles, while the distance from the sun to Neptune is 3230 miles, or about twenty times as great. Even the distance between Mars and Jupiter is two and one half times the distance from the sun to the outermost member of the terrestrial group, while the distance between Uranus and Neptune is nearly eight times as great. In a figurative sense the terrestrial planets flock together near the sun, while the members of the Jovian group wander singly and afar in space, Neptune to a distance 3230 miles from our mountain top. As we look from our point of vantage over the endless regions below and find besides the sun only a few little bodies above all the ocean of mist, bodies so small that they appear to us like particles of dust, we are

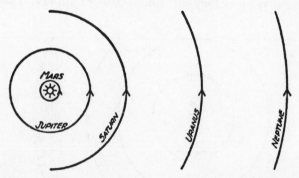

III-11. *Orbits of Mars and the Jovian planets—Jupiter, Saturn, Uranus, Neptune—to the same scale. On the same scale the orbit of Pluto would be an inch outside that of Neptune.*

deeply impressed with the extent and the emptiness of space. If there were a thousand planets instead of nine in the space they occupy, they would still be so far apart that each of them would appear from every other as an insignificant object in its sky.

Since the intensity of the sun's rays diminishes as the square of the distance from it increases, the Jovian planets receive from the sun very much less radiant energy per unit area than is received by the terrestrial planets. According to this law, a planet at twice the distance of the earth from the sun would receive one fourth as much heat per unit area as we receive. In order to compare the apparent diameter of the sun as seen from the various planets with its diameter as seen from the earth, and the amount of radiant energy received by the various planets with that received by the earth, we shall represent both of these quantities by 100 for the earth. Then the results for all the planets are as given in the following table:

Apparent Diameter of Sun and Energy Received from It by the Planets per Unit Area

Planet	Apparent Diameter of Sun	Energy Received from the Sun per Unit Area
Mercury	258.3	667.4
Venus	138.3	191.1
Earth	100.0	100.0
Mars	65.6	43.1
Jupiter	19.2	3.7
Saturn	10.5	1.1
Uranus	5.2	0.27
Neptune	3.3	0.11
Pluto	2.5	0.06

When we examine the numbers in this table, we discover that the mental picture of the solar system which we constructed from our observations on the mountain top is somewhat erroneous. We did not realize how large the sun would appear to be as seen from Mercury or how very small as seen from Uranus, Neptune, and Pluto. And much less did we suspect the very great differences in the amount of radiant energy received from the sun by the various planets. At one extreme, we find Mercury receiving six and two thirds as much per unit area as the earth; and at the other extreme, Pluto receiving one sixteenth of one per cent as much. If the surface conditions and atmospheres of these planets were similar to those of the earth, we could compute their surface temperatures, for we know how the temperature varies with the amount of energy received. Although the surface conditions and the atmospheres of the planets differ greatly from one to another, computations of their surface temperatures under the assumption that they are similar to the earth are interesting. The average temperature of the surface of the earth is about 60 degrees Fahrenheit. If Mercury were similar to the earth, its average surface temperature would be 343 degrees, or 131 degrees above the boiling point of water. On the other hand, the average temperature of Mars would be 38.7 degrees below zero, while that of Jupiter would be 232 degrees below zero. These results are obtained from hypotheses which are not strictly true, but nevertheless they give us some conception of the wide variations in temperatures on the surfaces of the various planets.

Now let us return to our mountain top and observe our planets again. No object is found where Mercury was a little while ago. Perhaps it is gone out to the region of the Jovian planets. No! Although it has moved it has remained at approximately the same distance from the sun. Repeated observations show us that it is revolving around the sun in an almost circular orbit in a period of 88 of our days. Similarly, we find that Venus makes its circuit of the sun in 225 days, and Mars in 22.6 months. When we come to the Jovian planets we find that although they also move, we cannot wait for them to complete their revolutions. From the times required by them to describe small arcs we compute their periods of revolution —12 years for Jupiter, 29.5 for Saturn, 84 for Uranus, 165 for Neptune, and 250 for distant Pluto. The planets near the sun not only describe shorter circuits of revolution about it, but they move with greater velocities in their orbits. For example, the orbital speed of Mercury is almost 30 miles per second and that of the earth is 18.5 miles per second, but Pluto creeps along its enormous orbit at a speed of less than 3 miles per second.

If in our imaginations we speed up a thousandfold the velocities of the planets in our model, we shall be able to see how the planetary mechanism works, just as we see the motions of the hands of a clock. Even with this increase in velocity, Pluto will make a circuit of the sun only once in three months. But with some patience we arrive at an understanding of all the motions. We find that all the planets move in the same direction, that their orbits are nearly circular, and that they are nearly in the same plane. By very, very careful and prolonged observations we find the remarkable fact that in their slight departures from circular orbits each planet moves so that the line from it to the sun sweeps over equal areas in equal intervals of time.

Our model has made the problem of learning how the planets move appear easier than it has actually been. Tycho Brahe, Kepler, and Newton did not stand on a mountain top and see the planets circling in simple orbits far below. They were on one of these moving worlds, on one of the little ones comprising the terrestrial group. What they saw was enormously complicated by the motions of the body on which they lived.

Mercury, as observed from the earth, is always apparently so near the sun that no permanently identifiable markings have been seen on its surface. Consequently, it has not been possible to determine the period of its rotation. No permanent markings have been seen on Venus because its surface is covered with an extensive atmosphere which is always filled with clouds. Uranus, Neptune, and Pluto are so remote from the earth that astronomers have not been able to determine their periods of rotation by direct observations. But Mars has surface markings which have been observed since they were discovered by Hooke in 1666. Although Jupiter and Saturn have no permanent surface features, these planets often have conspicuous markings lasting long enough for the determination of their periods of rotation. The period of rotation of Mars is 24 hours, 37

minutes, and 22.6 seconds, with an uncertainty not exceeding one tenth of a second. The period of rotation of enormous Jupiter is about 9 hours and 50 minutes, while that of
the nearly as great Saturn is about 10 hours and 2 minutes.
By certain indirect means astronomers infer that the day of
Venus is very long, perhaps equal to its year of 225 of our
days; that the period of rotation of Uranus is retrograde
with a period of about 11 hours; and that the period of
rotation of Neptune is about 15 hours and 48 minutes.

From the earth the moon appears to be a small body not
very far up in the sky. We know, of course, that it is higher
than the clouds, for sometimes they come beneath it and
shut it from view. We know it is beyond the trees over which
it rises. Indeed, we know from our books that its average
distance from the center of the earth is 238,000 miles. But
this number is theoretical knowledge, and not real in our
consciousness as is the height of a tree. Now it is possible to
determine how far away we subconsciously place the moon,
and the method of determining it is simple. We have at least
a vague impression of how large the moon appears to be.
Since we know how large an angle the moon subtends as
seen from the earth (it is about half a degree), we can
calculate how far away an object having a diameter equal
to our estimate must be to subtend this angle. Let us make
the calculation for our real impression of the size of the
moon and compare the result with our theoretical knowledge
of it.

To many persons the moon appears to be about eight
inches in diameter. A body eight inches in diameter subtends
an angle of one half of a degree at a distance of about eighty
feet. Consequently, those who say that the moon appears to
be eight inches in diameter really place it in their mind's eye
at a distance of eighty feet. As a matter of fact, the problem
is reversed psychologically. A person is conscious that the
moon is beyond his reach, that it is above the trees. For him
it vaguely has a distance (about 80 feet), though he does not
translate his impression into a number. But on the basis of
this impression of distance he estimates the moon's size, and
it turns out to be perhaps eight inches in diameter. How

absurd the result is as compared with the real distance and the real size of the moon! Eighty feet contrasted with 238,000 miles—reality, psychologically speaking, with theoretical knowledge! Large numbers do not speak a language that our minds can understand without an enormous amount of practice. That is the reason we decide to look at the solar family from a mountain top. Let us return to our mountain and see what the moon looks like in our model.

Through our telescope we discovered a little body 108 miles from the huge sun beneath our mountain, and we named it Earth. An astronomer measured it for us and found that it is 48 feet in diameter. At a distance of 108 miles a body 48 feet in diameter looks like a point to the unaided eye; indeed, it would look like a point if its diameter were ten times as great. But let us carefully examine this little body. Through our fine telescope we see that it is a tiny sphere, a world, and near it is a smaller world, about one fourth as great in diameter. To our delight we find that by screening off the light of the sun we can see also the smaller world without the aid of a telescope, but it is very close to Earth, so close that we cannot much more than discern that the two bodies are distinct. They look to us somewhat as Mizar and Alcor, at the bend in the handle of the Big Dipper, would appear if they were only three quarters as far apart. The little body is our moon, the yellowish disk which seems to be only eighty feet above us in our evening sky.

Let us examine more carefully the planets nearer the sun, Mercury and Venus, and then those more distant than Earth. Our skilled astronomer with the greatest telescope finds no moon attending Mercury and Venus, but with the utmost difficulty he discovers two near the planet Mars. These moons do not bear much resemblance to the companion of Earth; they are extremely close to Mars and not more than about ten miles in diameter. Jupiter has four moons, or satellites, ranging in diameter from 1900 to 3220 miles, the discovery of which by Galileo was one of the first astronomical achievements with the telescope. Jupiter has also five much smaller moons, none of them exceeding 100 miles in diameter, which were discovered from 1892 to 1908.[1] Saturn has nine known satellites, Uranus four,[1] and Neptune one.[1] So far are all these planets from the mountain top beneath which our model lies that all the satellites appear, even through a telescope, to be very close to their respective planets.

Prolonged observations show us that the moons do not stand still, but are revolving around the planets with which they are associated. As Earth, for example, moves forward in its orbit, the moon is sometimes seen ahead of it a very short distance, then between it and the sun, then behind, and finally opposite the sun. The distance the moon moves with respect to Earth is almost negligible in comparison with the distance the two move together in their circuit around the sun. And so it is with the satellites of all the other planets, their little orbits being only miniatures of the great orbital curves described by their primaries. It is an interesting, and probably significant, fact that in general the satellites revolve around their respective planets in the direction in which the planets rotate on their axes and revolve around the sun. There are, however, a few exceptions. The most remote of the satellites of both Jupiter and Saturn revolves round their respective planets in the retrograde direction; the planes of the orbits of four satellites of Uranus are almost perpendicular to the orbit of the planet; and the plane of the orbit of one satellite of Neptune is inclined about 50 degrees past the perpendicular to the plane of the orbit of the planet.

For convenience of reference, the known satellites of the planets are listed in the table on pages 163-64, together with their distances from the centers of the planets around which they revolve, their periods of revolution, and their diameters.

When the nonscientific person reads in a book that the average density of Mars is 3.96 times the density of water, he is likely to accept the result with mental reservations, for no astronomer has ever been to Mars. Since Mars shines entirely by reflected light, the spectroscope can give us no information respecting its composition, even at the

1. It is now known that Jupiter has twelve satellites, Uranus five and Neptune two.—Eds.

surface. Its period of revolution around the sun does not depend appreciably upon its mass. Consequently, we apparently know nothing about the planet itself except its size. But hold! It has two satellites, and Newton taught us how the period of revolution of a body depends upon the size of its orbit and the mass of the body around which it revolves. We solve the relationship inversely. From our knowledge of the periods of the satellites of Mars and the dimensions of their orbits, as determined directly from observations, we compute from Newton's equations the mass of the central body, Mars, that holds them under its gravitative control. From such observations, reasoning, and computations we determine the mass of Mars, actually with about as great percentage of accuracy as we determine the mass of the earth; and then from its measured diameter we compute its density, 3.96 times the density of water. Such are the paths that astronomers travel to reach their astonishing results!

The Satellite Systems

PLANET	SATELLITE	DISTANCE FROM CENTER OF PLANET Miles	PERIOD OF REVOLUTION Days	Hrs.	Mins.	DIAMETER Miles
Earth	Moon	238,857	27	7	43	2160
Mars	Phobos	5,828	0	7	39	10(?)
	Deimos	14,577	1	6	18	5(?)
Jupiter	Satellite V	112,600	0	11	57	100(?)
	Io	261,800	1	18	28	2320
	Europa	416,600	3	13	14	1960
	Ganymede	665,000	7	3	43	3100
	Callisto	1,170,000	16	16	32	3000
	Satellite VI	7,120,000	250	16	—	100(?)
	Satellite VII	7,290,000	260	1	—	30(?)
	Satellite X	7,200,000	260	—	—	20(?)

PLANET	SATELLITE	DISTANCE FROM CENTER OF PLANET Miles	PERIOD OF REVOLUTION Days Hrs. Mins.			DIAMETER Miles
	Satellite XII	13,000,000	600	—	—	14(?)
	Satellite XI	14,000,000	692	—	—	18(?)
	Satellite VIII	14,600,000	739	—	—	30(?)
	Satellite IX	14,700,000	738	—	—	15(?)
Saturn	Mimas	113,000	0	22	37	300
	Enceladus	147,800	1	8	53	350
	Tethys	183,000	1	21	18	750
	Dione	234,400	2	17	41	800
	Rhea	327,300	4	12	25	1000
	Titan	760,000	15	22	41	3000
	Hyperion	923,000	21	6	38	250(?)
	Japetus	2,200,000	79	7	56	1200(?)
	Phoebe	8,050,000	550	10	—	150(?)
Uranus	Miranda	75,000	1	9	—	200(?)
	Ariel	119,100	2	12	29	560(?)
	Umbriel	165,900	4	3	28	430(?)
	Titania	272,200	8	16	56	1000(?)
	Oberon	364,000	13	11	7	900(?)
Neptune	Triton	220,000	5	21	3	2500(?)
	Nereide	3,500,000	359	—	—	200(?)

It is evident that the masses of all other planets having satellites can be determined by the method used in the case of Mars. But Mercury, Venus, and Pluto are not accompanied by satellites; consequently, if we are to determine their masses, we must use other methods. What other possible methods are there? How do we determine the mass of a body here upon the surface of the earth? If we know the substance of which it is composed and, therefore, its density, we measure its volume and compute its mass. But since we cannot determine the composition of Mercury, Venus, and Pluto, we are not able to use this method. We might find how much velocity a given force will produce in the body in question in a unit of time and from this result compute its mass. But we cannot apply known forces to the planets. Finally, we might weigh the body; indeed, that is the way masses of sugar and meat and coal and everything else on the surface of the earth are determined.

Now the weight of a body is the attraction which the earth exerts on it (neglecting slight effects due to the rotation of the earth). Since the body attracts the earth equally, the attraction between every two bodies being equal in opposite directions, we actually determine the masses of bodies in everyday life by their attractions for the earth. Astronomers determine the mass of Mars and other planets having satellites by fundamentally the same method. Fortunately, in a few instances comets have passed so near to Venus that their motions have been influenced appreciably by the attraction of the planet. From these effects mathematical astronomers have been able to determine, at least roughly, the mass of Venus. The mass of Mercury is very uncertain and the mass of Pluto is quite unknown, except that its faintness implies that its diameter is probably a little less than that of the earth; and it is probable that its mass is also less. The mass of the sun, however, is easily computed from the periods of revolution of the planets and their distances from it.

It has been remarked that the weight of a body is due to the earth's attraction for it. Since attraction increases with mass and decreases as the square of the distance, the weight of an object at the surface of a planet depends upon both the mass and the radius of the planet. Since the masses and diameters of the planets vary greatly, if a unit mass were taken to their various surfaces its weight would undergo corresponding variations. The acceleration at the surface of a body (it is 32 feet per second for the earth) is the *surface gravity* of the body. The following table gives the surface gravity for the sun and each of the planets.

Distances, Diameters, Masses, Densities, and Surface Gravities

Body	Distance From Sun	Mean Diameter (Miles)	Mass (Earth = 1)	Mean Density (Water = 1)	Surface Gravity (g = 1)
Sun		864,400	332,000.	1.41	27.9
Moon		2,160	0.0123	3.33	0.16
Terrestrial Planets:					
Mercury	35,960,000	3,010	0.06	5.1	0.36
Venus	67,200,000	7,610	0.81	4.86	0.85
Earth	92,897,000	7,918	1.00	5.52	1.00
Mars	141,540,000	4,150	0.11	3.96	0.38
Jovian Planets:					
Jupiter	483,310,000	86,728	316.94	1.34	2.64
Saturn	886,120,000	75,500	94.92	0.71	1.17
Uranus	1,782,700,000	30,600	14.7	1.27	0.92
Neptune	2,793,400,000	27,100	17.2	1.58	1.12
Pluto	3,673,000,000	4,000(?)	0.7	5.3(?)	0.9(?)

This table exhibits the remarkable differences in dimensions, masses, and surface gravities of the principal bodies of the solar system. It emphasizes the dominance of the sun in every respect except that of density. For example, its mass is three million times that of Mars, and its surface gravity is one hundred times that of Mercury. The table also shows that the terrestrial planets are very much denser than the Jovian planets. Perhaps we should note that the earth is the densest (in the literal sense) body in the solar system. The surface gravity of a celestial object is not merely interesting because it enables us to compute how much we should weigh if we could migrate from one body to another, but it is the factor which determines whether a body can hold an atmosphere, and if so how rapidly the density of its atmosphere decreases with altitude. It is, in fact, a very important property of a planet or a satellite.

We are, perhaps, becoming too much involved in the details of the properties of the planets. So let us return to our mountain top and see whether there are not other members of the solar system which we have not as yet discovered. Naturally we search for unknown planets, planets nearer the sun than Mercury or more remote than Pluto. Our search turns out to be fruitless. Then we look for smaller planets among those we already know. We find one, then several, finally more than a thousand little *planetoids*, as we call them, revolving around the sun between the orbits of Mars and Jupiter, at an average distance of about four hundred miles from our mountain. The orbits of some of them are nearly circular, and the orbits of others are considerably elongated; the orbits of some of them are near the plane of the orbits of the larger planets, and the orbits of others are considerably inclined to this plane. The paths they travel are so interwoven that if they were made of wire and one were removed, all the remainder would be taken with it. The inner end of the orbit of one planetoid extends within the orbit of Mars, looping through but not crossing it. This little body, Eros, at its nearest approach to the earth comes within about sixteen

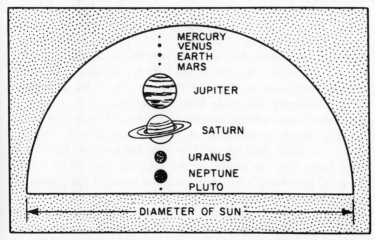

III-12. *The sun and planets to the same scale, showing that the sun is enormously larger in volume than all the planets combined and that the earth is a relatively small planet.*

million miles, nearer than any other celestial body except the moon. At the other extreme there are about a dozen planetoids which revolve at the distance of Jupiter from the sun in such a peculiar way that they form with Jupiter and the sun an equilateral triangle. The periods of the known planetoids lie between 1.76 years and 11.86 years, and the diameters of these bodies range from possibly five miles up to about five hundred miles. There may be tens of thousands of them so small that they have not been discovered.

A strange object is seen through our telescope, a fuzzy faint body two hundred miles away, somewhat beyond the orbit of Mars. It is approaching the sun and becoming more conspicuous; it looks like a little cloud with a gauzy tail streaming behind like smoke from a locomotive. We call it a *comet*. It rushes toward the sun at greater and greater speed; it becomes very bright, much brighter than any planet; its volume is a hundred times greater than that of Jupiter; its tail would reach from the sun to the earth; it has become a terrifying object nearly a mile in diameter and having a tail a hundred miles in length. Though it appeared destined to plunge directly into the sun, it only grazes its surface. Instead of rushing by in a straight line, it quickly passes nearly around the sun and recedes almost in the direction from which it came. But now an apparently absurd thing is noticed —the tail goes ahead of the body of the comet. As the comet recedes, its velocity decreases, its brightness rapidly declines, its tail diminishes in size, it loses its terrifying appearance, and it disappears by the time it reaches the orbit of Jupiter at a distance of 559 miles from our mountain.

In the course of time we observe several hundred comets, most of which are much smaller and fainter than the one we have described. Few approach so near the sun; few have such long tails; few are visible to the unaided eye. Their orbits lie in all possible planes, some near the plane of the planetary orbits and some nearly at right angles to this plane. Some comets describe elongated closed orbits, returning time after time in periods ranging from a few years up to thousands of years; possibly some of them come in from outer space and visit the solar system but once, returning, after passing around the sun, to the interstellar regions from which they came. In comparison to the planets, they are erratic bodies with orbits following no fixed pattern; they vary greatly in brightness and size; their tails are astonishing and inexplicable. It is difficult for one not a scientist to see in them evidence of an orderly universe, yet mathematicians determine their paths with precision and guide observers in looking for them when they are so far from the sun that they can be found only with great difficulty.

In spite of their huge size and terrifying appearance, comets do not threaten the destruction of a planet or the sun, for their masses are very small. How do astronomers know that their masses are small? The answer is obviously from their small attractive effects upon the bodies they pass near. For example, in 1886 a comet passed slowly across the orbit of Jupiter; indeed, for several months it was within the limits of the planet's satellite system. Although the attraction of the planet completely transformed the orbit of the comet, the comet did not in return have any appreciable effect upon Jupiter or any of its satellites. By such methods it has been proved that the masses of comets cannot exceed one millionth of the mass of the earth, though some comets are approximately a million times greater than the earth in volume. In a sense, comets are the relatively unsubstantial ghosts of the solar family.

Before terminating our outline survey of the solar family, let us in imagination start at the sun and make a brief visit to each of its principal members, not on the reduced scale on which we saw it below our mountain top, but on its actual scale, which is nearly a million times greater. In order to complete our journey before a geological age shall have passed, let us fly in a superstratospheric machine at the rate of 1000 miles an hour. With such a machine, starting on the earth's equator at noon, we could fly westward as fast as the sun moves in its diurnal motion. After passing every longitude of the earth at its noon, we should arrive at our starting point at noon the following day.

But we are starting from the sun, and before winging our way across the interplanetary spaces let us circle this great body. Although we continue our flight at the rate of 1000 miles per hour without stopping, we do not complete the circuit of the sun and return to our starting point until 113 days, or nearly four months, have passed. With enthusiasm for our longer journey, we set out for Mercury and the more distant planets with few fears that we shall be very long on our way. After a few days we look back, expecting to find the sun a little object vanishing in the distance; instead, we find it covering half the sky behind us. After four months it still covers an area 1500 times greater than that covered by the moon as seen from the earth. But, finally, after about four years and one month we arrive at Mercury. We fly around this little planet between breakfast and luncheon and immediately start for Venus. In three and one half years more, or in seven years and seven months after we left the sun, we arrive at Venus, which we circle in a day. Then we set sail for Earth, arriving at this little planet in the tenth year and seventh month of our wandering.

On our way between Venus and Earth we see an enormous comet. For a moment we were on the point of saying that we are passing the comet, for we are speeding along at the rate of 1000 miles an hour. But the comet is going about 100 times as fast, and it rushes obliquely across our path as though we were not moving at all. Just now, while it is near to us, perhaps a million miles away, its head is seen far in one direction and its tail in the opposite. We cannot say that its head is east or west or up or down, for there are no such directions out here in space. Nor can we say that the comet extends from one horizon to the other, for there is no horizon. Its head is in one direction and its tail fades out in the opposite direction, and near us it half fills the hemisphere. But in a few days we note that it is receding; in a few weeks it is definitely farther away, as it should be, since it moves at the rate of 90,000 miles per hour; before we reach Earth it has become a dim, fuzzy little body, vanishing in the depths of space.

It is just 10.6 years since we left the sun as we arrive at Earth. Ten days after we pass the orbit of the moon we approach the surface of our world. Another day is sufficient for our customary trip around the planets we visit, and then we start for Mars. We arrive at Mars in 5.6 years more or 16.2 years since we left the sun. In twelve hours we make a circuit around it and set out for Jupiter. We while away ten, twenty, thirty years looking at the planetoids, and Jupiter is still far in the distance. Finally, in the thirty-eighth year of this part of our journey, we arrive at the ninth satellite of Jupiter; in a year and two months thereafter at the surface of Jupiter itself. Our journey from the sun to Jupiter has required more than fifty-five years.

We arrive at Saturn in 101 years, at Uranus in 203 years, at Neptune in 318 years, and at Pluto in 420 years. At the distance of Saturn we look back and find that the sun has diminished in apparent size to a starlike point. But the illumination is not feeble, for the light we receive from it is 100,000,000 times greater than that which we receive from such a brilliant star as Arcturus. Even at the distance of Pluto the illumination from the sun is almost equal to that at the surface of the earth at noon on a cloudy day.

Having become accustomed to the hardships of interplanetary travel during the 420 years of our journey from the sun to Pluto, we propose to our good pilot that we continue on our way to Sirius, the brightest star and one of the nearest stars in the sky. With a tone of pity that we should know so little of the universe about us, he explains that the ship in which we have been riding is suitable only for local service, and that at its creeping pace of 1000 miles per hour 5,900,-000 years would be required for it to go to the relatively near star Sirius. Then for the first time we realize how isolated the solar family is in an ocean of space.

Aside from its dramatic impact, the following article is of importance on two counts: it represents one of the great triumphs of mathematical astronomy and it is a striking example of coincidence in scientific discovery. The calculations of Adams and Leverrier were performed simultaneously by two men, each of whom was completely ignorant of the work of the other. The history of science is studded with such coincidences—the invention of the calculus by Newton and Leibniz, the discovery of evolution by Darwin and Wallace, and many others. In astronomy, Janssen and Lockyer made independent observations of solar prominences without an eclipse. In August, 1868, the sun was totally eclipsed for 5½ minutes in a path that crossed India. A large prominence happened to be present on the sun's limb or edge. The French astronomer Jules Janssen observed the brilliantly colored lines in the prominence spectrum and asked himself whether these lines could not be seen without the existence of an eclipse. The next morning he succeeded in making the observation. Meanwhile, in England, Sir Norman Lockyer had ordered a powerful spectroscope with the plan of making the same observation. It arrived in October, he turned it on the sun and observed the same brilliant lines. He announced his discovery on the same day that news of Janssen's discovery reached England from India.

To describe such events as sheer coincidence is to offer only an incomplete explanation. In general, though by no means universally (note Roentgen's discovery of X rays), scientific discoveries are based on a fund of knowledge which is available to all specialists in a field. Moreover, there are fashions in science as in other fields of human activity. The scientific community places greater emphasis on certain problems than on others. Given such conditions, coincidental discovery ceases to be as surprising as it might otherwise appear.

Sir Harold Spencer Jones was born at Kensington, England, in 1890, was educated at Cambridge, did astronomical research at the Royal Observatory and the Cape of Good Hope Observatory, and became Astronomer Royal in 1933. He is the author of General Astronomy, Worlds Without End, and Life on Other Worlds. He died in 1960.

JOHN COUCH ADAMS AND THE DISCOVERY OF NEPTUNE

SIR HAROLD SPENCER JONES

ON THE NIGHT of 13 March 1781 William Herschel, musician by profession but assiduous observer of the heavens in his leisure time, made a discovery that was to bring him fame. He had for some time been engaged upon a systematic and detailed survey of the whole heavens, using a 7 in. telescope of his own construction; he carefully noted everything that appeared in any way remarkable. On the night in question, in his own words:

> In examining the small stars in the neighbourhood of H Geminorum I perceived one that appeared visibly larger than the rest; being struck with its uncommon appearance I compared it to H Geminorum and the small star in the quartile between Auriga and Gemini, and finding it so much larger than either of them, I suspected it to be a comet.

Most observers would have passed the object by without noticing anything unusual about it, for the minute disk was only about 4 sec. in diameter. The discovery was made possible by the excellent quality of Herchel's telescope, and by the great care with which his observations were made.

The discovery proved to be of greater importance than Herschel suspected, for the object he had found was not a comet, but a new planet, which revolved round the Sun in a nearly circular path at a mean distance almost exactly double that of Saturn; it was unique, because no planet had ever before been discovered; the known planets, easily visible to the naked eye, did not need to be discovered.

After the discovery of Uranus, as the new planet was

called, it was ascertained that it had been observed as a star and its position recorded on a score of previous occasions. The earliest of these observations was made by Flamsteed at Greenwich in 1690. Lemonnier in 1769 had observed its transit six times in the course of 9 days and, had he compared the observations with one another, he could not have failed to anticipate Herschel in the discovery. As Uranus takes 84 years to make a complete revolution round the Sun, these earlier observations were of special value for the investigation of its orbit.

The positions of the planet computed from tables constructed by Delambre soon began to show discordances with observation, which became greater as time went on. As there might have been error or incompleteness in Delambre's theory and tables, the task of revision was undertaken by Bouvard, whose tables of the planet appeared in 1821. Bouvard found that, when every correction for the perturbations in the motion of Uranus by the other planets was taken into account, it was not possible to reconcile the old observations of Flamsteed, Lemonnier, Bradley, and Mayer with the observations made subsequently to the discovery of the planet in 1781.

Further observations of Uranus were for a time found to be pretty well represented by Bouvard's Tables, but systematic discordances between observations and the tables gradually began to show up. As time went on, observations continued to deviate more and more from the tables. It began to be suspected that there might exist an unknown distant planet, whose gravitational attraction was disturbing the motion of Uranus. An alternative suggestion was that the inverse square law of gravitation might not be exact at distances as great as the distance of Uranus from the Sun.

The problem of computing the perturbations in the motion of one planet by another moving planet, when the undisturbed orbits and the masses of the planets are known is fairly straightforward, though of some mathematical complexity. The inverse problem, of analysing the perturbations in the motion of one planet in order to deduce the position, path and mass of the planet which is producing these perturbations, is of much greater complexity and difficulty. A little consideration will, I think, show that this must be so. If a planet were exposed solely to the attractive influence of the Sun, its orbit would be an ellipse. The attractions of the other planets perturb its motion and cause it to deviate now on the one side and now on the other side of this ellipse. To determine the elements of the elliptic orbit from the positions of the planet as assigned by observation, it is necessary first to compute the perturbations produced by the other planets and to subtract them from the observed positions.

The position of the planet in this orbit at any time, arising from its undisturbed motion, can be calculated; if the perturbations of the other planets are then computed and added, the true position of the planet is obtained. The whole procedure is, in practice, reduced to a set of tables. But if Uranus is perturbed by a distant *unknown* planet, the observed positions when corrected by the subtraction of the perturbations caused by the *known* planets are not the positions in the true elliptic orbit; the perturbations of the unknown planet have not been allowed for. Hence when the corrected positions are analysed in order to determine the elements of the elliptic orbit, the derived elements will be falsified. The positions of Uranus computed from tables such as Bouvard's would be in error for two reasons; in the first place, because they are based upon incorrect elements of the elliptic orbit; in the second place, because the perturbations produced by the unknown planet have not been applied. The two causes of error have a common origin and are inextricably entangled in each other, so that neither can be investigated independently of the other. Thus though many astronomers thought it probable that Uranus was perturbed by an undiscovered planet, they could not prove it. No occasion had arisen for the solution of the extremely complicated problem of what is termed inverse perturbations, starting with the perturbed positions and deducing from them the position and motion of the perturbing body.

The first solution of this intricate problem was made by a young Cambridge mathematician, John Couch Adams. Whilst still an undergraduate his attention had been drawn to the irregularities in the motion of Uranus. As soon as Adams had taken his degree he attempted a first rough solution of the problem, with the simplifying assumptions that the unknown planet moved in a circular orbit, in the plane of the orbit of Uranus, and that its distance from the Sun was twice the mean distance of Uranus, this being the distance to be expected according to the empirical law of Bode. This preliminary solution gave a sufficient improvement in the agreement between the corrected theory of Uranus and observation to encourage him to pursue the investigation further. In order to make the observational data more complete application was made in February 1844 by Challis, the Plumian Professor of Astronomy, to Airy, the Astronomer Royal, for the errors of longitude of Uranus for the years 1818-26. Challis explained that he required them for a young friend, Mr Adams of St John's College, who was working at the theory of Uranus. By return of post, Airy sent the Greenwich data not merely for the years 1818-26 but for the years 1754-1830.

Adams now undertook a new solution of the problem, still with the assumption that the mean distance of the unknown planet was twice that of Uranus but without assuming the orbit to be circular. During term-time he had little opportunity to pursue his investigations and most of the work was undertaken in the vacations. By September 1845, he had completed the solution of the problem, and gave to Challis a paper with the elements of the orbit of the planet, as well as its mass and its position for 1 October 1845. The position indicated by Adams was actually within 2° of the position of Neptune at that time. A careful search in the vicinity of this position should have led to the discovery of Neptune. The comparison between observation and theory was satisfactory and Adams, confident in the validity of the law of gravitation and in his own mathematics, referred to the "new planet".

Challis gave Adams a letter of introduction to Airy, in which he said that 'from his character as a mathematician, and his practice in calculation, I should consider the deductions from his premises to be made in a trustworthy manner'. But the Astronomer Royal was in France when Adams called at Greenwich. Airy, immediately on his return, wrote to Challis saying: "would you mention to Mr Adams that I am

The Northern Constellations, from an old Astronomical Atlas.
American Museum of Natural History.

The Ptolemaic System, from an old Astronomical Atlas. *Ameri-*

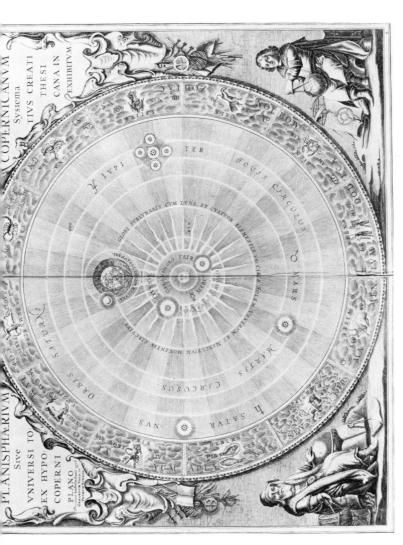

The Copernican System, from an old Astronomical Atlas.
American Museum of Natural History.

Galileo's Telescope.
*Drawing by Milford
Zornes.*

Newton's Telescope.
*Drawing by Milford
Zornes.*

The two hundred-inch mirror. Insert shows comparative size of Newton's telescope. *Mount Wilson and Palomar Observatories.*

The two hundred-inch Hale Telescope on Palomar Mountain. *Mount Wilson and Palomar Observatories.*

Radar telescope at Stanford University, prepared to bounce signals off the dark side of the moon. *Stanford University*.

Thirty-two dish radio telescope at Stanford University, used for research in solar-terrestrial physics, galactic radio astronomy, radio interferometry, and radiometry. *Stanford University*.

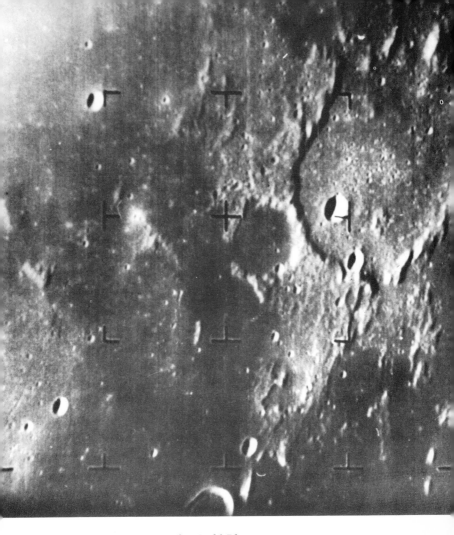

Wide World Photos

Photograph taken by the Ranger VII spacecraft before it impacted the Moon at 6:25 am Pacific Daylight Time, July 31, 1964. It was taken by the camera with a 75mm, f/2 lens at an altitude of 470 miles, and shows an area about 78 miles on a side. The smallest craters shown are about 800 feet in diameter. The large crater in the upper right-hand corner is Guericke. Numerous small secondary craters are shown on its floor as well as two large conical craters. The larger of the two is about four miles in diameter.

Mars, Jupiter, Saturn, and Pluto. *Mount Wilson and Palomar Observatories.*

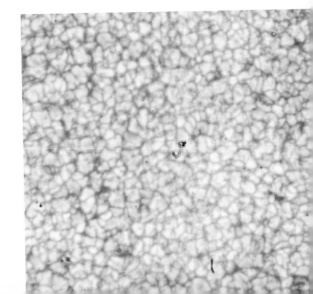

Photograph of granulations on the surface of the sun, taken from a balloon. *Martin Schwartzschild.*

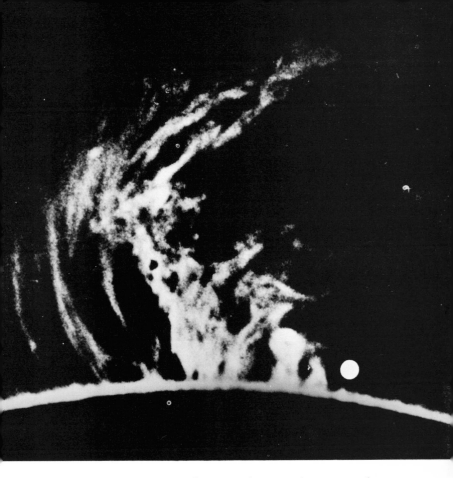

Large active prominence on the sun, 140,000 miles high, photographed in light of calcium. *Mount Wilson and Palomar Observatories.*

The above map shows the constellations visible in latitude 40 degrees north on November 1st at 9:00 P.M.

Double stars and Variables are indicated; the first-magnitude stars are the following:

α Geminorum — Castor α Tauri — Aldebaran α Aquilae — Altair
β Geminorum — Pollux α Lyrae — Vega α Piscis Austrinus —
α Orionis — Betelgeuse α Cygni — Deneb Fomalhout
α Aurigae — Capella

Map of the Winter Skies. *American Museum of Natural History.*

The above map shows the accepted geometrical patterns of all the constellations visible at 9:00 P.M. on July 1st, in latitude 40 degrees north. All the stars listed for study in the articles on *Double Stars* and *Variable Stars* are indicated as well as the first-magnitude stars which are the following:

α Aurigae — Capella	α Aquilae — Altair	α Boötis — Arcturus
α Cygni — Deneb	α Leonis — Regulus	α Virginis — Spica
α Lyrae — Vega		α Scorpii — Antares

Map of the Summer Skies. *American Museum of Natural History.*

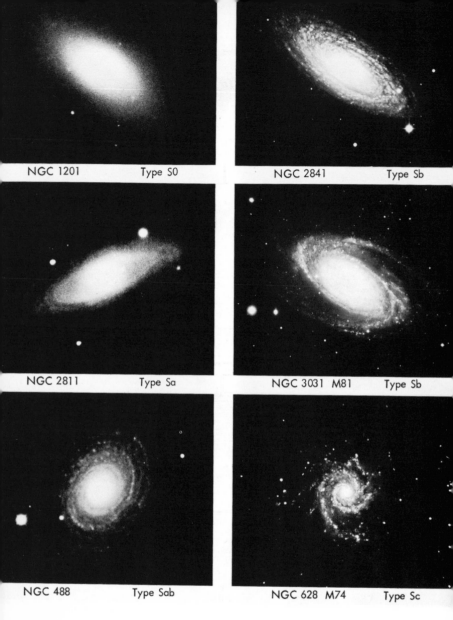

NGC 1201   Type S0

NGC 2841   Type Sb

NGC 2811   Type Sa

NGC 3031 M81   Type Sb

NGC 488   Type Sab

NGC 628 M74   Type Sc

Classification of Normal Galaxies. *Mount Wilson and Palomar Observatories.*

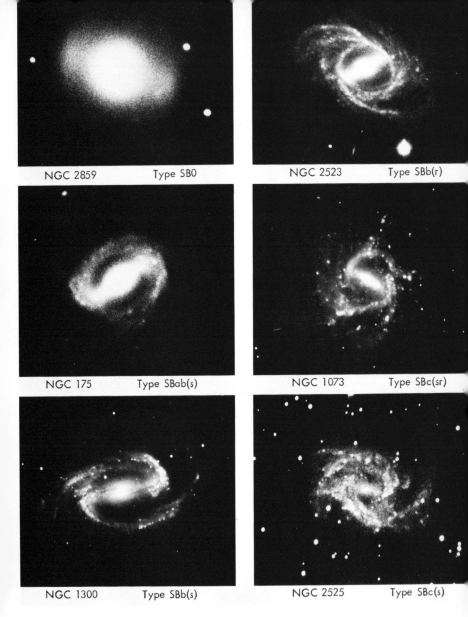

NGC 2859	Type SB0
NGC 175	Type SBab(s)
NGC 1300	Type SBb(s)
NGC 2523	Type SBb(r)
NGC 1073	Type SBc(sr)
NGC 2525	Type SBc(s)

Classification of Barred Galaxies. *Mount Wilson and Palomar Observatories.*

Nebulosity in Monoceros, taken with the 48-inch Schmidt telescope. *Mount Wilson and Palomar Observatories.*

Nebulosity in Monoceros, photographed in red light with the two hundred-inch telescope. *Mount Wilson and Palomar Observatories.*

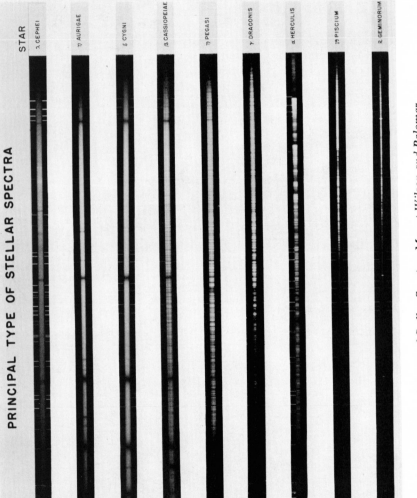

Principal Types of Stellar Spectra. *Mount Wilson and Palomar*

that of a disturbing planet exterior to Uranus. Assuming, as Adams had done, that its distance was twice the distance of Uranus and that its orbit was in the plane of the ecliptic, he assigned its true longitude for the beginning of 1847; he did not obtain the elements of its orbit nor determine its mass.

The position assigned by Le Verrier differed by only 1° from the position which Adams had given seven months previously. Airy now felt no doubt about the accuracy of both calculations; he still required to be satisfied about the error of the radius vector, however, and he accordingly addressed to Le Verrier the query that he had addressed to Adams, but this time in a more explicit form. He asked whether the errors of the tabular radius vector were the consequence of the disturbance produced by an exterior planet, and explained why, by analogy with the moon's variation, this did not seem to him necessarily to be so. Le Verrier replied a few days later giving an explanation which Airy found completely satisfactory. The errors of the tabular radius vector, said Le Verrier, were not produced actually by the disturbing planet; Bouvard's orbit required correction, because it had been based on positions which were not true elliptic positions, including, as they did, the perturbations by the outer planet; the correction of the orbit, which was needed on this account, removed the discordance between the observed and tabular radius vector. Airy was a man of quick and incisive action. He was now fully convinced that the true explanation of the irregularities in the motion of Uranus had been provided and he felt confident that the new planet would soon be found. He had already, a few days before receiving the reply from Le Verrier, informed the Board of Visitors of the Royal Observatory, at their meeting in June, of the extreme probability of discovering a new planet in a very short time.

Airy considered that the most suitable telescope with which to make the search for the new planet was the Northumberland telescope of the Cambridge Observatory, which was larger than any telescope at Greenwich and more likely to detect a planet whose light might be feeble. Airy offered to lend Challis one of his assistants, if Challis was too busy to undertake the search himself. He pointed out that the most favourable time for the search (when the undis-covered planet would be at opposition) was near at hand. A few days later, Airy sent Challis detailed directions for carry-ing out the search and in a covering letter said that, in his opinion, the importance of the inquiry exceeded that of any current work, which was of such a nature as not to be totally lost by delay.

Challis decided to prosecute the search himself and began observing on 29 July 1846, three weeks before opposition. The method adopted was to make three sweeps over the area to be searched, mapping the positions of all the stars ob-served, and completing each sweep before beginning the next. If the planet was observed it would be revealed, when the different sweeps were compared, by its motion relative to the stars.

What followed was not very creditable to Challis. He started by observing in the region indicated by Adams: the first four nights on which observations were made were 29 July, 30 July, 4 August and 12 August. But no comparison was made, as the search proceeded, between the observa-tions on different nights. He did indeed make a partial com-parison between the nights of 30 July and 12 August, merely to assure himself that the method of observation was ade-quate. He stopped short at No. 39 of the stars observed on 12 August; as he found that all these had been observed on 30 July, he felt satisfied about the method of observation. If he had continued the comparison for another ten stars he would have found that a star of the 8th magnitude observed on 12 August was missing in the series of 30 July. This was the planet: it had wandered into the zone between the two dates. Its discovery was thus easily within his grasp. But 12 August was not the first time on which Challis had observed the planet; he had already observed it on 4 August and if he had compared the observations of 4 August with the observa-tions of either 30 July or of 12 August, the planet would have been detected.

When we recall Airy's strong emphasis on carrying on the search in preference to any current work, Challis's subse-quent excuses to justify his failure were pitiable. He had delayed the comparisons, he said, partly from being occupied with comet reductions (which could well have waited), and partly from a fixed impression that a long search was required to ensure success. He confessed that, in the whole of the undertaking, he had too little confidence in the indications of theory. Oh! man of little faith! If only he had shared Airy's conviction of the great importance of the search.

But we have anticipated somewhat. While Challis was laboriously continuing his search, Adams wrote on 2 September an important letter to Airy who, unknown to Adams, was then in Germany. He referred to the assumption in his first calculations that the mean distance of the supposed disturbing planet was twice that of Uranus. The investigation, he said, could scarcely be considered satisfactory while based on anything arbitrary. He had therefore repeated his calculations, assuming a somewhat smaller mean distance. The result was very satisfactory in that the agreement between theory and observations was somewhat improved and, at the same time, the eccentricity of the orbit, which in the first solution had an improbably large value, was reduced. He gave the residuals for the two solutions, and remarked that the comparison with recent Greenwich observations suggested that a still better agreement could be obtained by a further reduction in the mean distance. He asked for the results of the Greenwich observations for 1844 and 1845. He then gave the corrections to the tabular radius vector of Uranus and remarked that they were in close agreement with those required by the Greenwich observations.

Two days earlier, on 31 August, Le Verrier had communicated a third paper to the French Academy which was published in a number of the *Comptes Rendus* that reached England near the end of September. Challis received it on 29 September. Le Verrier gave the orbital elements of the hypothetical planet, its mass, and its position. From the mass and distance of the planet he inferred, on the reasonable assumption that its mean density was equal to the mean density of Uranus, that it should show a disk with an angular diameter of about 3·3 sec. Le Verrier went on to remark as follows:

It should be possible to see the new planet in good telescopes and also to distinguish it by the size of its disk. This is a very important point. For if the planet could not be distinguished by its appearance from the stars it would be necessary, in order to discover it, to examine all the small stars in the region of the sky to be explored, and to detect a proper motion of one of them. This work would be long and wearisome. But if, on the contrary, the planet has a sensible disk which prevents it from being confused with a star, if a simple study of its physical appearance can replace the rigorous determination of the positions of all the stars, the search will proceed much more rapidly.

After reading this memoir on 29 September, Challis searched the same night in the region indicated by Le Verrier (which was almost identical with that indicated by Adams, in the first instance, a year earlier), looking out particularly for a visible disk. Of 300 stars observed he noted one and one only as seeming to have a disk. This was, in actual fact, the planet. Its motion might have been detected in the course of a few hours, but Challis waited for confirmation until the next night, when no observation was possible because the Moon was in the way. On 1 October he learnt that the planet had been discovered at Berlin on 23 September. His last chance of making an independent discovery had gone.

For on 23 September Galle, Astronomer at the Berlin Observatory, had received a letter from Le Verrier suggesting that he should search for the unknown planet, which would probably be easily distinguished by a disk. D'Arrest, a keen young volunteer at the Observatory, asked to share in the search, and suggested to Galle that it might be worth looking among the star charts of the Berlin Academy, which were then in course of publication, to verify whether the chart for Hour 21 was amongst those that were finished. It was found that this chart had been printed at the beginning of 1846, but had not yet been distributed; it was therefore available only to the astronomers at the Berlin Observatory. Galle took his place at the telescope, describing the configurations of the stars he saw, while d'Arrest followed them on the map, until Galle said: "And then there is a star of the 8th magnitude in such a position", whereupon d'Arrest exclaimed: "That star is not on the map." An observation the following night showed that the object had changed its position and proved that it was the planet. Had this chart been available to Challis, as it would have been but for the delay in distribution, he would undoubtedly have found the planet at the beginning of August, some weeks before Le Verrier's third memoir was presented to the French Academy.

On 1 October, Le Verrier wrote to Airy informing him of the discovery of the planet. He mentioned that the Bureau des Longitudes had adopted the name Neptune, the figure a trident, and that the name Janus (which had also been suggested) would have the inconvenience of making it appear that the planet was the last in the solar system, which there was no reason to believe.

The discovery of the planet, following the brilliant researches of Le Verrier, which were known to the scientific world through their publication by the French Academy, was received with admiration and delight, and was acclaimed as one of the greatest triumphs of the human intellect. The prior investigations of Adams, his prediction of the position of the planet, the long patient search by Challis were known to only a few people in England. Adams had published nothing; he had communicated his results to Challis and to Airy, but neither of them knew anything of the details of his investigations; his name was unknown in astronomical circles outside his own country. Adams had actually drawn up a paper to be read at the meeting of the British Association at Southampton early in September, but he did not arrive in sufficient time to present it, as Section A closed its meetings one day earlier than he had expected.

The first reference in print to the fact that Adams had independently reached conclusions similar to those of Le Verrier was made in a letter from Sir John Herschel, published in the *Athenaeum* of 3 October. It came as a complete surprise to the French astronomers and ungenerous aspersions were cast upon the work of Adams. It was assumed that his solution was a crude essay which would not stand the test of rigorous examination and that, as he had not published any account of his researches, he could not establish a claim to priority or even to a share in the discovery.

At the meeting of the French Academy on 12 October,

Arago made a long and impassioned defence of his protégé, Le Verrier, and a violent attack on Adams, referring scornfully to what he described as his *clandestine* work.

In England opinion was divided; some English astronomers contended that because Adams's results had not been publicly announced he could claim no share in the discovery. But for the most part it was considered that the credit for the successful prediction of the position of the unknown planet should be shared equally between Adams and Le Verrier. Adams himself took no part in the heated discussions which went on for some time with regard to the credit for the discovery of the new planet; he never uttered a single word of criticism or blame in connexion with the matter.

The controversy was lifted to a higher plane by a letter from Sir John Herschel to *The Guardian* in which he said:

> The history of this grand discovery is that of *thought* in one of its highest manifestations, of science in one of its most refined applications. So viewed, it offers a deeper interest than any personal question. In proportion to the importance of the step, it is surely interesting to know that more than one mathematician has been found capable of taking it.

At the meeting of the Royal Astronomical Society on 13 November 1846, three important papers were read. The first, by the Astronomer Royal, was an "Account of some Circumstances historically connected with the Discovery of the Planet Exterior to Uranus." All the correspondence with Adams, Challis and Le Verrier was given, as well as the two memoranda from Adams, the whole being linked together by Airy's own comments. The account made it perfectly clear that Adams and Le Verrier had independently solved the same problem, that the positions which they had assigned to the new planet were in close agreement, and that Adams had been the first to solve the problem. The second was Challis's "Account of Observations undertaken in search of the Planet discovered at Berlin on September 23, 1846", which showed that in the course of the search for the planet, he had twice observed it before its discovery at Berlin, and that he had observed it a third time before the news of this discovery reached England. The third paper was by Adams and was entitled "An Explanation of the observed Irregularities in the Motion of Uranus, on the Hypothesis of Disturbances caused by a more Distant Planet; with a determination of the Mass, Orbit, and Position of the Disturbing Body."

Adams's memoir was a masterpiece; it showed a thorough grasp of the problem; a mathematical maturity which was remarkable in one so young; and a facility in dealing with complex numerical computations.

With the independent investigations of both men published, there was no difficulty in agreeing that each was entitled to an equal share of the honour. The verdict of history agrees with that of Sir John Herschel who, in addressing the Royal Astronomical Society in 1848, said:

> As genius and destiny have joined the names of Le Verrier and Adams, I shall by no means put them asunder; nor will they ever be pronounced apart so long as language shall celebrate the triumphs of science in her sublimest walks.

The moon is our nearest celestial neighbor and aside from the sun itself the most dramatic spectacle in the heavens. Small wonder that it has played so important a part in both the superstitions and the scientific thinking of men. Among the ancients, it was regarded as a goddess. Its phases were supposed to influence such diverse matters as the success of crops and the workings of men's minds. We have seen how, with a single glance through his telescope, Galileo showed "that it does not possess a smooth and polished surface, but one rough and uneven, and just like the face of the Earth itself, is full of vast protuberances, deep chasms and sinuosities." Newton first verified the theory of gravitation through a study of the moon's motion and showed how it influenced the tides. Hevelius mapped it in 1647 and shortly thereafter Riccioli, a Spanish Jesuit, initiated the practice of naming its salient features after noted men (himself included). The surface has since been mapped in greater detail than many areas of the earth. In more

recent times, the study of its surface was abandoned by professional astronomers to amateur observers. Its light often
hindered other research. Unromantically, they would have
preferred that it did not exist. Yet the fundamental problem of
the origin and nature of the moon remains a mystery and in it,
as Jastrow shows, may lie the solution to a wider problem, the
history of the solar system.

The study of the moon has been revolutionized by recent
developments in technique. The Russians first photographed
the other side of the moon, but their photographs lacked
clarity. The Americans then obtained photographs of the
visible side of the moon, with a new order of clarity and detail.
These photographs throw light on problems which have baffled
astronomers since the beginnings of the science. They offer
new hope for a successful landing on the moon.

Robert Jastrow was born at New York in 1925 and received
his Ph.D. from Columbia University in 1948. He taught at
Columbia and Cooper Union, became a member of the
Institute for Advanced Studies at Princeton in 1949, and was
appointed Assistant Professor of Physics at Yale in 1953. He is
now at The Institute for Space Studies in New York City.

THE EXPLORATION OF THE MOON

ROBERT JASTROW

THE FIRST extraterrestrial body to be explored will undoubtedly be the moon. The moon is the earth's nearest
neighbor. Mars and Venus are at least 100 times more distant, and a rocket that would take months to reach one of
these planets can travel to the moon in a day or two. An
instrument station on the moon could communicate with the
earth with greater ease than one on Mars or Venus. The
moon is a way-station en route to the planets, and a testing

ground for the development of the rocket technology and scientific instrumentation of planetary exploration.

By a fortunate coincidence the moon also has a great importance for the scientist. In fact, a growing body of scientific opinion holds that the moon will in many ways more richly reward the effort to reach it than will either Mars or Venus. To investigators preoccupied with the remarkable developments in contemporary astronomy and physics, the moon has seemed a dead and changeless world. But there has been a growing realization that out of its very deadness and changelessness the moon may yield the answers to some fundamental and universal questions about the solar system and the universe at large. Harold C. Urey of the University of California at La Jolla has been the most vigorous and effective advocate of this point of view.

The moon is an astronomical Rosetta stone. Because its surface has preserved the record of ancient events, it holds a key to the history of the solar system. The air and water that support life on the earth continuously wear away the surface features of our planet. Processes in the interior of the earth heave up chains of mountains for demolition by the forces of erosion, and the cycles of building and erosion from one epoch to the next erase the record of the past. Similar processes presumably occur on Mars and Venus. The moon, on the other hand, has neither atmosphere nor oceans, and has never been eroded by wind and water. The lunar surface does disintegrate to some extent under a hail of small meteorites, and exposed rocks may flake as a result of the great difference between the temperature of the lunar night and that of the lunar day. But such erosion is slight in comparison to that on earth. Furthermore, the circular formations that dominate the moon's topography indicate that its crust has never undergone the violent changes which are involved in mountain-building processes on earth. Otherwise the circular craters of the moon would have been distorted out of all recognition in a few tens of millions of years, and the major features of the lunar surface would be the irregular linear structures so characteristic of the earth's surface. (One of the rare linear structures on the moon is the so-called Straight Wall, a cliff 60 miles long and 800 feet high.) The dead surface of the moon probably possesses features that are some four billion years old.

Upon this surface cosmic dust has rained for eons unimpeded by any atmosphere. Here is a biographical record of the solar system. Moreover, the cosmic sediment may contain complex organic molecules—precursors of living matter —and perhaps even living spores that have drifted in from other planets or from outside the solar system.

One of the primary objectives of the first-hand exploration of the moon will be to obtain evidence on its temperature history. Such evidence will help to settle uncertainties about the origin of the sun and the planets, and indicate whether the solar system is a common or a rare phenomenon in the universe. One of the older ideas of planetary creation—the "collision" hypothesis—postulates that a passing star tore great masses of material from the sun. Condensing first into hot, liquid protoplanets, this material then cooled to form the planets. But stars are so far apart that such encounters must be extremely rare. The collision hypothesis therefore implies that planets are similarly rare in our galaxy. The more widely accepted idea—the dust-cloud hypothesis—holds that stars arise from the condensation of the immense clouds of dust and gas that are observed in interstellar space. Variations in the density of such a cloud bring into action gravitational forces that form the stars, and local variations within the cloud give rise to planets. According to this scheme, planets may grow by the accretion of dust particles, or they may come into being when small, solid planetesimals fall together. In either case a planet would be cool at birth. The dust-cloud hypothesis implies that planets and planetary satellites such as the moon may be nearly as numerous as stars, because they are a natural accompaniment of star formation.

A cool birth does not exclude the later heating and melting of planetary bodies by the radioactive elements that they contain. However, in the case of a relatively small body such as the moon, the heat of radioactivity would be lost at the surface very rapidly. In fact, Urey, and more recently Gordon J. F. MacDonald of the University of California at

Los Angeles and the National Aeronautics and Space Administration, have shown that radioactivity alone could not raise the temperature of the entire moon to the melting point unless the primitive moon were already quite warm at the time of its creation. According to MacDonald's latest calculations, the heat generated by the radioactive elements would probably not be sufficient to produce extensive melting unless the moon were initially at a temperature greater than 600 degrees centigrade. This high initial temperature would be improbable in the product of a dust cloud, but it would be more than likely if the moon arose from hot gases pulled out of the sun in an encounter with another star.

Some evidence gained by remote observation from the earth indicates that the moon has never been molten. There is, first of all, the shape of the moon. If the moon were a warm body with a relatively plastic interior, its rotation about its own axis would give rise to an equatorial bulge like that of the earth. This bulge is produced by centrifugal forces that depend on speed of rotation. The earth's 24-hour rotation-period has produced a bulge of 21 kilometers (13 miles). Because the moon rotates more slowly on its axis—only once in 28 days—its equatorial radius should be only 50 meters greater than its polar radius. In actuality the equatorial radius is one kilometer greater. Moreover, there is a bulge in the side of the moon that always faces the earth. This "moon nose" has been pulled out by the gravitational attraction of our planet. According to calculations based on the known force of gravity, the nose should be about 40 meters high. In reality, it is about a kilometer high.

The explanation for these discrepancies probably lies in the fact that the moon was once much closer to the earth and rotated much faster on its axis. The enormous forces then prevailing molded the moon in its present shape. But these forces waned as the moon swung out on a more distant orbit and turned more slowly on its axis. This happened no later than a few tens of millions of years after the birth of the moon. In the subsequent four billion years the moon has retained the irregular shape it acquired in its infancy. If the moon had been plastic at any time, the bulges would have sunk into its interior. The preservation of these irregularities shows that for most of its history the interior of the moon has been quite cold and mechanically quite strong.

Measurements made with the help of artificial satellites have recently disclosed that the earth also departs significantly from its calculated shape. Bulges in the Northern and Southern hemispheres give it a slightly pearlike configuration. Furthermore, the equatorial bulge is somewhat greater than was expected. In fact, the present equatorial bulge must have come into existence some 100 million years ago, when the earth was rotating faster and its day was shorter. Thus the interior of the earth, unlike that of the moon, is sufficiently warm and plastic to respond to changes in rotation rate, although with a lag of 100 million years.

The orbit of the first closely tracked lunar satellite will be able to measure the irregularities in the shape of the moon with great accuracy. The same observations will yield another crucial bit of evidence to decide whether the moon has ever been molten. Certain characteristics of the satellite orbit will show whether the lunar material has a relatively even density. If the moon has ever been completely molten, its iron will have collected in its core, as has the iron of the earth. On the other hand, if the moon grew by the accretion of small, cool bodies, it is likely to have a "raisin-bread" structure in which chunks of metal are spread evenly among the lighter materials.

The chemical composition and physical characteristics of the lunar surface are also important clues to the temperature and other conditions both at the time of the moon's birth and during its later development. Telescopic observations have produced a tantalizingly incomplete picture of the lunar surface, a picture that is compatible with several different conjectures as to what the surface is really like. The dominant features of the lunar landscape are craters and dry "seas," or maria. At one time it was widely believed that the craters were volcanic in origin. The U. S. geologist G. K. Gilbert dealt this idea a heavy blow in 1892, when he pointed out that lunar craters have virtually none of the characteristics of volcanoes. Among the tens of thousands of craters on the moon, only a dozen resemble terrestrial volcanoes. Most students of the moon now agree that meteorite collisions and not vulcanism created the vast majority of the craters visible on the moon.

The absence of lunar volcanic activity reinforces the pictures of the moon as a relatively cold planetary body. It is true that in 1958 the Soviet astronomer Nikolai A. Kozyrev made observations that indicated such activity in the crater Alphonsus. However, an extended discussion at the Space Exploration Symposium in Washington brought general agreement that what Kozyrev had observed must have been simply the release of residual gas and not a true eruption.

In his 1892 lecture Gilbert asserted that meteorites had probably created some of the lunar seas as well as the craters. He reasoned that the flying fragments of a giant meteorite had carved the series of deep valleys that radiate from Mare Imbrium. The fragments would have had to be large and considerably denser than the material of the lunar surface. Gilbert suggested that they came from an object 100 miles in diameter. Striking the moon at an oblique angle, the meteorite first created the "inlet" in Mare Imbrium known as Rainbow Bay and then came to rest in the center of the sea.

Gilbert thought that Mare Imbrium itself was a lava flow produced by the heat of impact. However, Thomas Gold of Cornell University, Robert S. Dietz of the Naval Electronics Laboratory in San Diego and MacDonald have pointed out that a meteorite collision is more likely to pulverize rock than to melt it. A small amount of lava, they say, may appear at the point of contact, but most of the energy will go into creating dust and rubble that in an airless environment will drop back in the area of the collision to form a relatively flat bed.

Although this argument weighs against the idea that the seas were created by the melting of rock in major meteorite impacts, it is still possible that the seas are flows of lava, but lava that welled up through fissures in the surface during periods of internal activity. Gerard P. Kuiper and other students of the moon subscribe to this view of the formation of the maria, and it may turn out to be the correct one. However, difficulties are associated with it also. In particular, the irregular figure of the moon indicates that it has been relatively cold during a large part of its history, and a cold interior could not produce large lava flows at the surface.

At the same time it must be said that some features on the moon are hard to explain unless it is assumed that they are lava flows. The Sea of Tranquility, for example, has the irregular outline that is characteristic of the flow of a liquid over a rough terrain.

The answer to the question of what really does cover the lunar seas must await detailed reconnaissance and surface exploration. In the 67 years since Gilbert gave his lecture telescopic observations have yielded practically no new information about the moon. The resolving power of present-day telescopes is not appreciably greater than that of the telescopes in Gilbert's time. According to Kuiper, who has made some of the finest lunar photographs, the large telescopes of today might under the best seeing conditions be used visually to resolve objects a 10th of a mile across. Photographic resolution is considerably poorer; unlike the eye, the photographic plate cannot accommodate the wobbling of images caused by the instability of the earth's atmosphere. For all practical purposes a feature of the moon can be observed visually only if it is more than 1,000 feet across, and can be observed photographically only if it is more than 2,500 feet across.

In 1957 an important detail was added to the telescopic picture of the moon by a series of remarkable radio observations conducted at Jodrell Bank in England and at the U. S. Naval Research Laboratory. The observations took advantage of the fact that when light or any other electromagnetic radiation, such as radio waves, strikes the surface of a polished sphere, it is reflected back to the source as though from a single point within the sphere. If the surface of the sphere is not polished—that is, if the average size of the irregularities is equal to or greater than the wavelength of the radiation falling upon it—the reflected radiation will be diffused, and the entire illuminated area will appear uniformly bright, like a frosted light-bulb. The lunar surface does diffuse the visible light that it reflects. Light waves are of the order of .0001 centimeter long, and on this fine scale the surface of the moon is fairly rough. The radio observations showed, however, that the moon sharply reflects radio waves that are 10 centimeters (four inches) long. On this coarser scale the surface of the moon is relatively "polished": its irregularities must be, on the average, less than 10 centimeters in diameter.

This relative smoothness of the lunar surface poses a question. The surface should be covered with pits with a diameter of more than 10 centimeters, caused by the meteorites that undoubtedly rain steadily on the moon. Yet the pits are not there; at least there is no evidence for them. Of course the hail of meteroites must have chipped away at the rocks, and the moon must be covered with a layer of rock dust; the large meteorites that created the visible craters doubtless manufactured even more dust. But since there is no wind on the moon, even the dust should be pitted.

Some unknown agent distributes the dust over the lunar surface with such uniformity that the small pits and craters are filled in. Perhaps the continued bombardment of the surface by micrometeorites moves enough dust to make the surface virtually smooth.

Gold has proposed a more interesting and more original solution to the problem. He suggests that the solar protons which bombard the moon would give some neighboring dust particles a positive electric charge. Under the mutual repulsion of their like charge, the particles would hop about. Gold and his students have bombarded dust particles with electrons in the laboratory, and the particles act like Mexican jumping beans. Their hopping makes them migrate; if they are on a slope, for example, they will march downhill under the influence of gravity. Thus the moon's highlands should be scoured clean, and its depressions should be filled with dust to a considerable depth. The weight of the overlying dust would compact the deeper materials, but for some distance down it is possible that the lunar surface is relatively porous, perhaps with the texture of a rusk. If Gold is right, it would be well not to choose the otherwise smooth and inviting surface of a lunar sea for the first landing on the moon. The porous rusk might not be able to bear the modest lunar weight of an exploration vehicle, and so might swallow it up.

One of the first objectives of the lunar-exploration program will be to obtain views of the surface that are more detailed than those available from telescopes on the earth. A first step in this direction has been taken by the U.S.S.R. with *Lunik III*, which transmitted television pictures of the "back" of the moon. More revealing views of the lunar surface will be made by cameras mounted either in lunar satellites or in spacecraft designed to land on the moon. The images may be obtained by television or by photography; perhaps both methods will be developed and tried. The pictures relayed to earth by these cameras will provide the definition needed to determine the structure of the lunar surface and will at the same time permit the selection of landing sites for vehicles. Over limited areas the resolution of detail may be about 100 times better than that of the best terrestrial telescopes.

The region of extended shadows near the terminator— the line dividing light from dark on the moon—may prove to be a good place for such reconnaissance. Here all surface details are thrown into exaggerated relief, and it may be possible to detect differences in elevation of a few feet or less. An important supplement to the television studies will be an instrument designed to penetrate the surface and reveal its hardness or the degree to which it is compacted.

Even in advance of these achievements it is clear that the lunar landscape does not at all resemble the earlier conception of the moon as a Gothic spectacle of steep cliffs and needle-like spires. To a man standing within a typical lunar crater its slopes would appear rather gentle; indeed, they seldom exceed a grade of 10 degrees.

Beyond the initial objective of surface reconnaissance,

several experiments that are in prospect will make major contributions to knowledge of the moon. Perhaps the most important experiment in the early stages of lunar exploration will be carried out by the gamma-ray spectrometer. The instrument, mounted in either a lunar satellite or a landing capsule, might consist of a crystal to detect gamma rays emitted by radioactive uranium, thorium and potassium, and a pulse-height analyzer to separate the various wavelengths of the rays. Since the different elements emit gamma rays at different wavelengths, the analyzer will indicate how much potassium, thorium and uranium the lunar crust contains. The relative abundance of these elements will in turn reveal a great deal about the rocks of the lunar crust, because different kinds of rock contain different amounts of these elements. Moreover, the concentration of these elements will indicate how much of the heating of the young moon was accountable to radioactivity.

Finally, several years further in the future, the stage of serious lunar exploration by unmanned landings involving remotely controlled instrumentation can begin. The Soviet *Lunik I* has already made contact with the moon's surface, but it carried no instruments to report what it had encountered. The first instrumented landings may be rather rough. Nonetheless a seismometer that should sustain the impact of a rather hard landing is already being developed. This instrument, by reporting on moonquakes, could supply valuable information on the internal structure of the moon. With the development of the guidance and control needed for truly soft landings, an X-ray fluorescence spectrograph might be sent to determine the chemical composition of the lunar surface. This instrument, working wide-open in the high vacuum of the lunar environment, would bombard the rock with an electron beam. The atoms in the rock would respond by emitting X-rays at characteristic energies, thus identifying the metals in the rock.

Another important instrument would be a gravimeter for measuring small changes in the force of gravity at the surface of the moon. Such changes are produced by land tides that occur when the sun and the earth pull on the moon.

Land tides are similar to the earth's ocean tides, but their amplitude is much smaller, since solid land responds far less than water does to an attacking force. In a land tide the surface of the moon moves outward a few inches or a foot, and a gravimeter on it would move away from the center of the moon by that amount. Since the force of gravity grows weaker with increasing distance from the center of the attracting body, the gravimeter will record a decrease in the gravitational force as a result of this outward movement. A variation of six inches is only a ten millionth the radius of the moon, yet gravimeters are so sensitive that they can detect far smaller effects. The height and timing of lunar land tides will furnish precise measurements of the viscosity and elasticity of the moon's interior.

The soft-landing packages may also contain ionosphere and plasma probes, density gauges, magnetometers and television cameras. The latter could be fitted with telescopic lenses for inspecting the surrounding area to some distance and with lenses for close examination of materials near the vehicle. The ultimate in unmanned exploration may be a roving vehicle that will land on the moon's surface and then be piloted about by remote control. The machine would have to travel over the unfamiliar surface in a vacuum and under extreme temperature conditions, carrying delicate physical and chemical instruments that do their work as it proceeds, all under the control of an operator a quarter of a million miles away on the earth. But the vehicle would get away from the disturbed conditions at the landing site and would be able to correct the possibly misleading impressions gained from the limited number of sites at which earlier instruments will have landed. This self-propelled laboratory might be powered by solar batteries and would have to hibernate during the two-week lunar night, coming to life again during each lunar day.

The remote-control instrument station in its most complex form will reveal a great deal of information about the moon. But no matter how complex this instrumentation may become, it will never be able to grapple with unforeseen circumstances and to capitalize on unexpected opportunities. With the advent of manned flights a decade or more hence, lunar exploration will enter upon its most rewarding phase.

In an event which ranks with Galileo's first telescopic examination of Venus, a space probe launched from Cape Canaveral, Florida, in 1962 reached a point 21,598 miles from the planet after having made the longest trip ever initiated by man. During this trip, it collected some ninety million bits of experimental data which will require years for complete analysis. Already, however, it has cast new light on the nature of Venus, has given us more accurate measurements and basic physical data on the solar system, and has provided engineers with information of great value for the design of future spacecraft.

To quote the volume from which this selection was taken:

> The 447-pound spacecraft had to be catapulted from a launching platform moving around the Sun at 66,600 miles per hour, and aimed so precisely that it would intercept a planet moving 78,300 miles per hour (or 11,700 miles per hour faster than the Earth) at a point in space and time some 180.2 million miles away and 109 days later, with only one chance to correct the trajectory by a planned mid-course maneuver.
>
> And the interception had to be so accurate that the spacecraft would pass Venus within 8,000 to 40,000 miles. The chances of impacting the planet could not exceed 1 in 1,000 because Mariner was not sterilized and might contaminate Venus. Also, much more data could be gathered on a near-miss flight path than on impact. Furthermore, at encounter (in the target area) the spacecraft had to be so positioned that it could communicate with Earth, see the Sun with its solar panels, and scan Venus at the proper angles.

With the Russian moon rocket, Mariner is the earliest of many similar space probes to be expected in the near future.

Is there life on Mars? What is the true nature of the forces
acting between the earth and the sun? Is planetary colonization
possible? Questions like these, hitherto unanswerable, now
seem open to solution by means of new scientific and engineer-
ing techniques.

MARINER: MISSION TO VENUS

THE STAFF, JET PROPULSION LABORATORY,
CALIFORNIA INSTITUTE OF TECHNOLOGY.

HALFWAY BETWEEN Los Angeles and Las Vegas, the
California country climbs southward out of the sunken basin
of Death Valley onto the 3500-foot-high floor of the Mojave
desert.

On this immense plateau in an area near Goldstone Dry
Lake, about 45 miles north of the town of Barstow, a group
of 85-foot antennas forms the nucleus of the United States'
world-wide, deep-space tracking network.

Here, on the morning of December 14, 1962, several men
were gathered in the control building beneath one of the
antennas, listening intently to the static coming from a loudspeaker. They were surrounded by the exotic equipment of
the space age. Through the window loomed the gleaming
metal framework of an antenna.

Suddenly a voice boomed from the loudspeaker: "The
numbers are changing. We're getting data!"

The men broke into a cheeer, followed by an expectant
silence.

Again the voice came from the speaker: "The spacecraft's
crossing the terminator . . . it's still scanning."

At that moment, some 36 million miles from the Earth,
the National Aeronautics and Space Administration's Mariner spacecraft was passing within 21,600 miles of the planet
Venus and was radioing back information to the Goldstone

Station—the first scientific data ever received by man from the near-vicinity of another planet.

At the same time, in Washington, D.C., a press conference was in progress. Mr. James E. Webb, Administrator of the National Aeronautics and Space Administration, and Dr. William H. Pickering, Director of the Jet Propulsion Laboratory, stood before a bank of microphones. In a few moments, Dr. Pickering said, the audience would hear the sound of Mariner II as it transmitted its findings back to the Earth.

Then, a musical warble, the voice of Mariner II, resounded in the hall and in millions of radios and television sets around the nation. Alluding to the Greek belief that harmonious sounds accompanied the movement of the planets, Dr. Pickering remarked that this, in truth, was the music of the spheres.

Mariner II had been launched from Cape Canaveral, Florida, on August 27, 1962. Its arrival at Venus was the culmination of a 109-day journey through the strange environment of interplanetary space. The project had gone from the drawing board to the launching pad in less than 11 months. Mariner had taxed the resources and the manpower of the Jet Propulsion Laboratory, California Institute of Technology; the Atlantic Missile Range centering at Cape Canaveral; theoretical and experimental laboratories at several universities and NASA centers; numerous elements of the aerospace industry; and, of course, NASA management itself.

To the considerable body of engineeers scattered around the world from Pasadena to Goldstone to South Africa to Australia, the warble of Mariner was something more than "the music of the spheres." Intercept with Venus was the climax of 109 days of hope and anxiety.

To the world at large, this warbling tone was a signal that the United States had moved ahead—reached out to the planets. Mariner was exploring the future, seeeking answers to some of the unsolved questions about the solar system.

Venus, the glittering beacon of our solar system, has intrigued man for at least 4,000 years. The Babylonians first mentioned the brilliant planet on clay tablets as early as 2,000 years before Christ. The Egyptians, the Greeks, and the Chinese had thought of Venus as two stars because it was visible first in the morning and then in the evening sky. The Greeks had called the morning star Phosphorus and the evening star Hesperos. By 500 B.C. Pythagoras, the Greek philosopher, had realized that the two were identical.

Galileo discovered the phases of Venus in 1610. Because of the planet's high reflectivity, Copernicus falsely concluded that Venus was either self-luminous or else transparent to the rays of the Sun.

Venus was tracked across the face of the Sun in 1761, from which event the presence of an atmosphere about the planet was deduced because of the fuzzy edges of the image visible in the telescope. Throughout the eighteenth and nineteenth centuries, Venus continued to excite growing scientific curiosity in Europe and America.

Even the development of giant telescopes and the refinement of spectroscopic and radar astronomy techniques in recent times had yielded few indisputable facts about Venus. Until radar studies, made from Goldstone, California, in 1962, neither the rate nor the angle of axial spin could be determined with any degree of accuracy. The ever-shifting atmosphere continued to shield the Venusian surface from visual observation on Earth, and the nature of its atmosphere became an especially controversial mystery.

Venus is a virtual twin of the Earth; it approaches our planet closer than any celestial body except the Moon, a few vagrant comets, and other such galactic wanderers. Long fabled in song and legend as the most beautiful object in the sky, Venus has an albedo, or reflectivity factor, of 59% (the Moon has one of 7%). In its brightest or crescent phase, Venus glows like a torch, even casting a distinct shadow—the only body other than the Sun and the Moon yielding such light.

Venus' diameter is approximately 7,700 miles, compared with Earth's 7,900. Also as compared with 1.0 for the Earth,

Venus' mean density is 0.91, the mass 0.81, and the volume 0.92.

The Cytherean orbit (the adjective comes from Cytherea, one of the ancient Greek names for Aphrodite—or in Roman times, Venus—the goddess of love) is almost a perfect circle, with an eccentricity (or out-of-roundness) of only 0.0068, lowest of all the planets. Venus rides this orbital path at a mean distance from the Sun of 67.2 million miles (Earth is 93 million miles), and at a mean orbital speed of 78,300 miles per hour, as compared with Earth's 66,600 miles per hour.

It also has a shorter sidereal period (revolution around the Sun or year): 224 Earth days, 16 hours, 48 minutes. Estimates of the Venus rotational period, or the length of the Venus day, have ranged from approximately 23 Earth hours to just over 224 Earth days. The latter rotation rate would be almost equivalent to the Venusian year and, in such case, the planet would always have the same face to the Sun.

Venus approaches within 26 million miles of the Earth at inferior conjunction, and is as far away as 160 million miles at superior conjunction, when it is on the opposite side of the Sun.

The escape velocity (that velocity required to free an object from the gravitational pull of a planet) on Venus is 6.3 miles per second, compared with Earth's escape velocity of 7 miles per second. The gravity of the Earth is sufficient to trap an oxygen-bearing atmosphere near the terrestrial surface. Because the escape velocity of Venus is about the same as that of Earth, men have long believed (or hoped) that the Cytherean world might hold a similar atmosphere and thus be favorable to the existence of living organisms as we know them on the Earth. From this speculation, numerous theories have evolved.

Before Mariner II, Venus probably caused more controversy than any other planet in our solar system except Mars. Observers have visualized Venus as anything from a steaming abode of Mesozoic-like creatures such as were found on the Earth millions of years ago, to a dead, noxious, and sunless world constantly ravaged by winds of incredible force.

Conjectures about the Venusian atmosphere have been inescapably tied to theories about the Venusian topography. Because the clouds forming the Venusian atmosphere, as viewed from the Earth through the strongest telescopes, are almost featureless, this relationship between atmosphere and topography has posed many problems.

Impermanent light spots and certain dusky areas were believed by some observers to be associated with Venusian oceans. One scientist believed he identified a mountain peak which he calculated as rising more than 27 miles above the general level of the planet.

Another feature of the Venusian topography is the lack of (detectable) polar flattening. The Earth does have such a flattening at the poles and it was reasoned that, because Venus did not, its rate of rotation must be much slower than that of the Earth, perhaps as little as only once during a Venusian year, thus keeping one face perpetually toward the Sun.

Another school of thought speculated that Venus was covered entirely by vast oceans; other observers concluded that these great bodies of water have long since evaporated and that the winds, through the Cytherean ages, have scooped up the remaining chloride salts and blasted them into the Venusian skies, thus forming the clouds.

Related to the topographic speculations were equally tenuous theories about its atmosphere. It was reasoned that if the oceans of Venus still exist, then the Venusian clouds may be composed of water droplets; if Venus were covered by water, it was suggested that it might be inhabited by Venusian equivalents of Earth's Cambrian period of 500 million years ago, and the same steamy atmosphere could be a possibility.

Other theories respecting the nature of the Venusian atmosphere, depending on how their authors viewed the Venusian terrain, included clouds of hydrocarbons (perhaps droplets of oil), or vapors of formaldehyde and water. Finally, the seeemingly high temperature of the planet's surface, as measured by Earth-bound instruments, was credited by some to the false indications that could be given by a Cytherean ionosphere heavily charged with free electrons.

However, the consensus of pre-Mariner scientific thinking seemed generally to indicate no detectable free oxygen in the atmosphere; this fact inveighed against the probability of surface vegetation, because Earth-bound vegetation, at least, uses carbon dioxide and gives off oxygen into the atmosphere. On the other hand, a preponderance of carbon dioxide in the Venusian atmosphere was measured which would create a greenhouse effect. The heat of the Sun would be trapped near the surface of the planet, raising the temperature to as high as 615 degreees F. If the topography were in truth relatively flat and the rate of rotation slow, the heating effect might produce winds of 400 miles per hour or more, and sand and dust storms beyond Earthly experience. And so the controversy continued.

But at 1:53.13.9 a.m., EST, on August 27, 1962, the theories of the past few centuries were being challenged. At that moment, the night along the east Florida coast was shattered by the roar of rocket engines and the flash of incandescent exhaust streams. The United States was launching Mariner II, the first spacecraft that would successfully penetrate interplanetary space and probe some of the age-old mysteries of our neighbor planet.

If intelligent life had existed on Venus on the afternoon of the Earth's December 14, 1962, and if it could have seen through the clouds, it might have observed Mariner II approach from the night side, drift down closer, cross over to the daylight face, and move away toward the Sun to the right. The time was the equivalent of 12:34 p.m. along the Pacific Coast of the United States, where the spacecraft was being tracked.

Mariner II had reached the climax of its 180-million-mile, 109-day trip through space. The 35-minute encounter with Venus would tell Earth scientists more about our sister planet than they had been able to learn during all the preceding centuries.

Before Mariner, scientists theorized about the existence of clouds of cosmic dust around the Sun. A knowledge of the composition, origin, and the dynamics of these minute particles is necessary for study of the origins and evolution of the solar system.

Tiny particles of cosmic dust (some with masses as low as 1.3×10^{-10} gram or about one-trillionth of a pound) were thought to be present in the solar system and have been recorded by satellites in the near-Earth regions.

These microcosmic particles could be either the residue left over after our solar system was formed some 5 billion years ago, possibly by condensation of huge masses of gas and dust clouds; or, the debris deposited within our system by the far-flung and decaying tails of passing comets; or, the dust trapped from galactic space by the magnetic fields of the Sun and the planets.

Analysis of the more than 1,700 hours of cosmic dust detector data recovered from the flight of Mariner II seems to indicate that in the region between the Earth and Venus the concentration of tiny cosmic dust particles is some ten-thousand times less than that observed near the Earth.

During the 129 days (including the post-encounter period) of Mariner's mission, the data showed only one dust particle impact which occurred in deep space and not near Venus. Equivalent experiments near Earth (on board Earth satellites) have yielded over 3,700 such impacts within periods of approximately 500 hours. The cause of this heavy near-Earth concentration, the exact types of particles, and their source are still unknown.

The cosmic dust experiment performed well during the Mariner mission. Although some calibration difficulty was observed about two weeks before the Venus encounter, possibly caused by overheating of the sensor crystal, there was no apparent effect in the electronic circuits.

For some time prior to Mariner, scientists postulated the existence of a so-called plasma flow or "solar wind" streaming out from the Sun, to explain the motion of comet tails (which always point away from the Sun, perhaps repelled by the plasma), geomagnetic storms, aurorae, and other such disturbances. (Plasma is defined as a gas in which the atoms are dissociated into atomic nuclei and electrons, but which, as a whole, is electrically neutral.)

The solar wind was thought to drastically alter the configuration of the Sun's external magnetic field. Plasma moving at extreme velocities is able to carry with it the lines of magnetic force originating in the Sun's corona and to distort any fields it encounters as it moves out from the Sun.

It was believed that these moving plasma currents are also capable of altering the size of a planet's field of magnetic flux. When this happens, the field on the sunlit face of the planet is compressed and the dark side has an elongated expansion of the field. For example, the outer boundary of the Earth's magnetic field is pushed in by the solar wind to about 40,000 miles from the Earth on the sunward side. On the dark side, the field extends out much farther.

The solar wind was also known to have an apparent effect on the movement of cosmic rays. As the Sun spots increase in the regular 11-year cycle, the number of cosmic rays reaching the Earth from outside our solar system will decrease.

Mariner II found that streams of plasma are constantly flowing out from the Sun. This fluctuating, extremely tenuous solar wind seems to dominate interplanetary space in our region of the solar system. The wind moves at velocities varying from about 200 to 500 miles per second (about 720,000 to 1,800,000 miles per hour), and measures up to perhaps a million degrees Fahrenheit (within the subatomic structure).

With the solar plasma spectrometer working at ten different energy levels, Mariner required 3.7 minutes to run through a complete energy spectrum. During the 123 days, when readings were made, a total of 40,000 such spectra were recorded. Plasma was monitored on 104 of those 123 days, and on every one of the spectra, the plasma was always present.

Mariner showed that the energies of the particles in the solar winds are very low, on the order of a few hundred or few thousand electron volts, as compared with the billions and trillions of electron volts measured in cosmic radiation.

The extreme tenuousity or low density of the solar wind is difficult to comprehend: about 10 to 20 protons (hydrogen nuclei) and electrons per cubic inch. But despite the low energy and density, solar wind particles in our region of the solar system are billions of times more numerous than cosmic rays and, therefore, the total energy content of the winds is much greater than that of the cosmic rays.

Mariner found that when the surface of the Sun was relatively inactive, the velocity of the wind was a little less than 250 miles per second and the temperature a few hundred thousand degrees. The plasma was always present, but the density and the velocity varied. Flare activity on the Sun seemed to eject clouds of plasma, greatly increasing the velocity and density of the winds. Where the particles were protons, their energies ranged from 750 to 2,500 electron volts.

The experiment also showed that the velocity of the plasma apparently undergoes frequent fluctuations of this type. On approximately twenty occasions, the velocity increased within a day or two by 20 to 100%. These disturbances seemed to correlate well with magnetic storms observed on the Earth. In several cases, the sudden increase in the solar plasma flux preceded various geomagnetic effects observed on the Earth by only a short time.

The Mariner solar plasma experiment was the first extensive measurement of the intensity and velocity spectrum of solar plasma taken far enough from the Earth's field so that the Earth would have no effect on the results.

Speculation has long existed as to the amount of high-energy radiation (from cosmic rays and particles from the Sun with energies in the millions of electron volts) present within our solar system and as to whether exposure would be fatal to a human space traveler.

This high-energy type of ionizing radiation is thought to consist of the nuclei of such atoms as hydrogen and helium, and of electrons, all moving very rapidly. The individual particles are energetic enough to penetrate considerable amounts of matter. The concentration of these particles is apparently much lower than that of low-energy plasma.

The experiments were designed to detect three types of high-energy radiation particles: the cosmic rays coming from outside the solar system, solar flare particles, and radiation trapped around Venus (as that which is found in the Earth's Van Allen Belt).

These high-energy radiation particles (also thought to affect aurorae and radio blackouts on the Earth) measure from about one hundred thousand electron volts up to billions of volts. The distribution of this energy is thought to be uniform outside the solar system and is assumed to move in all directions in a pattern remaining essentially constant over thousands of years.

Inside the solar system, the amount of such radiation reaching the Earth is apparently controlled by the magnetic fields found in interplanetary space and near the Earth.

The number of cosmic rays changes by a large amount over the course of an 11-year Sun-spot cycle, and below a certain energy level (5,000 Mev) few cosmic rays are present in the solar system. They are probably deflected by plasma currents or magnetic fields.

Mariner's charged particles experiment indicated that cosmic radiation (bombardment by cosmic rays), both from galactic space and those particles originating in the Sun, would not have been fatal to an astronaut, at least during the four-month period of Mariner's mission.

The accumulated radiation inside the counters was only 3 roentgens, and during the one solar storm recorded on October 23 and 24, the dosage measured only about ¼ roentgen. In other words, the dosage amounts to about one-thousandth of the usually accepted "half-lethal" dosage, or that level at which half of the persons exposed would die. An astronaut might accept many times the dosage detected by Mariner II without serious effects.

The experiment also showed little variation in density of charged particles during the trip, even with a 30% decrease in distance from the Sun, and no apparent increase due to magnetically trapped particles or radiation belts near Venus as compared with interplanetary space. However, these measurements were made during a period when the Sun was slowly decreasing in activity at the end of an 11-year cycle. The Sun spots will be at a minimum in 1964–1965, when galactic cosmic rays will sharply increase. Further experiments are needed to sample the charged particles in space under all conditions.

The lack of change measured by the ionization chamber during the mission was significant; the cosmic-ray flux of approximately 3 particles per square centimeter per second throughout the flight was an unusually constant value. A clear increase in high-energy particles (10 Mev to about 800 Mev) emitted by the Sun was noted only once: a flare-up between 7:42 and 8:45 a.m., PST, October 23. The ionization chamber reading began to increase before the flare disappeared. From a background reading of 670 ion pairs per cubic centimeter per second per standard atmosphere, it went to a peak value of 18,000, varied a bit, and remained above 10,000 for 6 hours before gradually decreasing over a period of several days. Meanwhile, the flux of the particles detected by the Geiger counter rose from the background count of 3 to a peak of 16 per square centimeter per second. Ionization thus increased much more than the number of particles, indicating to the scientists that the high-energy particles coming from the Sun might have had much lower average energies than the galactic cosmic rays.

In contrast, the low-energy experiment detected the October 23 event, and eight or ten others not seen by the high-energy detectors. These must have been low-penetrating particles excluded by the thicker walls of the high-energy instrument. These particles were perhaps protons between 0.5 and 10 Mev or electrons between 0.04 and 0.5 Mev.

At 20,000 miles from the Earth, the rate at which high-energy particles have beeen observed has been recorded at several thousand per second. With Mariner at approximately the same distance from Venus, the average was only one particle per second, as it had been during most of the month of November in space. Such a rate would indicate a low planetary magnetic field, or one that did not extend out as far as Mariner's 21,598-mile closest approach to the surface.

Mariner II measured and transmitted data in unprecedented quantity and quality during the long trip. In summary, Mariner showed that, during the measuring period, particles were numerous in the energy ranges from a few hundred to 1,000 electron volts. Protons in the range 0.5 to

10 Mev were not numerous, but at times the flux (density) was several times that of cosmic rays.

Almost no protons were shown in the 10 to 800 Mev range, except during solar flares when the particles in this range were numerous. Above 800 Mev (primarily those cosmic rays entering interplanetary space from outside the solar system) the number decreased rapidly as the energy increased, the average total being about 3 per centimeter per second.

During one 30-day period in November and December, the low-energy counter saw only two small increases in radiation intensity. At this time, the mean velocity of the solar wind was considerably lower than during September and October. This might suggest that high-velocity plasma and low-energy cosmic rays might both originate from the same solar source.

Prior to the Mariner II mission, no conclusive evidence had ever been presented concerning a Venusian magnetic field and nothing was known about possible fluid motions in a molten core or other hypotheses concerning the interior of the planet.

Scientists assumed that Venus had a field somewhat similar to the Earth's, although possibly reduced in magnitude because of the apparently slow rate of rotation and the pressure of solar plasma. Many questions had also been raised concerning the nature of the atmosphere, charged particles in the vicinity of the planet, magnetic storms, and aurorae. Good magnetometer data from Mariner II would help solve some of these problems.

Mariner's magnetometer experiment also sought verification of the existence and nature of a steady magnetic field in interplanetary space. This would be important in understanding the charged particle balance of the inner solar system. Other objectives of the experiment were to establish both the direction and the magnitude of long-period fluctuations in the interplanetary magnetic field and to study solar disturbances and such problems in magnetohydrodynamics (the study of the motion of charged particles and their surrounding magnetic fields) as the existence and effect of magnetized and charged plasmas in space.

The strength of a planet's field is thought to be closely related to its rate of rotation—the slower the rotation, the weaker the field. As a consequence, if Venus' field is simple in structure like the Earth's, the surface field should be 5 to 10% that of the Earth. If the structure of the field is complex, the surface field in places might exceed the Earth's without increasing the field along Mariner's trajectory to observable values.

Most of the phenomena associated with the Earth's magnetic field are likely to be significantly modified or completely absent in and around Venus. Auroral displays and the trapping of charged particles in radiation belts such as our Van Allen would be missing. The field of the Earth keeps low- and moderate-energy cosmic rays away from the top of the atmosphere, except in the polar regions. The cosmic ray flux at the top of Venus' atmosphere is likely to correspond everywhere to the high level found at the Earth's poles.

In contrast to Venus, Jupiter, which is ten times larger in mass and volume and rotates twice as fast as the Earth, has a field considerably stronger than the Earth's. The Moon has a field on the sunlit side (according to Russian measurements) which, because of the Moon's slow rotation rate, is less than 1/3 of 1% of the Earth's at the Equator. Thus, a planet's rotation, if at a less rapid rate than the Earth's, seems to produce smaller magnetic fields. This theory is consistent with the idea of a planetary magnetic field resulting from the dynamo action inside the molten core of a rotating planet.

The Sun, on the whole, has a fairly regular dipole field. Superimposed on this are some very large fields associated with disturbed regions such as spots or flares, which produce fields of very great intensities.

These solar fields are drawn out into space by plasma flow. Although relatively small in magnitude, these fields are an important influence on the propagation of particles. And the areas in question are very large—something on the order of an astronomical unit.

Mariner II seemed to show that, in space, a generally quiet magnetic-field condition was found to exist, measuring something less than 10 gamma and fluctuating over periods of 1 second to 1 minute.

As Mariner made its closest approach to Venus, the magnetometer saw no significant change, a condition also noted by the radiation and solar plasma detectors. The magnetic field data looked essentially as they had in interplanetary space, without either fluctuations or smooth changes.

The encounter produced no slow changes, nor was there a continuous fluctuation as in the interplanetary regions. There was no indication of trapped particles or near-Venus modification in the flow of solar plasma.

On the Earth's sunny side, a definite magnetic field exists out to 40,000 miles, and on the side away from the Sun considerably farther. If Venus' field had been similar to the Earth's, a reading of 100 to 200 gamma, a large cosmic-ray count, and an absence of solar plasma should have been shown, but none of these phenomena were noted by Mariner.

These results do not prove that Venus definitely has no magnetic field, but only that it was not measurable at Mariner's 21,598-mile point of closest approach. The slow rotation rate and the pressure of the solar winds probably combine to limit the field to a value one tenth of the Earth's. Since Mariner passed Venus on the sunlit side, readings are required on the dark side in order to confirm the condition of the magnetic field on that side of the planet, which normally should be considerably extended.

Before Mariner, scientists had offered two main theories about the surface of Venus: It had either an electrically charged ionosphere causing false high-temperature readings on Earth instruments despite a cool surface, or a hot surface with clouds becoming increasingly colder with altitude.

The cool-surface theory supposed an ionosphere with a layer of electrons having a density thousands of times that of the Earth's upper atmosphere. Microwave radiations from this electrical layer would cause misleading readings on Earth instruments. As a space probe scanned across such an atmosphere, it would see the least amount of charged ionosphere when looking straight down, and the most concentrated amount while scanning the limb or edge. In the latter case, it would be at an angle and would show essentially a thickening effect of the atmosphere because of the curvature of the planet.

As the probe approached the edge, the phenomenon known as "limb brightening" would occur, since the instruments would see more of the electron-charged ionosphere and little if any of the cooler surface. The temperature readings would, therefore, be correspondingly higher at the limbs.

The other theory, held by most scientists, visualized a hot surface on Venus, with no heavy concentration of electrons in the atmosphere, but with cooler clouds at higher altitudes. Thus, the spacecraft would look at a very hot planet from space, covered by colder, thick clouds. Straight down, the microwave radiometer would see the hot surface through the clouds. When approaching the limb, the radiations would encounter a thicker concentration of atmosphere and might not see any of the hot surface. This condition, "limb darkening," would be characterized by temperatures decreasing as the edges of the planet were approached.

An instrument capability or resolution much higher than that available from the Earth was required to resolve the limb-brightening or limb-darkening controversy. Mariner's radiometer would be able to provide something like one hundred times better resolution than the Earth-based measurements.

At 11:59 a.m., PST, on December 14, 1962, Mariner's radiometers began to scan the planet Venus in a nodding motion at a rate of 0.1 degree per second and reaching an angular sweep of nominally 120 degrees. The radiometers had been switched on 6½ hours before the encounter with Venus and they continued to operate for another hour afterward.

The microwave radiometer looked at Venus at a wavelength of 13.5 millimeters and 19 millimeters. The 13.5-millimeter region was the location of a microwave water absorption band within the electromagnetic spectrum, but it was not anticipated that it would detect any water vapor on Venus. These measurements would allow determination of atmospheric radiation, averaging the hot temperatures near the surface, the warmer clouds at lower levels, and the lower temperatures found in the high atmosphere. If the atmosphere were a strong absorber of microwave energy at 13.5 millimeters, only the temperature of the upper layers would be reported.

Unaffected by water vapor, 19-millimeter radiations could be detected from deeper down into the cloud cover, perhaps from near or at the planet's surface. Large temperature differences between the 19- and 13.5 millimeter readings would indicate the relative amount of water vapor present in the atmosphere. The 19-millimeter radiations would also test the limb-brightening theory.

During its scanning operation, Mariner telemetered back to Earth about 18 digital data points, represented as voltage fluctuations in relation to time. The first scan was on the dark side, going up on the planet: the distance from the surface was 16,479 miles at midscan, and the brightness temperature was 369 degrees F. The second scan nearly paralleled the terminator (junction of light and dark sides) but crossed it going down; it was made from 14,957 miles at midscan and showed a temperature of 566 degrees F. The final scan, 13,776 miles at midpoint, showed 261 degrees F as it swept across the sunlit side of Venus in an upward direction.

The brightness temperature recorded by Mariner's radiometer is not the true temperature of the surface. It is derived from the amount of light or radio energy reflected or emitted by an object. If the object is not a perfect light emitter, as most are not, then the light and radio energy will be some fraction of that returned from a 100% efficient body, and the object is really hotter than the brightness measurement shows. Thus, the brightness temperature is a minimum reading and in this case, was lower than the actual surface temperature.

Mariner's microwave radiometer showed no significant difference between the light and dark sides of Venus and, importantly, higher temperatures along the terminator or night-and-day line of the planet. These results would indicate no ionosphere supercharged with electrons, but a definite limb-darkening effect, since the edges were cooler than the center of the planet.

Therefore, considering the absorption characteristics of the atmosphere and the emissivity factor derived from earlier JPL radar experiments, a fairly uniform 800 degrees F was estimated as a preliminary temperature figure for the entire surface.

Venus is, indeed, a very hot planet.

Mariner II took a close look at Venus' clouds with its infrared radiometer during its 35-minute encounter with the planet. This instrument was firmly attached to the microwave radiometer so the two devices would scan the same areas of Venus at the same rate and the data would be closely correlated. This arrangement was necessary to produce in effect a stereoscopic view of the planet from two different regions of the spectrum.

Because astronomers have long conjectured about the irregular dark spots discernible on the surface of Venus' atmosphere, data to resolve these questions would be of great scientific interest. If the spots were indeed breaks in the clouds, they would stand out with much better definition in the infrared spectrum. If the radiation came from the cloud tops, there would be no breaks and the temperatures at both frequencies measured by the infrared radiometer would follow essentially the same pattern.

The Venusian atmosphere is transparent to the 8-micron region of the spectrum except for clouds. In the 10-micron range, the lower atmosphere would be hidden by carbon dioxide. If cloud breaks existed, the 8-micron emissions would come from a much lower point, since the lower atmosphere is fairly transparent at this wavelength. If increasing temperatures were shown in this region, it might mean that some radiation was coming up from the surface.

As a result of the Mariner II mission, scientists have hypothecated that the cold cloud cover could be about 15 miles thick, with the lower base beginning about 45 miles above the surface, and the top occurring at 60 miles. In this case, the bottom of the cloud layer could be approximately 200 degrees F; at the top, the readings vary from about minus 30 degrees F in the center of the planet to temperatures of perhaps minus 60 degrees to minus 70 degrees F along the edges. This temperature gradient would verify the limb-darkening effect seen by the microwave radiometer.

At the center of Venus, the radiometer saw a thicker, brighter, hotter part of the cloud layer; at the limbs, it could not see so deeply and the colder upper layers were visible. Furthermore, the temperatures along the cloud tops were approximately equally distributed, indicating that both 8- and 10-micron "channels" penetrated to the same depth and that both were looking at thick, dense clouds quite opaque to infrared radiation.

Both channels detected a curious feature along the lower portion of the terminator, or the center line between the night and day sides of the planet. In that region, a spot was shown that was apparently about 20 degrees F colder than the rest of the cloud layer. Such an anomaly could result from higher or more opaque clouds, or from such an irregularity as a hidden surface feature. A mountain could force the clouds upward, thus cooling them further, but it would have to be extremely high.

The data allow scientists to deduce that not enough carbon dioxide was present above the clouds for appreciable absorption in the 10-micron region. This effect would seem to indicate that the clouds are thick and that there is little radiation coming up from the surface. And, if present, water vapor content might be 1/1,000 of that in the Earth's atmosphere.

Since the cloud base is apparently at a very high temperature, neither carbon dioxide nor water is likely to be present in quantity. Rather, the base of the clouds must contain some component that will condense in small quantities and not be spectroscopically detected.

As a result of the two radiometer experiments, the region below the clouds and the surface itself take on better definition. Certainly, heat-trapping of infrared radiation, or a "greenhouse" effect, must be expected to support the 800 degree F surface temperature estimated from the microwave radiometer data. Thus, a considerable amount of energy-blanketing carbon dioxide must be present below the cloud base. It is thought that some of the near-infrared sunlight might filter through the clouds in small amounts, so that the sky would not be entirely black, at least to human eyes, on the sunlit side of Venus. There also may be some very small content of oxygen below the clouds, and perhaps considerable amounts of nitrogen.

The atmospheric pressure on the surface might be very high, about 20 times the Earth's atmosphere or more (equivalent to about 600 inches of mercury, compared with our 30 inches). The surface, despite the high temperature, is not likely to be molten because of the roughness index seen in the earlier radar experiments, and other indicators. However, the possibility of small molten metal lakes cannot be totally ignored.

The dense, high-pressure atmosphere and the heat-capturing greenhouse effect could combine over long periods of time to carry the extremely high temperature around to the dark side of Venus, despite the slow rate of rotation, possibly accounting for the relatively uniform surface temperatures apparently found by Mariner II.

In 1961, the Jet Propulsion Laboratory conducted a series of experiments from its Goldstone, California, DSIF Station, successfully bouncing radar signals off the planet Venus and receiving the return signal after it had travelled 70 million miles in 6½ minutes.

In order to complement the Mariner mission to Venus, the radar experiments were repeated from October to December, 1962 (during the Mariner mission), using improved equipment and refined techniques. As in 1961, the experiments were directed by W. K. Victor and R. Stevens.

The 1961 experiments used two 85-foot antennas, one transmitting 13 kilowatts of power at 2,388 megacycles, the other receiving the return signal after the round trip to and from Venus. The most important result was the refinement of the astronomical unit—the mean distance from the Earth to the Sun—to a value of 92,956,200 ±300 miles.

Around 1910, the astronomical unit, plotted by classical optical methods, was uncertain to 250,000 miles. Before the introduction of radar astronomy techniques such as those used at Goldstone, scientists believed that the astronomical unit was known to within 60,000 miles, but even this factor of uncertainty would be intolerable for planetary exploration.

In radar astronomy, the transit time of a radio signal

moving at the speed of light (186,000 miles per second) is measured as it travels to a planet and back. In conjunction with the angular measurement techniques used by earlier investigators, this method permits a more precise calculation of the astronomical unit.

Optical and radar measurements of the astronomical unit differ by 50,000 miles. Further refinement of both techniques should lessen the discrepancy between the two values.

The 1961 tests also established that Venus rotates at a very slow rate, possibly keeping the same face toward the Sun at all times. The reflection coefficient of the planet was estimated at 12%, a bright value similar to that of the Earth and contrasted with the Moon's 2%. The average dielectric constant (conductivity factor) of the surface material seemed to be close to that of sand or dust, and the surface was reported to be rough at a wavelength of 6 inches.

The surface roughness was confirmed in 1962. Since it is known that a rough surface will scatter a signal, the radar tests were observed for such indications. Venus had a scattering effect on the radar waves similar to the Moon's, probably establishing the roughness of the Venusian surface as more or less similar to the lunar terrain.

Some of the most interesting work was done in reference to the rotation rate of Venus. A radar signal will spread in frequency on return from a target planet that is rotating and rough enough to reflect from a considerable area of its surface. The spread of 5 to 10 cycles per second noted on the Venus echo would suggest a very slow rotation rate, perhaps keeping the same face toward the Sun, or possibly even in a retrograde direction, opposite to the Earth's.

In the Goldstone 1962 experiments, Venus was in effect divided into observation zones and the doppler effect or change in the returned signal from these zones was studied. The rate of rotation was divided from three months of sampling with this radar mapping technique. Also, the clear, sharp tone characteristic of the transmitted radar signal was altered on return from Venus into a fuzzy, indistinct sound. This effect seemed to confirm the slow retrograde rotation (as compared with the Earth) indicated by the radar mapping and frequency change method.

In addition to these methods of deducing the slow rotation rate, two other phenomena seemed to verify it: a slowly fluctuating signal strength, and the apparent progression of a bright radar spot across from the center of Venus toward the outside edge.

As a result, JPL scientists revised their 1961 estimate of an equal Venusian day and year consisting of 225 Earth days. The new value for Venus' rotation rate around its axis is 230 Earth days plus or minus 40 to 50 days, and in a retrograde direction (opposite to synchronous or Sun-facing), assuming that Venus rotates on an axis perpendicular to the plane of its orbit.

Thus, on Venus the Sun would appear to rise in the west and cross to the east about once each Venusian year. If the period were exactly 225 days retrograde, the stars would remain stationary in the sky and Venus would always face a given star rather than the Sun.

A space traveller hovering several million miles directly above the Sun would thus see Venus as almost stopped in its rotation and possibly turning very slowly clockwise. All the other planets of our system including the Earth, rotate counterclockwise, except Uranus, whose axis is almost parallel to the plane of its orbit, making it seem to roll around the Sun on its side. The rotation direction of distant Pluto is unknown.

The Goldstone experiments also studied what is known as the Faraday rotation of the plane of polarization of a radio wave. The results indicated that the ionization and magnetic field around Venus are very low. These data tend to confirm those gathered by Mariner's experiments close to the planet.

The mass of Venus was another value that had never been precisely established. The mass of planetary bodies is determined by their gravitational effect on other bodies, such as satellites. Since Venus has no known natural satellite or moon, Mariner, approaching closely enough to "feel" its gravity, would provide the first opportunity for close measurement.

The distortion caused by Venus on Mariner's trajectory as the spacecraft passed the planet enabled scientists to calculate the mass with an error probability of 0.015%. The value arrived at is 0.81485 of the mass of the Earth, which is known to be approximately 13.173 septillion (13,173,000,-000,000,000,000,000,000) pounds. Thus, the mass of Venus is approximately 10.729 septillion (10,729,408,500,000,000,-000,000,000) pounds.

In addition to these measurements, the extremely precise tracking system used on Mariner proved the feasibility of long-range tracking in space, particularly in radial velocity, which was measured to within 1/10 of an inch per second at a distance of about 54 million miles.

As the mission progressed, the trajectory was corrected with respect to Venus to within 10 miles at encounter. An interesting result was the very precise location of the Goldstone and overseas tracking stations of the DSIF. Before Mariner II, these locations were known to within 100 yards. After all the data have been analyzed, these locations will be redefined or "relocated" to within an error of only 20 yards.

Mariner not only made the first successful journey to Venus—it also helped pinpoint spots in the California and Australian deserts and the South African veldt with an accuracy never before achieved.

IV. The Sun and Other Stars

IV.   The Sun and Other Stars

In ancient Babylon and Assyria, the sun was recognized as "the all-powerful ruler of the skies" as well as "the all-seeing guardian of justice." In Egypt, in the empires of the Incas and Aztecs, and in other prehistoric societies, it was worshipped as the giver of light and warmth. In Greek mythology, it was identified with Apollo, who rode on a golden chariot across the heavens. Only gradually did observers arrive at a realization of its proper size and distance. At first it was thought to circle our planet and the exact method was a matter of deep concern to philosophers. With Copernicus, it became established as the center of the universe. Herschel, however, identified it as merely one in a myriad of stars in our galaxy—the Milky Way. Now we know that it is not even at the center of our galaxy, which is itself only one among billions of other galaxies. The history of the sun has thus been one of successive upgrading and downgrading in cosmological importance.

From the point of view of the astronomer, the most important single statement that can be made about it is quoted in the article below: "The sun is a typical star." Because of its nearness to us, it gives us otherwise unattainable opportunities to examine the nature of all stars. The scientific examination of its surface began with Galileo's observation of sunspots. These sunspots, their periodicity, their magnetic fields and their possible effect on terrestrial phenomena, have since then come under intensive examination, as have the sun's corona and chromosphere, its flocculi and faculae and the forces which influence their behavior. Charles G. Abbott and his successors have examined the possibility of using the sun's energy for more direct satisfaction of human needs. The spectroscope and spectroheliograph, the radio telescope and balloon astronomy have opened up new avenues of research. With each discovery, new knowledge not only of the sun but of all the stars has been increased.

From such instruments and methods were obtained the facts contained in the following article on "The Sun" by Cecilia Payne-Gaposchkin. Born at Wendover, England, in 1900, she was graduated from Newnham College, Cambridge and received her Ph.D. at Radcliffe College in 1925. Since 1923 she has been associated with the Harvard College Observatory and is now professor of astronomy at Harvard.

THE SUN

CECILIA PAYNE-GAPOSCHKIN

FIVE THOUSAND stars are visible to the unaided eye; a four-inch lens reveals over two million; and over a billion are accessible with the 200-inch mirror. The fainter we go, the more rapidly do the numbers increase. The story is told that Edward C. Pickering, of Harvard, was describing a formula that expressed the number of stars brighter than any given magnitude.* One of his hearers remarked that the formula required *two* stars brighter than apparent magnitude—1, whereas there is only one such star—Sirius. "Ah!" said Pickering. *"You've forgotten the sun."* Perhaps familiarity breeds contempt; it is easy to forget that the sun is the nearest of the stars, the most readily studied, the only one that can be kept under continuous surveillance.

The sun is a typical star, a common kind of star. A quarter million stars have been analyzed in some detail, and 10 percent of them resemble the sun; it merely happens that most of them are far away, and our luminary is near by. A typical specimen of the cosmic population is, so to speak, on our doorstep—giving us a superb opportunity to study the construction and habits of stars in general.

---

* Magnitude is the astronomer's measure of stellar brightness—a logarithmic scale in which the smaller numbers express the greater brightness. A difference of one magnitude corresponds to a ratio in brightness of 2½.

THE LIGHT OF THE SUN. The sun is a gigantic globe of glowing gas, and so is every star that shines, though not one other is near enough to appear as a disk, even to the most powerful telescope. With over a hundred times the diameter of our planet, more than a million times its bulk, three hundred thousand times its mass, the sun is yet a small star and a lightweight. The dazzling surface, intolerable to the eye even at a distance of 93 million miles, many times brighter than the most powerful artificial light, pales in comparison to those of the hottest stars. Yet, in its degree, the sun displays the same capacities as other stars; close-ups of its face reveal nuances of expression that elude us at greater distances, and provide clues to the behavior of the other members of the cosmic population.

We take the steady dependability of sunlight for granted in everyday life, and not without reason. The most careful measurement has revealed only infinitesimal variations during the past half-century, and most of these have probably been caused by variations in the transparency of our own atmosphere.

The earth's temperature is almost entirely governed by the amount of heat received from the sun, and the very fact that life on earth has existed in unbroken sequence for hundreds of millions of years shows that *the sun has been shining steadily at least as long as that.* The earth receives energy at the rate of 4,690,000 horsepower per square mile from the sun, and has been doing so for hundreds of millions of years, and yet our tiny planet intercepts less than two thousand-millionths of the sun's radiated energy. Such numbers beggar the imagination.

Put in another way, the output of the sun is even more impressive. Modern physics recognizes not only the interconvertibility of various forms of energy, but also the equivalence of energy and mass. The famous Einstein equation states that

$$E = mc^2,$$

where E is the energy in ergs, m the mass in grams, and c the speeed of light, 3×10^{10} centimeters, or about 186,000 miles, per second. In the sense of this equation, light has weight just as matter does. The sun pours *four million tons* of radiant energy into space every second, and if (as we believe) this has been going on for at least a hundred million years, more than 10,000,000,000,000,000,000,000 (or 10^{22}) tons of light and heat have issued from our luminary in a steady stream! Large as the figure is, it represents less than one millionth of the total mass of the sun. As we shall see, the sun is actually converting its own substance into radiant energy. But it draws upon less than one million-millionth of its material capital a year—a very modest expenditure. Many stars are far more prodigal of their resources.

THE SURFACE OF THE SUN. The sun's steady output suggests tranquillity, but its surface is far from quiescent. Dark spots on it are often visible to the naked eye, and a completely unspotted sun is extremely rare. Closer scrutiny reveals a continually changing fine granulation over the entire disk. The sun's face is not a smooth unruffled sea of gas, but a heaving, churning expanse, with whirling tornadoes (sunspots) that break through from below, tongues of gas (spicules) that surge up and subside, clouds of glowing vapor (prominences) that float, swirl, and erupt high above the surface, and sudden localized blazes of intensely brilliant radiation (flares). On the sun these things can be seen; on the stars they can only be surmised or indirectly observed, but we can be sure that they are often even more spectacular than on the sun.

The whole surface of the sun—flares, granulations, even sun-spots—glows with intense brilliance. A complete array of color is present, from x-rays through the visible spectrum to radio waves, and perhaps it is no coincidence that the sun shines most brightly in the colors to which our eyes are sensitive. The fact that the sun is brightest in the yellow-green gives a clue to the temperature of its radiating surface. Common experience tells that the hotter a glowing surface, the bluer is the light by which it shines; and the quantitative formulation of this fact (Wien's law) enables us to say that the radiating surface of the sun has a temperature of about 6000°C (11,000°F). And this is true whatever the sun is made of.

THE COMPOSITION OF THE SUN. The brightness of the sun is not distributed among all colors with unbroken brilliance. When sunlight is passed through a prism, and spread into the artificial rainbow known as the *spectrum*, some colors are seen to be greatly depleted. The rainbow is broken up into an array of sharply bounded regions of color, separated by others, far less brilliant (the "Fraunhofer lines"). Something has robbed the sunlight of these colors, and the atoms above the solar surface have been convicted as the culprits.

Each atom has its own characteristic array of colors, and it can take up or give out these colors only, absorbing or emitting energy as it does so. The distribution of the colors in sunlight, and our knowledge of the behavior of atoms on earth, make possible a chemical analysis of the sun's surface, actually more delicate than we could perform in the laboratory if we had a chunk of the sun given us to analyze.* The results of the analysis show that the sun is made of the familiar chemical elements known on earth.

The matching of characteristic colors led at first to a qualitative analysis, and showed that *all* known atoms with spectrum lines in the accessible region of the sun ** are represented in its spectrum. A few simple compounds, such as cyanogen, are found, but most of the material is in the form of isolated atoms. In other words, the spectrum shows that *the outer layers of the sun are completely gaseous*. One can go further: the array of colors characteristic of an atom varies with temperature, and so the temperature of the low-lying atmosphere of the sun, which produces the Fraunhofer lines, can be determined; it agrees fairly well with the temperature inferred from the color of sunlight.

Growing knowledge of the physics of spectra has actually made it possible not only to identify the atoms above the sun's surface, but to count them. The sun, we find, is mainly hydrogen; there are more atoms of hydrogen, lightest and

* This is because of the great depth of the layer of atoms above the sun's surface, and the vast number accordingly available for the analysis. A large number of spectrum lines, only *predictable* on earth, can actually be *observed* in the spectrum of the sun!

** Molecules in the atmosphere of the earth, especially those of ozone, oxygen, and water vapor, obscure some parts of the sun's spectrum almost completely.

simplest of atoms, than of all other kinds put together. Next in order comes the second lightest atom, helium, and, with some notable exceptions, the numbers of heavier, more complex atoms fall off steadily in order of complexity.

This scheme of chemical composition is not peculiar to the sun. It is typical of the composition of the whole cosmos, not only the stars, but also the loose gas and dust that pervade interstellar space. The atomic makeup of all stars is not identical—and the differences, small as they are, may be of great significance—but the general uniformity is amazing, and it would be difficult to point with confidence to any cosmic object that does not consist mainly of hydrogen.

THE SUN'S SURFACE. Each atom has its characteristic array of colors, and a photograph of the sun in a single color records the atoms of one kind by themselves. Luckily the sun is so bright that even a very restricted range of color can be photographed, either with the instrument known as a spectroheliograph or by an ingenious arrangement of light filters. Pictures of the sun made by light of calcium or hydrogen show not only increased detail, but revealingly different detail. Whereas a direct photograph, in light of all colors, shows only dark sunspots and vague granulations, calcium light reveals brilliant variegations in the neighborhood of the sunspots, and greatly accentuates the contrast of the granulation. Even before a sunspot swirls through the surface, bright calcium "flocculi" herald its presence; and they remain for some time to mark the place after the spot has died away. The bright areas shown by the calcium atoms reflect the greater disturbances, more violent motions, and probably hotter regions, near the tornadoes that are sunspots.

Hydrogen poses are more difficult to take, because hydrogen does not cut so wide a swath in the spectrum as calcium, and less light is available for the photograph. This may seem surprising, for there is much more hydrogen than calcium above the sun's surface; but it is a consequence of the idiosyncrasies of the two kinds of atoms. At the sun's temperature nearly all the calcium atoms are in the right state to emit light, but the atom of hydrogen is more recalcitrant, and is only about one-millionth as prone to emit as calcium at 6000°C. Hydrogen atoms are more than ten thousand times as common as atoms of calcium, but even so, the lines they produce in the spectrum of the sun are less than one-hundredth as intense.

Photographs in hydrogen light show the disturbed regions near sunspots, but with less brilliance, because of the difficulty of stimulating the atoms. Both the hydrogen and the calcium photographs reveal slowly changing patterns of dark filaments silhouetted against the bright surface of the sun. The filaments are not really dark; they seem so only by contrast. When one of them extends beyond the sun's edge it is seen as a glowing prominence—a great cloud of gas poised above the surface. Some prominences are so brilliant that they show up as bright streaks, even against the face of the sun.

Prominences are protean in form, and have an infinite variety of motions. Some hang poised over the surface. Some spurt upward, in filamentary surges, like geysers, and seem to dissipate into space. Some rise and fall like fountains. But a surprising majority shower downward, not upward, and many give the impression of being sucked into a point at the surface.

We are far from understanding the motions of prominences. Some are associated with sunspots, but many are not. The variegated brilliance of the sun's surface may affect them. Electric forces may be of importance; magnetic forces probably play a crucial role. Whatever be the significant factors in producing the protean variety of solar prominences, they are important also in stars of very different kinds. For, as we shall see, prominence activity is characteristic of many stars, and often on a scale that makes the sun's activities seem puny.

Whether or not the motions of prominences are governed by magnetic forces, very intense magnetic fields are observed on the sun. The spectrum of a sunspot tells the story, through the medium of the spectra of the individual atoms in the tornado. An atom in a magnetic field absorbs and radiates in a special way; its peculiar series of colors subdivides into an intricate pattern, and the stronger the magnetic field, the more is the subdivision accentuated. The sunspot behaves like a tremendous electromagnet, many thousand miles across; no doubt electrically charged particles, whirling around the axis of the tornado, play the part of the current in the electromagnet, and a powerful magnetic field is produced along the axis of the spot. Sunspots, like prominences, are incompletely understood, but that they possess magnetic fields of several thousand gauss * is certain. Large as such fields are, even larger magnetic fields are found for certain peculiar stars *as a whole;* and like many sunspots, they reverse their polarity at regular intervals.

The times when sunspots are thickly scattered over the sun's face are marked by striking events nearer home. The Aurorae, the Northern Lights, gleam and shimmer in the sky. Magnetic storms disrupt communications and intrude on radio programs. The disturbances that produce spots on the sun have direct effects on our planet.

Disturbed areas of the sun are showering particles into space at high speeds, and a rain of electrons, protons, and even heavier particles pours down into our atmosphere. An electrically charged shower plays upon the atoms and molecules of the upper air, and excites the auroral glow. Oxygen in the high atmosphere emits its peculiar red and green light; molecules of nitrogen and other substances contribute their characteristic colors. The spectrum of the rain of solar hydrogen has recently been photographed by Meinel. The earth receives showers of particles that left the sun a few hours ** ago. Even more significant: the sun is continually spraying matter into space. Many stars, as we shall see, are doing the same.

Prominences are not the only features that rise above the sun's bright edge. At the crucial moment of a total eclipse, when the moon's disk cuts off the body of the sun, a brilliant rim of rosy light—the chromosphere—appears around it. The spectrum of the chromosphere shows that it consists of radiating atoms, the same atoms that were revealed by the

---

* The gauss is the unit of magnetic field. The magnetic field of the earth, which affects the compass, is small—a fraction of a gauss.

** The particles travel at 125 to 625 miles a second, and make the trip from sun to earth in from 200 to 40 hours.

Fraunhofer lines in a layer nearer the sun's surface, but with a difference. The pattern of colors that they radiate is modified in a way that admits of but one explanation—the temperature of the chromosphere, from five to ten thousand miles above the solar surface, is more than three times the temperature of the atoms that produce the absorption spectrum of the sun! Even helium, which is far more refractory than hydrogen, and requires a far higher temperature to excite it, appears not only in normal form, but even in the "ionized" condition, with one electron torn away—a situation found only at the surfaces of the hottest stars, at temperatures of over 30,000°C.

The chromosphere consists of a sort of hairy rim of tiny spicules, or jets, which spurt upward and disappear in a few minutes. The spicules may be related to the minute granules that pepper the face of the sun, and seem equally short-lived.

Other stars than the sun possess chromospheres, and with some of them, unlike the sun, the chromosphere is far larger than the star itself, and shines so brilliantly that the glowing atoms in the spectrum produce *bright spectrum lines* on the background of the star's light. Some chromospheres are poised, like the sun's, above the star's surface, with little motion. The shining atoms around other stars are flowing or spurting steadily outward, and some stars occasionally blow great chromosphere bubbles, which thin out gradually and dissipate into space.

Outside the chromosphere of the sun gleam the pearly streamers of the corona, which extend to distances comparable to the size of the sun itself. Like the chromosphere, the corona has a spectrum given by glowing atoms, but for many years its nature was a mystery. No such colors had been produced by any atoms on earth, and they used to be ascribed to a mysterious substance, *coronium,* that was unknown elsewhere. Now we know, from the work of the Swedish physicist Edlén, that the corona consists of well-known, common elements (such as iron, calcium, and nickel) but under conditions that represent temperatures never attained on earth. The corona—the "iron crown" of the sun—seems to be at a temperature of about a million degrees!

Other stars, too, have coronas, and some of them are intensely brilliant. The spectral colors of the sun's iron crown have been found in the light of certain peculiar stars that have suffered sudden explosion.

Perhaps the most remarkable thing about the outer regions of the sun is the increasing temperature of successive outward layers. The reversing layer and the photosphere * have temperatures of about 6000°; the chromosphere is at about 20,000°; and the corona, at 1,000,000°. The sunspots, which look like depressions in the solar surface, are even cooler than the reversing layer; their spectra and colors point to a temperature not far from 4000°.

The remarkable temperature stratification of the sun is not an isolated phenomenon. Other stars show it, and some of them display an even greater span of conditions. If we did not know that the sun is a single star, the variety of its spectra might tempt us to doubt; other stars whose spectra look as though they must be complex may be similarly put together.

THE SUN'S ROTATION. From the human point of view, the most important thing about the sun is the fact that it has planets, and that one of them presents physico-chemical conditions favorable to life. But from the standpoint of the sun, all the planets are negligible: even Jupiter, the largest, weighs less than one thousand as much as our luminary. Within the planetary system, Jupiter is the only really influential member; it is the most potent factor, for example, in governing the motions of the comets and asteroids, the lesser members of the system. In one respect, Jupiter excels even the sun: the giant planet possesses most of the total energy of rotation of the solar system—far more than the sun itself. True, the sun is spinning, but spinning very slowly. It takes nearly a month to make one complete turn. This fact has always been one of the great difficulties in the path of a theory of the

---

* The photosphere, or "sphere of light," is the glowing surface of the sun; the reversing layer is the atmosphere of absorbing atoms that lies above it. Temperatures, here and later, are given on the centigrade scale.

origin of the solar system; almost all the theories that have been moderately successful in other ways seem to require that the sun possess the greater part of the energy of rotation of the whole.

The slow spinning of the sun is far from being unusual. Most stars that resemble the sun in size and temperature are also turning slowly on their axes. Some stars, it is true, spin very rapidly, but these are usually the massive stars of high temperature. Stars such as the sun rotate rapidly only when constrained to do so by being members of twin systems; they raise huge tides in each other and always stay face to face. Any star that spins rapidly is distorted into a spheroid; even the solid or semisolid planets like the earth, Jupiter, and Saturn are more or less flattened at the poles by rotation. Jupiter looks like an orange, even in a small telescope. But the sun is so nearly spherical that no polar flattening has ever been detected.

Slowly as the sun rotates, it still does so in a remarkable manner: it spins faster at the equator than at the poles, so that its surface must be in a state of shear—that is, some parts of the surface must continually be slipping past others. Possibly the differential rotation plays some part in producing sunspot vortexes. And if even the slowly turning sun spins faster at the equator than at the poles, what of the stars that turn on themselves in a few hours, and are highly distorted? What, too, of the internal rotation of the sun? We can see the surface only; and a different internal rate of rotation is not only possible but likely. A star that turns very slowly will probably not churn up its interior and mix its constituents; but one that is spinning fast may be much better mixed. The degree of mixing of the materials within a star may well be a crucial factor in its history.

THE SUN'S INTERIOR. Which brings us to the problem of the sun's interior. So far we have spoken only of the parts of the sun that can be seen, a mere skin. Conditions within are very different. Without going beyond the elementary laws of physics, it can be shown that the sun, and all other stars, are gaseous not only at the surface, but all the way through.

Moreover, both temperature and pressure must necessarily rise toward the center.

In fact, it is well known that the central temperature of a star must depend essentially on its size and mass, and is proportional to the average mass of the individual particles of which it consists. This average mass of the particles, the so-called "mean molecular weight," would be least for a star that was all made of hydrogen, and would increase somewhat —but not very much—with larger proportions of heavier elements. The reason for this rather surprising statement is that *the interiors of the stars are so hot that atoms are stripped of nearly all their electrons.* Each electron counts as one particle in the average mass of the individual particles, and the masses of electrons are negligible, even in comparison with those of the nuclei of hydrogen, lightest of elements. In units of the hydrogen nucleus, a star all of hydrogen would have a "mean molecular weight" of ½; if the star were all helium, whose nucleus weighs four times as much as hydrogen, and which can part with two electrons, the average molecular weight would be 4/3, or 1.33; even if the stars were all uranium (92 electrons, atomic weight 238 times hydrogen), the mean molecular weight would only be $\frac{238}{93}$, or 2.55. As most stars consist mainly of hydrogen, the mean molecular weight will usually be between ½ and 1½; and the central temperature, for stars of the same mass and size but different composition, will therefore not differ by a factor of more than 2 or 3.

If, in addition to size and mass, the total energy output (luminosity) of a star is known, the same elementary theory permits the calculation of the mean molecular weight, which can be fitted by a certain number of different combinations of hydrogen, helium, and heavier elements.

The sun is found to have a central temperature near to 18 million degrees; and the temperature almost certainly increases steadily from the surface inward. Thus we have the odd paradox that the sun is actually coolest at the surface, or even a little below it, in the cores of the sunspots, and the temperature goes up again as we pass outward through the chromosphere to the corona.

High temperature and enormous pressure prevail within

the sun. The high temperature is responsible for the fact that the sun's substance behaves like an ideal gas, even at the center; it strips the atoms of their attendant electrons, resolves them into fragments far smaller than at the surface, and permits them to pack more closely without violating the laws that govern the behavior of gases.

THE SUN'S SOURCE OF ENERGY. The hot interior of the sun is the source of its light and heat. At 18 million degrees the atoms are able to interact, to convert some of their substance into energy. No other source is adequate to have produced the tremendous outpouring, steady over millions of years. The source of the sun's energy was long a puzzle. Combustion, chemical reaction, gravitational contraction, the drawing of energy from the environment, all were shown to be hopelessly inadequate. Nuclear energy seemed the only avenue of salvation, long before the details of the actual process were understood. "Does energy issue freely from matter," speculated Eddington a quarter of a century ago, "at 40 million degrees as steam issues from water at 100 degrees?"

Modern nuclear physics provides an affirmative answer. The actual processes have been observed in the laboratory. The interior of the sun liberates energy by a catalytic action similar to those of atomic chemistry; but the reactants are the naked nuclei, not atoms clad in their haze of electrons. Hans Bethe and C. F. von Weiszäcker discovered independently, nearly at the same time, that hydrogen cores combine, by a chain of reactions set off by carbon nuclei; four hydrogens interlock to produce a helium core. The helium is lighter than the sum of the hydrogens by about 0.7 percent, and this deficiency of mass is turned into energy, which passes from the interior to the surface in a steady flow. Only at temperatures between 15 and 20 million degrees can the reaction produce enough energy to supply the sun. The rate of production varies at about the eighteenth power of the temperature, and most of the sun's energy accordingly issues from its substance in the central region where the temperature is highest. At 15 million degrees the "light" given out resembles x-rays (even more "violet" than ultraviolet light); it flows outward, passed from hand to hand, so to speak, by the electrons and atoms of the overlying layers, and is steadily "reddened" in the process so that when it reaches the surface the observable color is primarily yellow-green.*

The sun shines by feeding on its own substance, and its diet is exceedingly simple. So far as we know, our luminary subsists entirely upon hydrogen. The same food sustains the other stars; stellar infants may possibly have a somewhat different diet, but their infancy is brief, if only because foods other than hydrogen are in short supply. Digestive processes may differ somewhat from one kind of star to another. If the temperature is well below 15 million degrees, the cycle catalyzed by carbon may be replaced by others, such as the *direct* combination of protons (hydrogen nuclei) to form helium—the "proton-proton" reaction. The food remains the same; hydrogen is consumed and helium is left behind.

Although the sun has been steadily digesting its own interior for tens, and even for thousands, of millions of years it still consists almost entirely of hydrogen, enough to keep things going at the present rate for at least an equal interval. Most other stars are equally rich in the vital substance, and have an equally bright future. In fact, paradoxically enough, the future of stars that are consuming hydrogen is even brighter than their past. For the brightness of a star of given size and mass depends primarily on the mean molecular weight of its substance. As the hydrogen supply slowly falls, the mean molecular weight gradually increases, and the star grows a little brighter, so long as it does not drastically alter its internal arrangements.

The great astronomer Eddington showed, even before the actual process of stellar nutrition was identified, that the more massive a star is, the more energy does it pour out. The energy output of a star of given composition is, in fact, proportional to something between the cube and the fourth power of its mass. The greater majority of the stars whose

---

* Actually the sun's surface gives out a surprising amount of radiation of very short wavelength, far more than would be expected if its light were distributed according to the elementary laws of radiation by a so-called "black body" (a technical term, which sounds rather paradoxical, and denotes a surface that absorbs and radiates ideally according to certain laws that are deducible from quantum theory).

masses are known conform to this rule (the "mass-luminosity law") fairly closely. Most of the differences are within the limits that would be expected from the possible range of mean molecular weight with composition—a range that was shown earlier to involve a factor not greater than two or three. But some stars, as we shall see later, are nonconformists, and they are important finger posts for theories of stellar evolution.

If a star's luminosity (which can be expressed in terms of tons of radiation per second for all stars, just as for the sun) were simply proportional to its mass, all stars of similar composition would have the same life expectancy. But a star much more massive than the sun is consuming itself much faster. A star of twice the mass is twelves times as prolific; at ten times the mass the factor is over a thousand, and at a hundred times the mass of the sun a star would be well over a million times as prodigal, and its life expectancy a million times shorter. The total life of a star like the sun (in the style to which we are accustomed) is about 5000 million years; if there were stars a hundred times as massive, their active lives would be reckoned in thousands rather than in millions of years, and they must become effectively bankrupt during an interval over which the sun can radiate with virtually unchanging brightness.

Such bankrupt stars actually exist. They can be recognized by the fact that their brightness is far lower than we should expect from the mass-luminosity law. Their light is feeble; they have exhausted their internal nuclear resources, have spent all their available hydrogen, and exist only on their very limited gravitational capital.* Such a destiny probably awaits all stars, but for most of them it lies in the far future. Even for the sun we see it as inevitable.

The sun, indeed, holds a mirror to the cosmos. Like all other stars it is a globe of glowing gas, hotter and denser within. Its surface is a seething, surging sea of atoms. Plumes of gas float above it; glowing filaments surge upward; shining fountains cascade downward. Giant tornadoes swirl through

---

* A star can convert gravitational energy into light and heat by contracting in size.

the surface. Spicules rise and dissipate like darting flames. Dazzling flares blaze up and vanish. A brilliant chromosphere rings it; and around it gleams the aura of the corona. Powerful magnetic forces play across the surface; atoms and electrons spray into space. As it spins on its axis the equator pulls steadily ahead; and across its face proceeds the slow rhythm of the sunspot cycle, waxing and waning every eleven years. The spectacle is impressive in itself. As the mirror of the cosmos it is stupendous. Other stars are doing the same things, and these stellar habits are the clue to their history.

The sun is made of hydrogen, "with a smell of other substances," and so are most other stars. The steady consumption of hydrogen keeps it shining; most stars are sustained in no other way. Wherever we look in the cosmos we see the play of the same forces, the march of the same phenomena —but often on a scale that makes the sun seem puny.

To early astronomers, the study of astronomy consisted in large part of celestial geography. The great constellations and the animal and human forms they were supposed to represent were charted and studied. With the invention of the telescope, the positions of a far greater number of stars became known with greater accuracy. Flamsteed at the Royal Observatory catalogued three thousand stars. Sir William Herschel observed the heavens systematically as they appeared from his latitude, and his catalogues of nebulae and clusters were issued about the end of the eighteenth century. His son John continued his work from the southern hemisphere. Since then, such studies have been extended by numerous observers. J. L. E. Dreyer's New General Catalogue of Nebulae and Clusters of Stars, originally issued in 1888, with later supplements, is in general use today.

In "Stars and Stellar Systems" George Gamow leads us on a tour of the heavens. He is a well-known physicist who has written numerous technical and popular books and articles on science, including Matter, Earth and Sky from which this article is taken. Born at Odessa in 1904, he was educated at Odessa and the University of Leningrad. After study at

Göttingen, Copenhagen, and Cambridge, he became professor of physics at George Washington University in 1934. He is now a member of the faculty of the University of Colorado.

STARS AND STELLAR SYSTEMS

GEORGE GAMOW

WHEN ONE LOOKS at the starry sky on a clear moonless night, one easily gets the impression that stars are practically innumerable. This impression is, however, far from being correct, for the number of stars visible to the naked eye in both celestial hemispheres is only about 6,000, while the number of stars that can be seen at any one time is less than half that because of the poor visibility near the horizon. But, of course, even the use of ordinary binoculars increases the number of visible stars to about 100,000, while the number of stars that can be photographed by the 200-inch telescope of the Palomar Mountain Observatory exceeds a billion. The brightest stars in the sky have their own personal names, mostly of Arabic and, in a few cases, of Greek or Latin origin. Thus, Aldebaran means "the flower" in Arabic; Antares stands for the "rival of Mars," which was so named because of its reddish color, while the names of Castor and Pollux date back to the ancient Greek legend about the two brothers.

Only a score of stars possess personal names; the others are designated according to the constellations to which they belong. As with the names of stars, the names of most of the constellations are of ancient origin, being associated with various animals, such as the *Great Bear*, or mythological heroes, such as *Orion*. The book *Almagest*, written by Ptolemy about 150 A.D., contains the description of 48 original constellations and designates the bright stars in each constellation as various parts of mythological or zoological figures. The ancient Greeks never went to the Southern

Hemisphere so the regions of the sky there are deprived of any mythological interpretation. This gap was filled later, mostly by the early navigators, who used more prosaic names such as *Southern Cross* and *Triangulum*. At present we recognize 88 constellations which cover the entire celestial sphere. And, instead of the vague boundaries of the various constellations that were introduced in conjunction with the shape of the imaginary figures they were supposed to represent, modern astronomy draws the boundaries of the constellations in a less romantic, but more definite way. Within each constellation the stars are designated by the letters of the Greek alphabet, generally in the order of their decreasing brightness. Thus, Aldebaran, being the brightest star in the constellation of Taurus (the bull), is also known as α Tauri (possessive form of Taurus), while the fourth brightest star in the constellation of Cepheus is called δ Cephei. (The Greek alphabet runs α, alpha; β, beta; γ, gamma; δ delta, etc.) When the astronomers ran out of Greek letters to designate stars in a given constellation, numbers were used; thus 61 Cygni means the 61st star in the constellation of the Swan. Most faint stars are called simply by the catalogue number in which their exact position, brightness, etc, are listed. For example, Ross 248 pertains to the number in Ross's Stellar Catalogue.

Ancient astronomers beginning with Ptolemy described the brightness of stars by dividing them into six classes, or *magnitudes*, the first magnitude being ascribed to the brightest ones, and the sixth magnitude to those that were barely visible to the naked eye. The exact measurements of relative stellar brightness showed later that a difference of one magnitude between two stars in Ptolemy's terminology corresponds to an intensity ratio of about two and a half, and it was decided to make the old notion more precise by *defining* the difference of one stellar magnitude as *corresponding exactly to the ratio 2.512 in intensity*. This introduced the modern scale of stellar magnitudes which extends from negative values for very bright stars (-1.6 magnitude for Sirius) down to the 23rd magnitude, which represents the observation limit of the 200-inch Palomar reflector. In Table 1 we list the 20 brightest stars with their personal

Table 1. The Brightest Stars

	Personal name		Constellation affiliation	Stellar magnitude	Color
1	Sirius	α	Canis Majoris	—1.58	Blue
2	Canopus*	α	Carinae	—0.86	Yellowish
3	*	α	Centauri	0.06	Yellow
4	Vega	α	Lyrae	0.14	Blue
5	Capella	α	Aurigae	0.21	Yellow
6	Arcturus	α	Boötis	0.24	Orange
7	Rigel	β	Orionis	0.34	Blue
8	Procyon	α	Canis Minoris	0.48	Yellowish
9	Achernar*	α	Eridani	0.60	Blue
10	*	β	Centauri	0.86	Blue
11	Altair	α	Aquilae	0.89	Blue
12	Betelgeuse	α	Orionis	0.92	Red
13	*	α	Crucis	1.05	Blue
14	Aldebaran	α	Tauri	1.06	Reddish
15	Spica	α	Virginis	1.21	Blue
16	Pollux	β	Geminorum	1.21	Orange
17	Antares	α	Scorpii	1.22	Red
18	Fomalhaut	α	Piscis Austrini	1.29	Blue
19	Deneb	α	Cygni	1.33	Blue
20	Regulus	α	Leonis	1.34	Blue

* Not visible as far north as latitude 40°N.

names and their relation to various constellations. The third column gives the stellar magnitude, while the last one describes the color of the star, which is determined by its surface temperature.

Since most of us live in the medium northern latitudes (from approximately 32°N for New Orleans and Los Angeles to approximately 45°N for Boston and Seattle), we can observe considerably more than half the entire celestial sphere. The stars that are located within about 45° from the north celestial pole never sink below the horizon and can be seen every clear night of the year. The stars located in a belt 45° north and 45° south of the celestial equator, i.e., in the vicinity of the ecliptic can be seen only during the seasons of the year when the sun in its annual trip around the celestial sphere is on the opposite side of the belt. The stars located within 45° of the south celestial pole cannot be seen at all from our geographical location.

In the northerly direction the picture is always about the same except that the constellations located in this part of the sky revolve around the Pole Star (or Polaris), which is located at the end of the handle of the Little Dipper (part of the constellation *Ursa Minor*, i.e., the small bear). Probably the most familiar stellar configuration, commonly known as the Big Dipper (part of the constellation *Ursa Major*, i.e., the great bear) is located between the Little Dipper and the zenith during the spring months, and between it and the horizon in the fall. Thus, it looks as if somebody is pouring soup from the big dipper into the small one in April, and vice versa in October. Just across the Pole Star from the Big Dipper is the constellation *Cassiopeia*, which looks like the letter *W* in the spring and like the letter *M* in the fall. Two other prominent constellations in this region of the sky are *Cepheus*, which looks like a kite, and *Draco*, which resembles a long serpent stretching over 135 degrees of celestial longitude between *Cepheus* and *Ursa Major*.

In the southern direction, the sky looks rather different during the different seasons of the year since, as we stated above, the stars located in these regions can be seen only when the sun moves to the opposite point on the celestial sphere. During spring evenings, high above the horizon we see the constellation *Leo* (lion) with its brightest star, Regulus (or α Leonis), already mentioned above, and the constellation, *Virgo* (maiden), with its brightest star, Spica. Still closer to the horizon we can see the constellations, *Hydra* and *Canis Major* (Great Dog), with Sirius as its brightest star.

The midsummer picture of the sky looks rather different from that presented in the spring. The center of the "southern exposure" is now occupied by the constellations *Ophiuchus* (serpent holder), *Hercules, Libra* (scales), and *Boötes* (herdman), with Arcturus as its brightest star. Close to the zenith is located the constellation *Corona Borealis,* a diadem of five bright stars. In the constellation *Hercules* is located one of the most beautiful of the globular clusters of stars.

When the autumn leaves begin to fall and the evenings become noticeably cooler, the dominant features of the starry sky are the constellations *Andromeda, Pegasus, Pisces* (fishes), *Cygnus* (swan), and *Aquila* (water carrier). In the constellation *Andromeda,* not far from its second brightest star (β Andromedae), is located a very interesting celestial object known as the Great Andromeda Nebula, which can be seen by the naked eye as a faint elongated nebulosity. Photographs taken by means of a large telescope show a very complicated structure consisting of a central elliptical body and two spiral arms wound around it. This is the nearest large neighbor in space to our stellar system of the Milky Way and is another giant swarm of stars about one hundred billion strong.

During the snowy winter months around Christmas and New Year's day, the evening sky is dominated by the constellation *Orion,* with three bright stars forming his "belt" and *Taurus* (bull) containing the so-called Crab Nebula, which resulted from a violent stellar explosion observed by Chinese astronomers about nine centuries ago. The well-known stellar cluster, the *Pleiades,* appears almost straight above our heads.

Travelers to the Southern Hemisphere can borrow a stellar map from the ship's captain and have fun identifying constellations that are never seen from our country. The most famous features of the southern sky are the Southern Cross (*Crux*) and two shapeless luminous patches, first described by Magellan and known as the Large and Small Magellanic Clouds. These two faint nebulosities are known now to be formed by billions of individual stars, and they, along with the Great Andromeda Nebula, are our nearest neighbors in the countless society of stellar systems populating the infinite space of the universe.

There does not seem to be any definite record of what ancient Greek astronomers thought about the nature and distances of stars, and the statement that stars are actually giant suns comparable to our own, but located much farther away, was first made by Copernicus in his epoch-making book on the solar system. For the observation of stellar parallaxes, the base line supplied by the diameter of the earth is hopelessly short, but fortunately we can use a much longer base line provided by the revolution of the earth around the sun. At one time we are on one side of the sun and six months later we are on the opposite side, 300,000,000 km from the former position. (Figure IV-1.) Thus, a star which is located comparatively close to us must show a parallactic displacement with respect to the background of more distant stars if observed half a year apart. The famous Danish astronomer, Tycho Brahe (1546–1601), was probably the first to attempt the observation of the yearly parallactic displacement of stars, but he came out with a negative result and interpreted his failure as proof that the earth is really at rest. We know now that this failure was due partially to the imperfection of contemporary astronomical instruments, but mostly to the fact that Tycho Brahe did not happen to pick up stars that are really close to us. The first

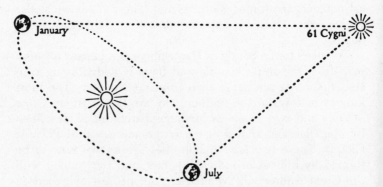

IV-1. *Measuring the distance to a star by the parallax meth-od, using the diameter of the earth's orbit as a base.*

reliable measurement of stellar parallax came much later, in
the year 1838, when the German astronomer, F. W. Bessel,
found that the star known as 61 Cygni shifts by about two-
thirds of an angular second in six months' time.

As in the case of parallactic measurements that are referred
to in terms of the earth's semi-diameter, stellar parallaxes
are always referred to in terms of the mean semi-diameter of
the earth's orbit, and thus represent the angle which this
semi-diameter would subtend if seen by an observer located
on the star in question. The exact value of the parallax of
61 Cygni is $0''.300 \pm 0.003$ and corresponds to a distance
of 108,000,000,000,000 kilometers, 690,000 astronomical
units, or 11 light-years. It may be noticed here that stellar
distances often are expressed in units that are directly derived
from the measurement of the parallax. The unit is known as
a *parsec*, and represents the distance from which the radius
of the earth's orbit would subtend an angle of one second.
Thus, if the parallax of a given star is $4''$, its distance is
one quarter of a parsec and, inversely, a star with a parallax
$0''.25$ is 4 parsecs away. One parsec equals 206,265 astronomical units, or 3.256 light-years. In measuring very
large distances, such as the diameter of our stellar system of
the Milky Way, or the distances to other galaxies scattered
through space, we often use the term, *kiloparsec*, which is
defined as one thousand parsecs. We may mention here still
another unit that was once introduced, in a none-too-serious
manner, at the Pulkovo Observatory (Russia). The unit was
known as a *Marsec*, and was defined as the distance from
which the tallest Russian astronomer, Dr. Markov, would
appear to subtend an angle of one second. Since Dr. Markov
must have been at least 6'6" tall, one marsec is about 260
miles. With today's precise instruments, we can measure
stellar parallaxes that are as small as $0''.005$ and correspond
to a distance of 200 parsecs or 650 light-years. To appreciate
the smallness of this angle, we should remember that it is the
angle under which a tall man, like Dr. Markov, would be
seen at a distance of 200 marsecs, i.e., 52,000 miles, or about
one-fifth the distance to the moon!

Measurements of parallax have been carried out for well
over two thousand stars, and Table 2 gives the data for 20

of the nearest stars. The names of the stars given in this table demonstrate the rather cumbersome astronomical nomenclature.

Table 2. The Twenty Nearest Stars

Name	Distance in light-years	Luminosity (in terms of the sun)
α Centauri A		1.3
α Centauri B	4.28	0.36
α Centauri C		0.00007
Barnard's Star	5.05	0.00044
Wolf 359	8.0	0.000023
Lalande 21185	8.4	0.0058
Sirius A	8.6	30.0
Sirius B		0.01
Ross 154	9.1	0.0003
L789-6	9.8	0.0001
Ross 248	10.8	0.00016
ε Eridani	10.8	0.33
τ Ceti	10.9	0.4
Procyon A	11.1	6.9
Procyon B		0.00052
61 Cygni A	11.1	0.069
61 Cygni B		0.036
Ross 128	11.2	0.00044
Groomb 34A	11.7	0.0076
Groomb 34B		0.00058

In addition to their distances, the table also gives the brightness of the various stars in terms of the brightness of the sun, which can easily be calculated from their apparent brightness and their distance from us. An inspection of this table is very useful for acquiring a general idea about the world of stars. We notice that only three of them (Sirius A, Procyon A, and α Centauri A) are brighter than the sun.

Three stars are between 1 and 0.1 of the sun's brightness, three between 0.1 and 0.01, while the remaining eleven are well below one per cent of the luminosity of the sun. Thus we conclude that, as stars go, our sun must be considered as a rather bright object, with most of the stars being considerably fainter.

The brightest star in the table (Sirius A) is only 30 times brighter than the sun, but if we go farther into space we will pick up stars compared with which our sun looks very insignificant indeed. Rigel (β Orionis), located 540 light-years away, is 21,000 times brighter than the sun and is still one of the brightest stars in the sky in spite of its great distance from us. But the real Goliath in stellar society is a variable supergiant known as S. Doradus, which, at its maximum, exceeds the brightness of the sun by a factor of 500,000. It seems to consist of two components, each equal to 250,000 suns, which alternately eclipse one another every 40 years. But S. Doradus is very far away from us, being located within the larger Magellanic Cloud that floats in space some 150,000 light-years away from our system of the Milky Way, and, in spite of its terrific brightness, it is invisible to the naked eye.

Inspecting Table 2, we also notice another important characteristic of stellar society, *the tendency of stars to gather into groups of two or more.* Stars belonging to such systems are given one name and are distinguished by the letters, A, B, C, etc. placed after the name. We see, indeed, that 11 out of 20 stars included in the table belong to such multiple systems, forming 4 doublets and one triplet.

Among the important problems of positional astronomy, touched on briefly in Gamow's article, is the measurement of distances of celestial objects. By trigonometric methods, ancient astronomers were able to make rough determinations of the distances of moon and sun, and by the method of stellar parallaxes discovered by Bessel, also involving relatively simple trigonometric calculations, the distances of the nearer stars were estimated. But even with the most sensitive instruments, the trigonometric method is inapplicable to distant stars and galaxies.

There is another, more indirect method which does not suffer from this handicap, and which has been used to estimate the most distant objects in the universe. It is based on the variability of starlight and is described in the following article. Such variability forms an interesting chapter in the story of astronomy. The variability of Algol was probably known to the Arabs, although they had no idea of the cause. The Chinese observed the formation of a "new star" in the constellation Taurus in 1054. Tycho Brahe studied a supernova in Cassiopeia in 1572. Double stars, rotating about each other, appear to vary because light from one star is periodically eclipsed by its companion. Another group of variables known as cepheids provide the key to the measurement of such remote objects as star clusters and nebulae. Thus Edwin P. Hubble, from his observation of cepheids in distant nebulae, proved conclusively that they are external galaxies comparable in size to our own. Their exact distances remain under study.

Edna E. Kramer received her Ph.D. in mathematics from Columbia University and served as a mathematical consultant in the Division of War Research at Columbia during World War II. She is the author of numerous articles in mathematical and educational journals and of Mathematics Takes Wings and The Main Stream of Mathematics, from which the following selection is taken.

CEPHEID VARIABLES

EDNA E. KRAMER

CEPHEUS was king of Ethiopia, the legends say, and Cassiopeia was his beautiful wife. Humility was not one of the queen's virtues, and she boasted that she was as handsome as any goddess. This enraged the sea nymphs and, as a result, Neptune, god of the sea, threatened to destroy the kingdom of Ethiopia unless Princess Andromeda was offered as a human sacrifice to a sea monster. To save their land, the king and queen were forced to chain their daughter to a rocky cliff. Before the monster Cetus could harm her, however, out of the sky flew Perseus. This fearless youth, born in Argos, had become a flier by borrowing Mercury's magic sandals. First he had slain the snaky-haired witches known as the Gorgons, carrying away with him the head of one of them, Medusa, which had the power of petrifying all who gazed upon it. He fell in love with Andromeda on sight and rescued her by distracting Cetus and getting him to focus on Medusa's head. Having turned the sea beast to stone he removed Andromeda's fetters and married her amidst all the pomp and circumstance of a royal wedding festival.

Starry memorials to the Ethiopian royal family illuminate the northern and northeastern skies on autumn nights. Cassiopeia is represented by a choice constellation, the *chair* or great *W*, at the end of a line from the Big Dipper through the North Star. Cepheus resembles a church steeple with summit directed toward Polaris (the North Star), which appears a dull star to the naked eye. Andromeda's head rests on Pegasus, the flying horse of Perseus, whose celestial form resembles that of a graceful dancer more than that of a fighter.

Such was the mythical astronomy of the ancients. It still assists the amateur stargazer in identifying heavenly bodies. Between 8 and 10 p.m. of October nights Cepheus is visible to the north and fairly high in the sky in mid-northern latitudes. The twentieth-century scientific story of this constellation may seem even less credible than the ancient version, for in the eyes, or the crown jewels, or the gleaming scepter of the king of Ethiopia can be read the secret of the *size of the universe*. The flickering of certain stars in Cepheus contains the mathematical key to stellar distances, however great, and makes possible the cartography of the heavens.

That mathematics in general and astronomy in particular deal with *variables* is part of their essence. That apparent brightness varies from star to star is a commonplace. But it is not generally known that many individual stars fluctuate

in brilliance from day to day, hour to hour. For certain stars
of this kind the astronomers use the name *Cepheid variable,*
since the discovery of the phenomenon we shall now describe was due to the observation of a particular star in the
constellation of Cepheus. This star was δ Cephei (read
Delta of Cepheus), the name signifying that it is approximately the fourth brightest star in the particular constellation (δ or delta is the fourth letter of the Greek alphabet).

This star was found to perform periodic oscillation in brilliance, waxing from dull to bright to dull over and over again
in regular cycles. Later observations revealed that the length
and breadth of the heavens were populated with stars be-
having this way. For some Cepheids the cycle is run through
daily. Others wax and wane more slowly, the lengthiest
period observed to date being about 32 days. The star δ
Cephei, requiring 5⅓ days for a performance, is an average
Cepheid.

In 1912 Henrietta S. Leavitt, a worker at the Harvard
Observatory, made a minute telescopic study of about 25
Cepheid variables, all about equally distant from the Earth,
since they were located in the same star cluster, the Lesser
Magellanic Cloud, so named because Magellan observed
this group of stars on his historic journey around the earth.
Because distance was constant for the Cepheids in question,
any difference in brilliance from star to star was intrinsic
and not caused by a variation in remoteness. Thus these
stars could be compared for luminosity as if they were elec-

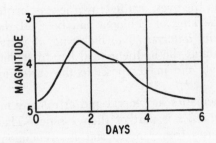

IV-2. *Variations in brightness of δ Cephei.*

tric light bulbs in the same room, or suns in a row with our own, or rather suns at the standard distance used in astronomy—about 2×10^{14} miles, called 10 parsecs (a parsec = 2×10^{13} miles).

Miss Leavitt discovered that the brighter Cepheids oscillated more slowly than the less brilliant ones. Just what turns the lights on and off in the Cepheids and regulates the time the process takes has not been completely explained to date, but the theory of Professor Shapley of Harvard ascribes the behavior to "pulsation." Cepheids are considered rather "young" stars, condensed from nebulae and still in the process of condensation. It is believed that they have reached a period in their life history when the gravitational forces working toward condensation are practically balanced by the internal forces tending to disrupt them. This is pictured as the cause of the pulsation. A Cepheid is visualized as a sort of gigantic inflated balloon from which air is released until it reduces somewhat in size, when it is reinflated until its original volume is regained. Then, according to the Shapley theory, the whole procedure is duplicated again and again, the time from start to finish being the same for each performance. Balloons of different sizes with different means of inflation and deflation would lead to different time intervals for the trick. So it is that the varied masses and temperatures of Cepheids bring about different pulsation periods.

Miss Leavitt was not concerned with the "why" of the pulsations. She merely observed some additional Cepheids and then fitted her total data with a mathematical formula indicating the dependence of intrinsic brightness on period. Professor Shapley then made studies of Cepheids throughout the heavens and a general *period-luminosity law* was the result. Astronomers at the Harvard Observatory have by now examined the behavior of close to 600 Cepheid variables. Having obtained periods directly through telescopic observation, they compute intrinsic brilliance indirectly by the Leavitt-Shapley formula. This luminosity or actual sun power is not directly discernible either by the naked eye or the telescope, since suns that outshine ours a millionfold may, because of their remoteness, leave but faint impres-

sions on photographic plates attached to the most powerful
telescopes. But the Period-Luminosity Law furnishes a scale
that rates our Sun and the Cepheids side by side. For example, if a star winks in the same manner and with the
same period 5⅓ days, as δ Cephei, it is known from the
formula that it has 700 sun power. This means that if its
distance were the same as the Sun's (93,000,000 miles), it
would shine 700 times as brightly as the Sun.

Once the true sun power is assigned, it is an easy matter
to figure by means of the "inverse square law" the distance
responsible for the apparent brightness. To understand this
law let us explain if two variables, x and y, are so related
that

$$y = \frac{k}{x^2}$$

where k is some constant, y is said to vary *inversely* as the
square of x. In the theory of light, the inverse square law
is: *Intensity of illumination varies inversely as the square
of the distance from the source of light.* If x is a particular
distance and y the intensity at this distance, then we have
just stated that

$$y = \frac{k}{x^2}$$

For a different distance X and associated intensity Y

$$Y = \frac{k}{X^2}$$

Dividing these two equations, we obtain the proportion

$$\frac{y}{Y} = \frac{X^2}{x^2}$$

If $x = 1$ foot and $X = 2$ feet

$$\frac{y}{Y} = \frac{4}{1} \quad \text{or} \quad Y = \frac{1}{4}y$$

In other words, if distance is doubled, intensity becomes one-fourth as great. In the same way, if distance is trebled, intensity is one-ninth as great.

We have just seen that it is possible by the Period-Luminosity Law to get an intrinsic or standard brightness rating for stars, which means that this law gives the value of y when $x = 2\times 10^{14}$ miles (i.e. $x = 10$ parsecs). The apparent brightness Y, obtained by telescopic photography, corresponds to the actual (unknown) distance X. Then

$$\frac{X^2}{100 \text{ parsecs}} = \frac{\text{standard brightness (known)}}{\text{apparent brightness (known)}}$$

X^2, and then X, the distance to the star, can be figured from this equation.

In this way distances are obtained not only for Cepheids but also for the different groups of stars throughout the heavens of which these variables are members. Thus ω Centauri (omega of the Centaur) is a star cluster with thousands of stars but at least 76 Cepheids whose periods have been observed. The luminosities of these Cepheids were determined by the Period-Luminosity Law. Then their distances were found as just explained. Thus the range of distances of the stars in the cluster became known, since astronomic theory places all of them "close" together. The average distance is 20,000 light years, which means that the photographs taken today picture the cluster as it was 20,000 years ago. In summary, then, Cepheid study is one tool whereby we

Can by the strength of our own thought, ascend
Through universe after universe.

In the following article, we come to grips with one of the major subjects of contemporary research. Even the largest telescopes reveal stars only as pinpoints of light, and as we have seen, their study has been hampered by numerous factors. The spectroscope offered a new method of examination and classification. Joseph Fraunhofer compared the spectra of the sun and other stars, but to quote the Russian-born astronomer Otto Struve, "the first fairly comprehensive attempt at classification was undertaken by the Italian astronomer Father Angelo Secchi in the 1860's 'to see if the composition of the stars is as varied as the stars are innumerable.' " He succeeded in classifying four thousand stars into four main types. In 1886, E. C. Pickering at Harvard began a study which resulted in The Draper Catalogue of Stellar Spectra, named in honor of a pioneer American spectroscopist. The classifications were gradually modified to become the Harvard sequence which McCrea describes.

The question of whether such classification was merely an indication of chemical composition or whether it could be related to the history of a star was hotly debated by astronomers. An outgrowth of the debate was the famous Hertzsprung-Russell diagram, relating luminosities to temperatures, which McCrea also describes and which has become one of the foundation stones of astrophysics.

William Hunter McCrea was born at Dublin in 1904, was educated at Trinity College, Cambridge and the University of Göttingen, taught at the Imperial College of Science and at Queens University in Belfast, and was governor of Royal Holloway College from 1946 to 1949. He is the author of Relativity Physics and The Physics of the Sun and Stars, from which the following excerpt is taken.

STARS: DATA AND CLASSIFICATION

W. H. McCREA

A QUITE RUDIMENTARY study of the general facts known about the stars is sufficient to show that they are objects of the same general character as the Sun. That is to say, each is an effectively independent body held together by its own gravitation and emitting radiation from its own resources. Also the characteristic quantities associated with the stars are such that the values of these quantities for the Sun are well within the ranges of values for the stars in general. It turns out, indeed, that the Sun is a "pretty average" star in almost every respect. Consequently, it is not surprising to find that the observational data available for the study of the stars are of the same character as those we have for the Sun, though for any individual star[1] they are less detailed and precise. It seems true to say that no observations of what may be called the *static* properties of the stars raise any fundamentally new problems not met with in the case of the Sun.

Where new problems do arise is in connection with the variability of certain stars (using this term to include the phenomena of novæ). Stellar variability, when properly understood, will certainly help also in the better understanding of stars which are not classed as variables and which are in a majority. However, in the present state of knowledge, it is convenient to exclude variable stars from the discussions in this and the succeeding chapter.

The data we are about to survey are mostly provided by stars in the nearer regions of the galactic system. But there is every reason to believe that, so far as our purposes go, these stars form an adequate sample for the whole of the

1. In this chapter we mean by "star" a star other than the Sun.

Galaxy. We are interested here only in the stars as individual bodies and the data concern their masses, sizes, luminosities, spectral energy-curves and line-spectra. We take these in turn, giving in each case some general remarks upon the principles of the determination, then a summary of the results, followed by brief comments upon them. This chapter summarizes observational results; the next will discuss the physics of the stars.

STELLAR MASSES. We know the mass of the Sun only because we can measure its gravitational pull on the Earth or some other member of the solar system. Similarly, we can know the mass of a star only from its gravitational pull upon some other body. Of course, even if any other star does possess a planetary system we cannot hope to observe the planetary bodies directly and so to use their motions to infer the mass of the star. Fortunately, however, there are a great many cases where a star possesses a companion body in the form of another star and the two revolve around each other under their mutual gravitational attraction. Indeed, probably more than half the stars are members of such combinations of two or, occasionally, more stars. If the circumstances of the orbital motion can be sufficiently fully observed, then the mass of each star in a binary system can be inferred. Somewhat less complete knowledge of the motion may provide information concerning the combined masses or the relative masses even though it does not give both. The essential point is that we know the masses of certain stars almost as directly as we know that of the Sun, and have useful information about the masses of certain other stars.

A word should be said here about a common feature of observational astronomy. As soon as astronomers have "direct" measurements of a particular quantity "A" in a sufficient number of cases they look for some empirical correlation between its value and some other observable characteristic "B". If, then, the characteristic "B" can be observed in further cases in which "A" cannot be measured directly, the empirical relation may be employed to infer "indirect" values of "A" in these additional cases. Stellar mass is an instance of such a quantity "A". Without going into details, it may be stated that there exist more or less reliable estimates of the masses of many more stars than those for which direct determinations are possible.

Nevertheless, such indirect estimates are for the most part useful only for statistical studies or for general verification of certain theories. As fundamental data for the study of the physical constitution of the stars we ought, so far as possible, to rely upon only the most direct available determination of the various quantities required.

RESULTS. The smallest known stellar masses are about one-fifth the mass of the Sun. A few stars are known to have masses over 100 times that of the Sun, the greatest known mass being about 400 solar masses. But *the great majority of known stellar masses lie within about 0·4 to 4 times the solar mass, i.e. a range of about* 10 : 1.

COMMENTS. Compared with the enormous ranges for other characteristics of the stars, this is a very small spread of values. It has long impressed astronomers as probably having some fundamental significance.

It is now generally believed that the mechanism of star-formation tends normally to produce objects of a standard mass, within about an order of magnitude.

STELLAR RADII. Suppose the distance of a particular star is known. Its size could be measured directly if its apparent angular diameter could be measured. But the biggest apparent angular diameter of any star is probably much under one ten-thousandth of one degree; for the vast majority of stars it can be only a minute fraction of this amount. Now an apparent diameter of one ten-thousandth of a degree is far too small to be measured by any of the usual methods for measuring angles.

What has just been said explains why, for direct observation, a star always behaves as a point-source of light. Every star is much too remote to provide an observable "disk" such as that provided by the Sun, Moon and planets.

Nevertheless, an ingenious method originated by A. A.

Michelson does exist for measuring angles down to a few millionths of a degree. Light entering a telescope in precisely one direction can be made to interfere with itself and to produce an interference pattern at the focus. Light entering simultaneously in a very slightly different direction will produce a similar pattern slightly displaced in regard to the first. Using a null method, this effect yields a measurement of the small angle between the two directions. Applied to a star it will, in principle, yield a measurement of its apparent angular diameter. The method has been successfully applied in practice to a few stars. But the overwhelming majority of the stars must remain forever outside the capability of this, the only method which may be described as a "direct" measurement of their sizes.

Fortunately, double stars once again come to our aid and in certain special cases provide an extremely convenient method of inferring accurate values of stellar diameters—the most accurate which we possess. The special cases are those of "eclipsing binaries", i.e. double stars whose orbits happen to be seen edge-on, or nearly so.

Consider, for definiteness, a case where the orbit is precisely edge-on and one star is appreciably bigger than the other. Then, once in each revolution the smaller star is lost to sight behind the bigger. When this occurs, the luminosity of the pair is reduced from the sum of the luminosities of the two components to that of the larger component alone. The time required for this reduction to take place is the time taken for the smaller star to travel a distance equal to its own diameter, while the duration of its total eclipse is the time for it to travel a distance equal to the difference of the two diameters. These times are easily observed from the "light-course." If, as is sometimes the case, the actual speed of revolution of the pair can also be measured from the Doppler effect in the spectra, then these times can be translated into distances travelled and thus the absolute dimensions of the system can be inferred. The method has so far been successfully applied to some 50 eclipsing binaries.

By far the most abundant data on stellar radii are derived, however, by the method of comparing the total luminosity of a star with its luminosity per unit area. The results are less accurate than those derived from eclipsing binaries.

RESULTS.   It is found that the radii of the stars range from less than $\frac{1}{100}$ that of the Sun to about 500 times that of the Sun, i.e. from less than the Earth's own radius up to something of the order of the radius of Jupiter's *orbit*.

STELLAR DENSITIES.   The mean density of a star is, of course, known if both its mass and radius have been measured. Stellar densities so determined range from about one million times that of the Sun down to about one-millionth of that of the Sun. Thus there are stars in which one cubic inch of the material has an average mass of 20 tons, while there are others whose mean density is about one-thousandth the density of ordinary air.

MAIN SEQUENCE, WHITE DWARFS, GIANTS.   Inspection of the data shows that there is not a steady gradation of the stars through the million-million-fold density range just mentioned. This fact is exceedingly important since it furnishes, in the approach we are making, the first indication of the possibility of *classifying* the stars.

Among all the stars for which good data are available, it is found that the majority form a set occupying only a relatively small central interval in the full density range. In fact, most members of the set have densities between about 10 times and $\frac{1}{10}$ the solar value. This set of stars is called the *main sequence* and we shall see that the name has been aptly bestowed.

The stars possessing the extremely great densities mentioned form a set quite unmistakably separated from the main sequence. They are called the *white dwarfs*.

Finally, the stars of very low density are *giants*. The density criterion makes it natural to treat these as a set to be distinguished from the main sequence, but this criterion alone does not yield a clear demarcation between the two sets. The further characteristics we are about to consider will clarify and amplify the classification, but it is instructive to have noticed that such a simple characteristic as the density shows the existence of more than one genus of stars.

STELLAR LUMINOSITIES. On the basis that mass and size are physically more rudimentary, we have deferred till now the observationally more immediately obvious characteristic of a star, which is its *brightness*.

We suppose we are dealing with stars whose distances are known. So, if the apparent brightness of the star is measured, it is a simple matter to calculate what its brightness would be if it were placed at some standard distance from the Earth. This latter quantity is what astronomers call the star's *absolute magnitude*, when it is expressed in their agreed scale of measurement.

Provided the brightnesses have been observed for light in a fixed frequency-range, the comparison of the absolute magnitudes of the stars gives the ratios of their true brightnesses *in that particular light*. For instance, if all the observations were visual, so that we should obtain what are called "visual" magnitudes, then the comparison would be for light within the frequency range in which the human eye is perceptive.

RESULTS. Once again, there is an enormous range of values. The brightest known stars are of the order of 20,000 times as luminous as the Sun, while the Sun itself is of the order of 20,000 times as luminous as the faintest stars.

It is noteworthy that the main sequence itself extends over almost the whole range of observed luminosities, even though it occupies only a relatively small portion of the density-range.

The giants are found to be all very bright stars and the white dwarfs very faint. It should be noted that this is by no means inevitable, *a priori*, merely from the fact that the giants have large radii and the white dwarfs small radii.

COMMENTS. For the astrophysicist the most fundamental characteristic of a star's radiation is the *total* energy-output in all frequencies taken together. This is expressed by what astronomers call the *absolute bolometric magnitude* (bolo-metric = radiation-measuring), using a conventional scale analogous to that for visual magnitudes.

Were all stars to possess the same spectral energy-curve then, if a given star is found to be, say, ten times as bright as the Sun in visible light, its total luminosity would also be ten times the total luminosity of the Sun. Thus the visual luminosities already mentioned would suffice for the comparison of total luminosities.

A star's spectral energy-curve is the complete specification of the *colour* of its radiation. Even as seen by the naked eye, the stars differ greatly in colour; for instance, Sirius and Rigel are bluish white, by comparison Capella looks yellowish white, while Aldebaran and Betelgeuse look red. The stars therefore do *not* all possess the same energy-curve and it follows that visual magnitudes do not suffice for the comparison of bolometric magnitudes. We have to say briefly how the latter are determined.

The apparent magnitudes of the stars can be compared photographically, i.e. by the relative intensities of their images on a photographic plate, as well as visually. Now suppose some star "A" is taken as the standard for both methods of comparison. Then if "S" is any other star, it is found in general that the apparent photographic magnitude of "S" relative to "A" differs from the apparent visual magnitude of "S" relative to "A". Since the maximum sensitivity of the photographic plate occurs at a different (higher) radiation-frequency from that of the human eye, it follows that the proportion of "photographic" to "visible" radiation is in general different for "S" and "A". This is merely another way of saying that the colours of "S" and "A" are different. But it is also evident that the difference between the photographic and visual magnitudes of "S" may be regarded as an actual *measure* of the colour of "S". As determined by a suitably standardized procedure, it constitutes in fact the accepted measure called the *colour-index*.

Now, were it known that, although the stars have different energy-curves, these are all black body curves and differ merely in the black body temperatures, then a theoretical colour-index could be calculated for each value of the temperature. Comparison of the results with the observed colour-index of any particular star "S" would then enable the black body temperature of "S" to be inferred. Since the ratio of total to visible radiation for that temperature could also be calculated, the total luminosity of "S" could also be inferred.

In other words, the assumption that the stars radiate like black bodies makes it possible to convert the visual magnitude into the bolometric magnitude when the colour-index is known. This is the principle used in the practical determination of bolometric magnitudes. The effect of this allowance for colour is very appreciable; for example, Sirius is about 27 times as bright as the Sun in visible light, but according to this method the total luminosity of Sirius is about 39 times the total luminosity of the Sun. As an example of a less marked effect, the corresponding ratios for Capella are about 120 and 130, respectively.

The first consequence of all this discussion is merely that care must be taken always to specify what kind of luminosity is being considered, whether visual, photographic, or bolometric. The second is that, while visual and photographic magnitudes are derived directly from observation, the conversion to the more fundamental bolometric magnitude involves a specific hypothesis about the form of the energy-curve. Unfortunately, as we shall see, the hypothesis is not of general validity. It probably yields approximately correct results over a fairly wide range of colours but the accuracy in estimating true total luminosities is not very great.

This is a situation which calls for comment. It has been described at some length in order to illustrate, in a specific instance, the difficulties and uncertainties involved in securing the fundamental data of astrophysics.

The situation must not be misunderstood. The observations themselves are carried out with almost incredible care and precision. It is their *interpretation* to give the required fundamental quantities which is subject to considerable uncertainty in some cases. As a result of a most elaborate programme of observations a value may be got, for instance, for the total luminosity of a given star. Yet, when all is said and done, no one may care to say, in the particular case, whether the true value may not be perhaps twice or one-half the "observed" value!

This might appear to be a confession of gross uncertainty. Nevertheless, when we remember that the whole range of luminosities of the stars is of the order of 400,000,000 to 1, such a determination would place the given star in its correct position in the range with astonishing precision—a factor of two is neither here nor there! Therefore precise observations are, after all, rewarded by precise results when taken in the proper context.

These are really matters of ordinary common sense. When applied to astrophysical theory they merely mean that the theory must be compared with the observational results in contexts in which these are adequately precise and not in those in which their uncertainties render comparison fruitless. Experience shows that this precaution leaves ample scope for trustworthy progress.

EFFECTIVE TEMPERATURES. The value of the total luminosity of a star, together with the value of its radius, gives the value of the star's *effective temperature Tê*. This quantity really provides merely a convenient way of describing the total radiation per unit area of the star's surface. It is found that the effective temperatures of the stars range from less than 3,000 degrees up to 50,000 and possibly to about 100,000 degrees.

As defined, the effective temperature of a star is not a directly observable quantity. But the effective temperature is related to the colour, as is known both theoretically and observationally. Using a theoretical or empirical relation, the observed colour of a star may therefore be made to yield an *estimate* of its effective temperature (subject to some margin of uncertainty). Using this estimate, if the total luminosity of the star can be measured, we can then derive an estimate of its radius. As already mentioned, this principle provides the most common, but not the most accurate, means of determining stellar radii.

Line Spectra: Spectral Sequence

A science which has to deal with a great number of differing individual objects cannot handle its material without an adequate system of classification. The characteristics of the stars which we have so far considered do not serve this purpose, partly because they cannot be determined with precision for any but a small fraction of the stars and partly because they are over-simple. Imagine a botanist attempting to classify plants according to their weight, size, colour, etc.! Just as the botanist looks deliberately for features that, in addition to exhibiting systematic variations, are of a sufficient complexity in their variations to make a reasonably detailed classification possible, so the astronomer must expect the classification of the stars to depend upon more complex characteristics than mass, size and luminosity.

Now the only observable feature of a star not yet mentioned is its line-spectrum. This is found to be in general certainly very complex and so it does hold promise of providing a means of detailed classification. Moreover, it has the fortunate merit of being by far the most readily observable intrinsic feature of the stars. Most important of all, it does vary systematically from star to star in the fashion about to be described.

Before entering upon this description it is, however, desirable to satisfy ourselves that the resulting classification is likely to be of fundamental and not just superficial significance. For we know from the case of the Sun that the spectrum is formed by an infinitesimal fraction of the total material of a star. Without going into any specific theory, we know, however, that the spectrum depends in a highly sensitive manner upon the physical state of that material, while that physical state in turn depends in a highly sensitive manner upon the radiation passing through it and upon the surface gravity of the star. The radiation and surface gravity are determined by the luminosity, mass and radius of a star. Thus the line spectrum is a very sensitive function of these three fundamental characteristics. It provides, in fact, a function of these characteristics which can be studied with incomparably greater accuracy than that with which any one of them can be studied by itself, hence its profound significance.

CLASSIFICATION. The spectra of literally hundreds of thousands of stars have been carefully studied, classified and catalogued, and so the observational material available for the study is indeed vast.

The spectra of the majority of stars are in a general way similar to the Fraunhofer spectrum of the Sun. They show dark lines produced by the same chemical elements and, to a great extent, the self-same lines. But in the spectrum of any particular star it is in general noticeable that the lines occur with relative intensities different from those in the solar spectrum. Also, a certain proportion of stellar spectra show molecular, as opposed to atomic, absorption as more prominent features than does the solar spectrum. Finally, a small proportion of spectra contain bright, as opposed to dark, atomic lines.

Consider now a representative collection of stellar spectra. It is discovered by inspection that they can be arranged in a single sequence—we may imagine them all laid out in a single row—such that if attention be directed to any particular spectral line which figures prominently anywhere in the sequence, then, looking along, the row from one spectrum to the next, the intensity of this line is seen gradually to rise to a maximum and then gradually to diminish again. Or, if in the case of a few lines the behaviour is sometimes different, it is at any rate something perfectly orderly along the sequence. In fact, once the spectra have been sorted into this particular order, everything in them exhibits a nice smooth gradation along the sequence. Also it is found that, with relatively few exceptions, every stellar spectrum fits naturally into place somewhere in the sequence. In other words, a spectrum can be labelled just by its position in the sequence.

This is a remarkable result. Looking at such a complex thing as a typical stellar spectrum we might have expected some much more elaborate system of classification to be required. It is as though the botanist had discovered some characteristic by which he could allot to every plant a definite position in one single "natural order", using the term natural order in its most literal sense!

The only way to introduce a classification into such a sequence is to make a convenient number of quite *arbitrary* divisions and to describe a member by the division in which it is located. The spectral sequence is divided into a number of spectral *classes*[1] six of which, called classes B, A, F, G, K, M, include about 99 per cent of known stellar spectra. The classes have been chosen so that a typical member of a particular class exhibits some important groups of spectral lines at their greatest relative prominence in the sequence. Each class is further divided into ten sub-divisions labelled 0 to 9. Thus Sirius has spectral class A0, Rigel B8, the Sun G2, Capella G4, Aldebaran K5, Betelgeuse M0.

Although there is no difference of opinion about the order in the sequence, different observatories have unfortunately placed the divisions at slightly different positions in the sequence. The correspondence between the various systems in use is, of course, well known.

Spectra near the beginning of the sequence are said to be "early" type and those towards the end "late" type spectra. These terms must not be used with any other connotation as, for instance, in regard to ages of the stars. Classes O and B are characterized by lines of helium, oxygen and nitrogen. Metallic lines appear in Class A0 and persist through the rest of the sequence. For any particular element, lines of ionized atoms appear first and give place to those of neutral atoms later in the sequence. The later Classes, from K5 onwards, show molecular bands to an increasing extent. Hydrogen lines are the only ones which appear throughout the sequence; they are strongest in Class A0.

Class O, which precedes B and is one of the less abundant classes amongst known spectra, shows mainly bright lines. Certain late type spectra show some bright lines as well as absorption lines and bands. Otherwise bright lines occur

1. The terms and notation are partly the result of the historical development of the system. It may be mentioned that the sequence as a whole is called the Harvard sequence, and the classes are called Draper classes after the astronomer who first assigned them.

elsewhere in the sequence only as exceptional features of some individual stars. Such features present problems of much interest but they need not distract us here.

Finally, it must now be stated that the foregoing actually describes only a first approximation to the true state of affairs. But it is such a good first approximation that it is legitimate to present it in the way we have done. The required slight elaboration will be mentioned in due course.

INTERPRETATION. From purely spectroscopic data, without any theory of stellar atmospheres, it is readily seen that the progression in the spectral features along the sequence is purely one of steadily diminishing degrees of excitation and ionization of the atoms producing the spectra. This can be expressed by saying that *the spectral sequence is a temperature sequence* with the temperature decreasing from early to late type spectra. Moreover, the sequence as so far described cannot then be anything more than this; for were it to depend upon any other parameter independent of the temperature it would not be a *single* sequence.

The relevant "temperature" is really one defined by the state of excitation and ionization of the outermost layers of the stellar photosphere. The temperature so defined may not be numerically the same as the "effective temperature" of the star. But, without any detailed theory of stellar atmospheres, we may reasonably expect that, if one star is hotter than another as judged by this "excitation temperature" it will also be hotter as judged by its effective temperature. That is to say, if the stars are arranged in order of decreasing effective temperature then they would necessarily be found to be in order of decreasing "excitation temperature", i.e. they would in fact be in the order of the spectral sequence.

This expectation is found to be borne out by the values of independently determined effective temperatures for stars of known spectral class (apart from the slight modification mentioned on p. 274). This means that a characteristic effective temperature can be associated with each spectral class. Therefore the determination of the spectral class provides also a determination of the effective temperature. This accounts for the importance of spectral class from the standpoint of general astrophysics.

The following table summarizes the correspondence between temperature and spectral class, giving the temperature only in round numbers.

Spectral Class	Effective Temperature
O	50,000–25,000
Bo	25,000
Ao	11,000
Fo	7,500
Go	6,000
Ko	5,000
Mo	3,500
N	3,000–2,000

Correlations

The fundamental observable characteristics of a star are most conveniently taken to be its mass M, absolute luminosity L, and spectral class S.

At this stage in our presentation of the subject there is no definite reason for expecting the quantities M, L, S to be themselves related in any way. But it is an obvious next step to examine the observational data to see if any such relation exists. There could, of course, be at most two distinct relations between the three quantities, for the simple reason that two relations would serve to determine two of the quantities in terms of the other one. If such relations exist we expect to discover them by seeing how one of the quantities, say L, varies with each of the other two, M, S. The results of doing this are of momentous importance.

In the first instance it would be simpler and more natural to work directly with the observed luminosity (visual or photographic) and spectral class, rather than with the derived bolometric luminosity and effective temperature, respectively. But, for the sake of subsequent theoretical discussion, it is far more convenient to use the latter quantities. Therefore, in what follows, the "observed luminosity" and the "observed effective temperature" mean the bolometric luminosity and the effective temperature derived from the observed luminosity and the observed spectral class in accordance with the best current estimates of the relations between these quantities.

This procedure does not vitiate the "observational" or "empirical" character of the correlations about to be described. All it does, so far as the work of the present chapter is concerned, is to determine the particular "code-numbers" in terms of which we choose to express the observed luminosities and spectral classes. It is only when, in the following chapter, we attempt to reach a theoretical explanation of the correlations that we need to regard these code-numbers as having the particular significance of bolometric luminosities and effective temperatures. At that stage we shall, in fact, so regard them—with the reservation that the numbers used may not be altogether accurate measures of these quantities on account of uncertainties in our knowledge of stellar spectral energy-curves.

HERTZSPRUNG-RUSSELL DIAGRAM. A diagram can be constructed in which the observed luminosities of the stars are plotted against their observed spectral classes; in such a diagram each "dot" represents the observed values of these characteristics for a particular star. The result is the famous Hertzsprung-Russell diagram, named after the two astronomers who first studied extensive sets of data in this manner.

The first figure shows a "skeleton" diagram with a few well-determined points. The second shows, in a schematic way, what the diagram looks like when a large sample of the available data has been plotted.

The Hertzsprung-Russell diagram reveals that luminosity and spectral class *are* related characteristics of the stars. It does more: it shows that the stars divide themselves into sets each characterized by a different form of the relation between luminosity and spectral class. The features of the diagram may be summarized as follows:

(a) The predominant feature is a set of stars represented by points along a track (m in Figures IV-3, IV-4) which stretches obliquely right across the diagram. This is called the *main sequence* of stars. As we have seen, its existence is indicated by considerations regarding density and, as a matter of fact, it is found that stars which belong to the main sequence in the diagram would also be classified as main sequence stars on the density criterion.

(b) In the early spectral classes there is a set of stars of very small luminosity (w.d. in Figures IV-3, IV-4). These are the *white dwarfs* and are the stars already mentioned as possessing phenomenally great densities. Their name accords with their being, in fact, white, in agreement with their early spectral class, and small, in agreement with their low luminosity. The figure contains too few points representing white dwarfs for any relationship between their characteristics to be revealed, beyond the fact that the points occur in one small part of the diagram.

(c) In spectral classes F and "later" there is a set of stars (g in Figures IV-3, IV-4) of very much greater luminosity than the main sequence stars of the same classes. These are called *giant stars;* they are in fact very much larger as well as more luminous than main sequence stars of the same effective temperature. The giants form a fairly definite sequence of their own in which the variation of the luminosity from one class to another is quite different from that in the main sequence.

(d) In almost every spectral class there occur *super-giants* (s.g. in Figure IV-4) of 10 to 100 times the luminosity of the normal giants. The giants and super-giants are the stars previously mentioned as possessing very low densities.

Further analysis of the diagram is in fact possible, but the foregoing suffices for present purposes.

RELATIVE NUMBERS. The average giant star is over ten thousand times as luminous as the average of the known white dwarfs. So a giant has about the same apparent magnitude as has a dwarf at a distance one hundred times smaller; that is to say, the volume of space in which giants can be seen is of the order of a million times that in which

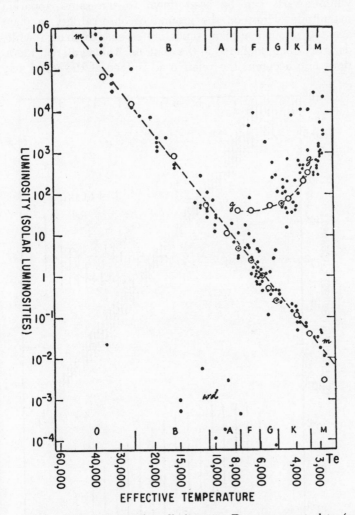

IV-3. Hertzsprung-Russell diagram. Dots represent data for
individual stars. Open circles represent currently accepted mean
values for various spectral classes. Spectral classes for main
sequence are indicated at the foot and for giants at the top.
N.B. In this and the following diagrams the quantities are
plotted on logarithmic scales.

white dwarfs can be seen down to the same apparent magnitude. Thus, on the ground of observability, a giant star has about a million times better chance than a white dwarf of being included in the diagram. Taking all considerations into account, the relative advantage of the giant may

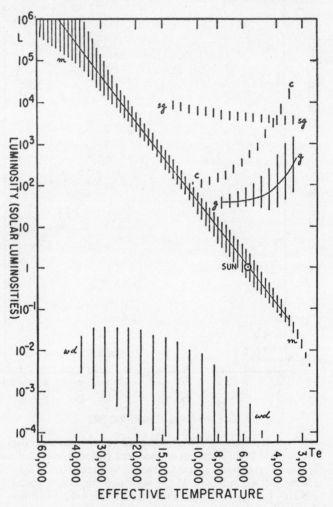

IV-4. *Hertzsprung-Russell diagram—schematic.* m = main sequence; wd = white dwarfs; g = giants; sg = super-giants; c = cepheid variables.

not be as large as a million to one, but it is certainly enormous. Consequently, the Russell-diagram as usually constructed does not, and is not intended to, give for the stars of the various sets a representation of the relative numbers in which they occur throughout the stellar system. To conclude that, just because the giants feature rather prominently in the diagram, they are a relatively numerous set of stars would be no more reasonable than to conclude, just because cabinet ministers and criminals feature prominently in the newspapers, that therefore cabinet ministers and criminals form a large proportion of the entire population.

A separate investigation is needed in order to estimate the relative numbers of the various sets of stars. It is sufficient to state here that the proportion of white dwarfs amongst all the stars in the Sun's neighbourhood in the galactic system has been estimated to be about 1 in 10. The proportion of giants is probably less than one per cent. Owing to their great luminosities, giants are in a majority amongst stars visible to the naked eye. But the great majority of *all* stars belong to the main sequence, while within the main sequence the proportion of stars of relatively small luminosity is known to be large.

Thus the main sequence forms literally the "main" bulk of the stars. In attempting to understand the constitution of the stars it is natural to begin with those of the main sequence. And if, in the next chapter, we succeed in describing in principle the solutions of the chief problems presented by these stars we shall have attained our main objective.

It must be finally pointed out that, if in the Russell diagram a curve is drawn to lie centrally along the track of the main sequence, the points representing the observed L, S-values for the individual stars are noticeably *scattered* about this curve. A certain amount of this scatter must be due to uncertainties in the observations. But, as regards order of magnitude, it is believed to denote a real spread in the stellar characteristics, and we shall have to refer to it again. The same applies to the giant sequence. Also in each spectral class in which giants occur, there are stars of intermediate brightness between giants and main sequence stars, but these intermediate types are relatively rare and do not serve to destroy the distinctions which have been made between the two principal sets.

ABSOLUTE MAGNITUDE EFFECT. What has been said about the spectral sequence being a single sequence is in agreement with all the facts of observation down to all but the last detail. We might indeed be somewhat surprised were the difference between a giant and a main sequence star—a difference which in class M is represented by a factor of as much as 300 in the linear dimensions—to show no trace of an effect upon the spectrum. Actually there is some effect which may be described as follows: Any non-exceptional star can be assigned without ambiguity to a particular spectral class. But within that class the strengths of certain of the less prominent lines or bands in the spectrum are found to depend in a definite manner upon the absolute magnitude of the star. This *absolute magnitude effect* is so well-established empirically for classes F-M that it provides in practice one of the standard methods for obtaining absolute magnitudes of stars and hence their distances.

In classes F-M it is customary to denote the spectrum of a typical main sequence[1] star by a prefix "d" and that of a typical giant by "g". Thus the solar spectrum is classified as dG2 and the spectrum of Capella as gG4.

It is found observationally that the brighter stars of a given spectral class have slightly lower effective temperatures than those of the less bright stars.

We may digress for a moment to notice the explanation of these effects. The appearance of the spectrum of a star depends upon the degrees of excitation and ionization of its atmosphere. These degrees depend upon the temperature and, in the case of ionization, upon the density also. But the density effect is subsidiary and is in any case such that to a first approximation a decrease in density has the same effect as a slight increase in temperature. It follows that, as we know, the spectral sequence is predominantly a tempera-

1. Main sequence stars of later spectral classes used to be called "dwarfs", hence the choice of the prefix "d". But, except for this purpose, the name has largely dropped out of use for stars of the main sequence.

ture sequence. But it also follows that almost the same spectrum is produced by two stellar atmospheres of different densities if that having the lower density is at a slightly lower temperature. This explains why the effective temperature (or any other significant temperature) decreases slightly with increasing luminosity in any one spectral class, and thereby verifies that the atmosphere of stars of any such class have lower density the greater the luminosity of the star. Finally the density effect, though similar to a temperature effect, possesses small residual differences and these constitute the absolute magnitude effect as observed. These arguments, which are adequate to explain the principles of the observed effects, are as far as the matter can be taken without appeal to specific theories of stellar atmospheres.

MASS-LUMINOSITY RELATION. A diagram can next be constructed in which the observed luminosities of the stars are plotted against their observed masses. The result is shown in Figure IV-5. Such a diagram contains fewer entries than can be inserted in a Russell-diagram simply because the mass can be determined for far fewer stars than the spectral class. But there are ample data to show that there is in fact a close correlation between the two characteristics applying to all stars except apparently the white dwarfs. This is the *mass-luminosity relation*, first made famous by Eddington's theoretical studies in 1917.

That such a relationship should exist, as an empirical fact, must be truly astonishing to anyone making a first acquaintance with it. For it shows that the luminosity of a star depends primarily only upon its mass. General physical preconceptions would lead one to expect the luminosity to depend upon all kinds of features concerning the star's past and present physical state and chemical composition. But, even if it does, the existence of the mass-luminosity relation shows that either the dependence must be relatively slight or else the features must themselves depend almost only upon the mass. Even so, having discovered the existence of main sequence stars, giants and super-giants, one might expect at least that any dependence of luminosity upon mass would be different for these different sets of stars.

Yet this is not the case; the mass-luminosity relation evidently ignores or transcends such differences.

Such considerations almost compel the view that the mass-luminosity relation is of deeper significance than the class-luminosity relation. This is not surprising. For, if the luminosity, i.e. the energy-output, of a star depends principally upon the mass of a star it must do so by virtue of some very fundamental properties of matter. On the other hand, the spectral-class is practically the effective temperature, and for a given luminosity the effective temperature de-

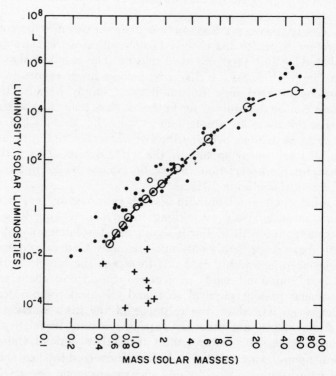

IV-5. *Mass-luminosity relation; dots represent main sequence and giant stars; crosses represent white dwarfs; open circles represent average values for main-sequence stars.*

pends only on the radius. Therefore the class-luminosity relation can be regarded as showing that a star of given luminosity must assume a certain size. This must be a matter of stellar architecture and so is expected to depend upon other than the most fundamental properties of matter. What is surprising is that there should exist a mass-luminosity relation at all.

CHEMICAL COMPOSITION. As in the case of the Russell-diagram, the mass-luminosity diagram shows a significant amount of scatter. The two diagrams together can be taken as showing that L and S both depend upon M. The scatter shows, however, that L and S do not depend upon M alone, but that the stars must differ from one another in regard to some other characteristic upon which L and S depend to a subsidiary extent. This characteristic cannot be any of those already studied, since we have already noted how these are related to L and S.

There is, however, a further regard in which it would be natural to expect one star to differ from another. This is its *chemical composition. A priori*, this might have been thought to constitute a major factor and some surprise may be felt that so little scope has been left for its operation. On a superficial view one might have concluded, for instance, that the striking differences between various stellar spectra is simply evidence of differences of chemical composition. Actually, we have seen that the spectral differences are explained with no appeal whatever to differences of chemical composition. However, any differences in composition which could affect the luminosity must concern the interior of a star and therefore cannot be directly observable.

The empirical situation is that there is no known observable characteristic that accounts for the observed scatter in the M-L and M-S relations, but that the internal chemical composition is a characteristic which has not yet been allowed for. There is therefore strong presumption that it will be found to supply the required explanation.

It should be stated that there are apparently *systematic* differences between the Russell-diagrams for certain groups of stars in the sky. If these stars are all plotted in a single diagram, the differences merely contribute to the scatter we have mentioned. The scatter in the individual diagrams, on the other hand, is considerably less. Such effects are receiving much attention at the present time and are usually interpreted as indicating systematic differences in chemical composition.

How can astronomers have the audacity to describe the internal constitutions and the life histories of objects billions of light years away, which sometimes are barely visible in even the largest telescopes? The answer to this question lies in a process of the most rigorous theoretical research, the foundations of which were laid down by the Englishman, Sir Arthur Eddington. Eddington was among the greatest of modern astronomers. He was primarily, though not exclusively, a theoretician. One of his most famous observations was that of the deflection of light during an eclipse, which he describes later in this volume. In 1927, he explained how a star, lest it disintegrate, must reach a state of equilibrium between gravitational forces tending to cause it to collapse and opposing expansive forces within it. On this premise he showed how, knowing certain factors, other factors in stellar constitutions could be arrived at by mathematical means.

At the time he stated, "The road to a knowledge of the stars leads through the atom; and important knowledge of the atom has been reached through the stars." When he wrote, scientists did not have sufficient knowledge of atomic processes in the stars to make accurate estimates of their life cycles. Bethe's discovery of the carbon cycle opened a new avenue of investigation, which is discussed by Allan Sandage in the following article. Sandage is one of the foremost younger contemporary astronomers. He was assistant to Edwin P. Hubble, the great California cosmologist, from 1951 to 1953, obtaining his Ph.D. from the California Institute of Technology in 1953. Since then, he has been a member of the staff of the Mt. Wilson and Palomar Observatories and has become a leading authority on stellar evolution and cosmology. His great predecessors have relied in varying degrees on both observation and theory. The

*manner in which he and they have attacked this problem is a
classic example of the differing methods by which science
attains its objectives.*

THE BIRTH AND DEATH OF A STAR

ALLAN SANDAGE

THE MASTER PROBLEM in the field of stellar evolution is
to describe, explain, and understand the life histories of the
stars, from the time they were created and began to shine,
until the time they exhaust their fuel supply and become
dark clinkers on the stellar ash heap.

It was not so many years ago that the topic of stellar
evolution was considered to be nothing but speculation—a
fit subject of conversation on those dark and stormy nights
when observational astronomers have leisure. But today,
stellar evolution is a rapidly developing field of astronomical
research, touching almost every branch of astrophysics. The
genesis of this change occurred in 1938 when the physicist
Hans Bethe found that the source of stellar energy is atomic.
Reasoning from general principles of nuclear physics, Bethe
outlined the now famous set of catalytic nuclear reactions
called the carbon cycle, which operates in the stars and
which converts four hydrogen atoms into one helium
nucleus with a subsequent release of energy. This discovery
opened the door to detailed studies, both by the theoretical
astrophysicists and the observational astronomers, of the
way in which the structures of the stars change as they age.

The problem of tracing the life history of a single star like
the sun is most difficult because the time scale for stellar
evolution is enormous. Put in familiar terms, the astronomical problem is similar to the dilemma of a biologist if he
were required to describe the aging process in human beings
by observing the human scene for half a minute. We shall
later see that the life-span of the sun is about 12 billion

years. Because the human span is short, any particular astronomer can observe the sun for less than one part in a hundred million of the total solar lifetime.

Now, obviously, the biologist cannot direct his attention to a single individual and expect to find evidence of aging in 30 seconds. He must rather devise some indirect method to solve his problem, such as surveying a large sample of the human population and noting age parameters among this sample. Variations in the size of individuals could be one difference which depends upon age. The degree of wrinkling of the face or the baldness of the human head would be others. A careful study of such differences would permit our biologist to construct a reasonable picture of human development. This snapshot method of solution is the only one available to the astronomer, and by its use a theory of stellar development has emerged.

Inspection of the stars in our immediate neighborhood gives evidence of a large diversity of age. Unmistakable signs of extreme youth are found side by side with extreme old age. The oldest stars date to nearly the beginning of the universe, while the youngest are less than a million years old. Astronomers determine stellar ages the same way that a heat engineer finds the burning time of a coal furnace, when he knows the amount of coal contained within his furnace and knows the rate at which his fuel is being consumed.

As we have seen, the source of stellar energy is atomic, obtained from the conversion of hydrogen into helium. We know from nuclear physics how much energy is released per nuclear conversion. We also know how many hydrogen atoms are available in a given star (that is to say, we know the star's mass). We therefore know the total potential energy content of the stars. For any particular star, observational astronomy gives the *rate* at which this available energy is being used up and radiated into space. Ipso facto, the age of that star is determined.

Direct measurements of stellar distances and light intensities show that some stars are spendthrift of their fuel supply. They release into space over one-millionth of their energy store every year. At this rate, their entire available energy supply will be exhausted in a million years and they will die of fuel starvation. Because such stars are visible in our skies today we know they must have been created less than a million years ago.

A million years is an extremely short time in terms of the total age of the universe. It is about equal to the time that has elapsed since some rudimentary form of man first emerged upon earth. We therefore have good evidence for the creation of stars within very recent geological times. It is indirect evidence to be sure, because a star has never actually been seen in the process of creation, but something almost as convincing is observed.

It is a remarkable fact that these very young and highly luminous stars are found in and *only* in regions of our galaxy containing large amounts of free cosmic gas and dust. This strongly suggests that the birthplace of new stars is in the dust clouds between the older stars, and that this dust is the material out of which stars condense.

These observations are so suggestive that astronomers now believe (perhaps somewhat optimistically) that they know what physical processes must take place in the creation of new stars. Presumably, when the density of a cloud of gas and dust becomes large enough, a sizable segment of the cloud becomes gravitationally unstable and begins to collapse under its own weight. The packing of matter into a smaller and smaller space due to slow collapse releases energy from the gravitational field and the gas and dust becomes hot. And as this pre-star condenses more and more, the central temperature within the globule goes higher and higher until, at the stage where the volume has shrunk a billion, billion times, the temperature and density are large enough for collisions between the hydrogen atoms to begin. These collisions lead to nuclear reactions of the same type as in a hydrogen bomb. At this stage an explosion does *not* occur, however, because a new star has the unfailing ability to adjust itself to release this energy gradually, contrary to the conditions inside a bomb. When nuclear reactions begin, the contraction of our protostar stops and a stable star is born.

Stable Stars

A stable star is one of nature's most magnificent inventions. The large amount of matter within a star is in equilibrium at every point; that is to say, it neither collapses nor expands. This means that a star arranges itself so that the forces acting on every small element of volume in the interior just balance. These forces are the gravitational force tending to pull the material toward the center, and the pressure of the gas tending to push the material outward. From the laws of physics we know that the pressure of the gas is determined by the temperature, and the gravitational pull by the total mass. The higher the mass of the star, the higher the central temperature must be to overcome the increased gravitational force.

But this is not the whole story, because the rate of nuclear reactions also depends critically on temperature. At high temperatures the hydrogen atoms are speeding about at breakneck speeds and collisions are frequent. High temperature therefore means high energy production and a very luminous star is the result. From similar arguments it can be shown that the final radius of our stable star depends upon the distribution of pressure, which is also given once the mass is known. Hence all the conditions of a stable star—i.e., its radius, its luminosity, and, as a direct consequence, its surface temperature—are determined by the total mass.

This means that there is a unique relation between surface temperature and the luminosity of the stars, and these are quantities which can be found directly by observation. The astronomer summarizes this information in the so-called color magnitude diagram (Figure IV-6), where the observed data are plotted for all stars. New stars which are just at the beginning of their evolutionary life lie on a line in this diagram which is called the main sequence.

It is now of interest to follow the history of a star as time goes on. By fairly easy calculation it can be shown from the theory of stable gas masses that the internal conditions of an aging star must change with time because of the presence of the waste products of the nuclear burning—namely the created helium atoms. These helium atoms are the ashes of the nuclear flame and remain deep in the stellar interior, close to their place of formation.

At first glance it would seem that helium atoms replacing the original hydrogen would not make much difference to the balance of forces within the star but this is not correct. Atom for atom, helium weighs four times as much as hydrogen and this weight difference per particle means that, for the same temperature, there is a difference in pressure of hydrogen and helium gas.

Detailed consideration of the relevant physical processes

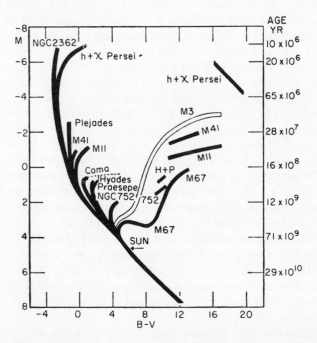

IV-6. *Color-magnitude diagram for stars in the individual clusters named above. The horizontal scale (B-V) is a measure of color or surface temperature. Blue stars are to the left, red stars to the right. The vertical scale is a logarithmic measure of the energy output.*

shows that the star compensates for the change in its internal chemical composition by increasing in radius and luminosity. It must brighten and expand to remain stable as the helium content increases. This change occurs quite gradually until 12 percent of the original hydrogen supply has been transferred into helium. During this period of gradual change, the star remains close to the main sequence. The sun is now in this stage of its evolution, because it has converted only 6 percent of its available hydrogen supply into helium.

Theory tells us that when 12 percent of the fuel has been exhausted, the star can no longer compensate for its increased helium content by small changes, but must drastically increase in radius and move rapidly from the main sequence. At this point the star is near the end of its life, because it swiftly increases in luminosity, consumes its remaining fuel at a tremendous rate, and finally sinks into obscurity and death as its fuel is depleted.

These predictions from the theory of stellar structure are *not* idle speculation. First, they follow from very basic principles of physics, and second, *they are observed to occur* in clusters of stars. We cannot, of course, follow the evolution of a single star for reasons of time scale already explained. However, individual stars in a group are all the same age but have an initial range of mass. They evolve at different rates because the rate of hydrogen consumption increases rapidly with the mass. Hence, in a cluster, we find stars at all different stages in their evolutionary history. We follow the evolution by the snapshot method.

The observational data are shown in Figure IV-7. The data for a number of different clusters are superimposed on the same diagram. Some stars in this diagram are still near the main sequence, while others have reached the 12 percent limit and have increased rapidly in radius and moved to the right.

From the data in these diagrams we date the stars in the various clusters by the coal furnace method already described. In particular, we can determine the age of the oldest cluster, M 67, to be about 5 billion years. Notice the position of the sun. It has moved slightly from the sequence because it has already consumed part of its fuel and is contaminated with helium. It is still below the 12 percent limit and is comfortably close to the main sequence. The sun has lived perhaps half of its total life span. It is now approaching middle age.

If the theory outlined above is correct, and observation confirms it at every point, we can predict the evolutionary track of the sun for future time and, in particular, de-

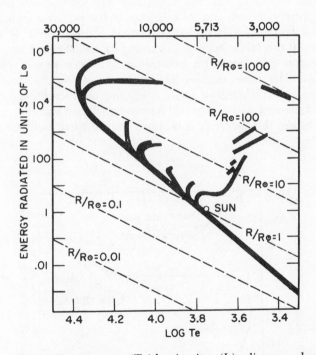

IV-7. Temperature (Te)-luminosity (L) diagram showing the position of stars in certain clusters that were shown in Figure IV-6. The main sequence is the straight line running from the upper left to lower right. New, unevolved stars lie on this sequence; evolved stars lie to the right. The radii of the stars in different parts of the diagram are shown by dotted lines. The unit ☉ is the present radius of the sun; L ☉ is the luminosity of the present sun.

termine the effect of such evolution on the conditions of the earth.

There is good reason to believe that the sun's evolutionary track in the color magnitude diagram should be quite similar to the tracks in M 67. From this similarity transformation we construct the predicted track of the sun, which is shown in Figure IV-8.

In another 6 billion years the sun will have reached the 12 percent limit and will then begin to expand rapidly in radius, moving to the right in the color magnitude diagram. At its maximum size the aging sun will grow to 30 times its present radius, and will appear in the sky as a dull red globe 15 degrees in diameter, instead of its present ½ degree. In this stage, our sun is burning its fuel at a tremendous rate and will soon after exhaust its hydrogen supply. Now begins the slow decline in brightness along the nearly horizontal track shown in the diagram, until finally the sun must die and most likely will become a white dwarf.

During this interval, conditions on the earth will not re-

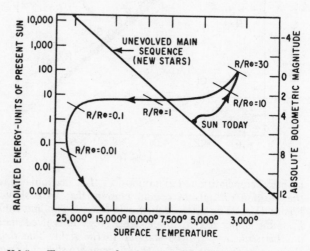

IV-8. *Temperature-luminosity diagram showing the evolutionary track of the sun. The radius of the sun, in terms of its present value, is shown along the track.*

main as they are today but the temperature at the surface must go up. Our state of knowledge of stellar evolution is now advanced to a point where fairly definite predictions of these temperature changes can be made. Figure IV-9 shows the calculated values of the radiation temperature of the earth plotted against the radius of the sun. There will be a catastrophe to most forms of life when the sun reaches four times its present radius. At this point the earth's temperature will be about 70 degrees centigrade. As the sun continues to expand it will brighten and will drive the temperature first above the boiling point of water and then to the melting point of lead, until finally, at the sun's greatest brightness, the earth's temperature reaches more than 800 degrees centigrade. Life will have ceased, the oceans will have boiled away, and conditions will be miserable.

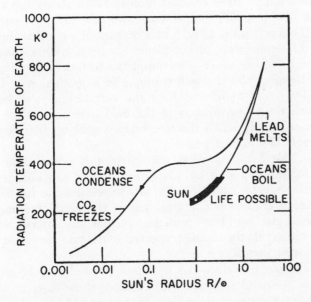

IV-9.   How the radiation temperature of the earth will change when the sun alters its radius. Temperature is on the absolute or Kelvin scale, where zero corresponds to minus 273 degrees centigrade.

Under these conditions it would be interesting to compute what the atmosphere of the earth would be like. For one thing the oxygen-carbon equilibrium, which is now in operation due to plant life, will probably be destroyed. For another, the water originally in the oceans will exist as dense clouds high about the earth's surface. These clouds will reflect a large fraction of the sun's rays and the temperatures may be somewhat lower than those shown in the diagram, but not much lower.

From the high of 800 degrees centigrade, the temperature of the earth will decrease as the sun declines in brightness. It will eventually cool until the oceans rain down over the scorched land. This will be a brief period followed by continued cooling until the oceans freeze. And as the sun becomes dimmer and dimmer, the coldness on the earth will be profound.

It is of great interest to compute the time scale of these future temperature changes. Figure IV-10 shows the variation of the earth's temperature with time. The present age of the sun is taken to be 6 billion years. We see that the rise in the temperature of our planet has been gradual over the past 6 billion years—amounting to less than 20 degrees centigrade. The rise will continue in a gradual way for 6 billion years more and then the catastrophic rise begins which dooms civilization to the final heat death. The end comes rapidly when the temperature goes up 500 degrees in only 500 million years.

In the 6 billion years remaining it is conceivable that biological evolution by adaptive processes can change the human species sufficiently rapidly to compensate for the remaining gradual temperature rise of the earth. Presumably a biologist could in principle predict the course which evolution of the human species must take to meet the changing conditions.

The picture which has just been painted may be one of great terror to sensitive people. From these facts of astrophysics it appears quite likely that human life is doomed by natural processes, if not by man's folly. It is as if the Lord were playing a mad game with things of his creation. After 12 billion years of trial and error, chance mutations and

evolution of living matter, the Lord tires of this play and
puts his toys away with fire.

But let us not despair of *our* plight. Our sun is only one
among millions in our galaxy and our galaxy is but one
among millions in the universe. Most astronomers now believe that solar systems like our own are common. If this
view holds, then there may be other places much like our
own where life exists.

We on this planet are lucky. The rate of aging of our sun
is slow. We have another 6 billion years to live. Many stars
more massive than the sun exist and here the rate of aging
is more rapid. Planets circling these stars go through the
same temperature cycles as ours but at a more rapid rate.

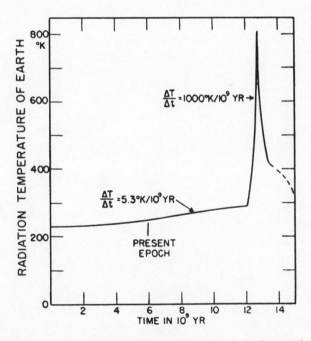

IV-10. *How the radiation temperature of the earth will
change as time goes on. Average change of temperature per
unit time is shown here.*

It follows that there may be people in the universe *this very day* facing the dilemma of the heat death. God made the sun of such a mass that we yet have time ahead. A 10 percent increase of the original solar mass would put us today at the end of life. Is it chance, or does it have some purpose that our sun was not so massive?

V. Galaxies, Cosmology, and Relativity

V. Galaxies, Cosmology, and Relativity

What are galaxies? No one knew before 1900. Very few people knew in 1920. All astronomers knew after 1924.

Galaxies are the largest single aggregates of stars in the universe. They are to astronomy what atoms are to physics. Each galaxy is a stellar system somewhat like our Milky Way, and isolated from its neighbors by nearly empty space. In popular terms, each galaxy is a separate "island universe" unto itself.

The above description, written by Allan Sandage, is a contemporary statement of a cosmological problem which has a long background in history. The idea of constellations of stars which seemed to form patterns in the sky was, as we have seen, familiar to ancient astronomers. The concept of "aggregates," related into scientific systems, was unknown until 1750. In that year a teacher and craftsman named Thomas Wright of Durham, England published An Original Theory or New Hypothesis of the Universe, beautifully illustrated with engravings from his own hand, in which he postulated the existence of many star systems, enclosed by spheres, of which our own galaxy was one. His theory was ignored by astronomers and his book largely forgotten. However, the German philosopher Immanuel Kant, who read an abstract of it in a Hamburg journal, used it as the basis for an evolutionary hypothesis which came to the attention of nineteenth-century astronomers and helped rescue Wright's work from oblivion. The theories of both men, as well as a similar suggestion by the Swedish scientific and religious thinker Emanuel Swedenborg, were theoretical and philosophical. It remained for Sir William Herschel to arrive independently at his theory of the Milky Way, shaped like a disk or grindstone with the sun at or near the center, on the basis of exact observation. Herschel considered the nebulae as similar and independent systems. His great paper on the subject was delivered to the Royal Society in 1784.

In the twentieth century, the view that there were no external galaxies, that they were all elements in our own galaxy, became popular. The problem was essentially one of measurement of distances. As we have seen, the turning point in the controversy was reached by Hubble, whose discovery of cepheid variables in distant galaxies eliminated the possibility that they were members of the Milky Way system. Hubble's observation of the so-called "red shift" in distant stars, due to the Doppler effect, led to his theory of an expanding universe, which remains one of the leading hypotheses of modern cosmology.

What we now know about the galaxies themselves is the subject of the following article. The author was born at Toronto, spent most of his youth in Japan, and after studying at the University of Toronto, obtained his Ph.D. at Harvard in 1932. He has worked at three of Canada's largest observatories, is well known for his study of the spectra of meteors, and is head of upper atmosphere research at the National Research Council of Canada.

GALAXIES

PETER M. MILLMAN

THE STARS we see, even on the clearest night, all belong to our own star system or galaxy. This galaxy has the form of a large flattened disk and is outlined by the Milky Way. In the galaxy are located some 100,000 million stars, and between the stars is finely divided matter in the form of gas and dust. We have found that this star system of ours has the immense diameter of 80,000 light-years. This means that light, which can girdle the earth seven times in less than a second, would take 80,000 years to travel from one side of the galaxy to the other. But this is only the beginning of immensity because our galaxy, with all its stars and gas and dust, is only one of a great multitude of other similar galaxies that we observe in the depths of space far beyond the limits of our own star system.

During the evenings of late summer the constellation Andromeda, the Chained Maiden, rises in the north-east. Above the three principal stars in this figure you can just detect with the naked eye a little misty patch somewhat elongated in shape. This is the Great nebula in Andromeda, one of the closest of the other galaxies. If you take a trip to the southern hemisphere two more of our neighboring galaxies can be seen: the famous clouds of Magellan, or the Magellanic Clouds. These look like detached portions of the Milky Way, and were named after the Portuguese navigator who in the sixteenth century led the first expedition to circumnavigate the globe. The Andromeda nebula and the two Magellanic Clouds are the only external galaxies, or island universes as they have often been called, that are visible to the naked eye. In telescopes many more can be seen visually as small hazy objects with little detail. But only photography gives us a true impression of the actual numbers of these external star systems. They are found in the hundreds-of-thousands, and in certain parts of the sky, among the faintest objects that can be photographed with large telescopes, there are actually more galaxies than stars recorded on the plates. When we realize that each one of these galaxies is a great star system in its own right, it is almost more than the mind can comprehend.

If I were asked to pick the most universal and significant units in our physical world I would say atoms, stars, and galaxies, on the basis of universality, and I would add men on the basis of subjective significance, since without man's ability to reason there would be no discussion at all. Now it so happens that these four units, atoms, men, stars, and galaxies, form a rough sequence of increasing size which, in very round figures, has equal steps. You could lay 10,000 million atoms in a row on a man's body. If you placed 10,000 million men in a row they would reach from side to side of an average star, and if you placed 10,000 million stars side by side they would extend across an average galaxy. Since atoms, men, stars, and galaxies, all vary a good deal in size, one should not attempt to apply this yardstick in too exact a manner.

What are some of the characteristics of these galaxies of

stars that we observe in such number? There can be no doubt that the most obvious feature seen in the majority of galaxies is a spiral structure. This spiral form was discovered in 1845 by the Earl of Rosse, an Irish nobleman who was an amateur astronomer with plenty of money. He had erected at Birr Castle a reflecting telescope with a metal mirror six feet in diameter. Just two months after this great instrument was put into use it was found that a nebula in Canes Venatici, the Hunting Dogs, not far from the Big Dipper, had spiral arms winding out from the centre, and this is still known as Lord Rosse's spiral. In the next few years some fourteen nebulae were observed to be of the spiral type. However, the spiral form of these objects is revealed much better in photographs and today the study of their structure is carried out entirely by means of photography. The term spiral nebula, used for many years in referring to these systems, has now been replaced by the designation spiral galaxy.

About one-fifth of the galaxies show no spiral structure at all. A few of this group are quite irregular in shape but most have a regular outline that varies from circular through elliptical to a narrow spindle shape. These are called the elliptical galaxies but in reality most of them probably approach a disk-like form. When seen from a direction at right angles to the plane of the disk they appear circular, and when seen edge-on they appear elongated.

The elliptical galaxies exhibit practically no detail. Their surface brightness is greatest at the centre and grades down to very low values at the outer edge. Two good examples of elliptical galaxies appear as companions to the Great nebula in Andromeda. In most photographs these elliptical systems look like hazy, symmetrical gas clouds but the nearby examples have been resolved into stars with the 100-inch telescope on Mt. Wilson, and with the 200-inch telescope on Mt. Palomar. The stars are relatively close together at the centres of such galaxies but thin out greatly towards the edges.

One of the pioneers in investigating the galaxies was the late E. P. Hubble of the Mt. Wilson and Palomar Observatories. He suggested a simple observational classification for these systems, based entirely on the dominant visual characteristics (Figure V-1). The elliptical galaxies were graded according to the degree of their apparent flattening or ellipticity, and the spiral galaxies were graded according to the prominence of the central nucleus relative to the arms. An interesting variation appears in about a third of the spirals, where the arms do not curve directly out of the nucleus or central core, but seem to start from the ends of a straight bar running through this core. These are called the barred spirals and they have a somewhat artificial appearance.

Strangely enough, in spite of many suggestions and much

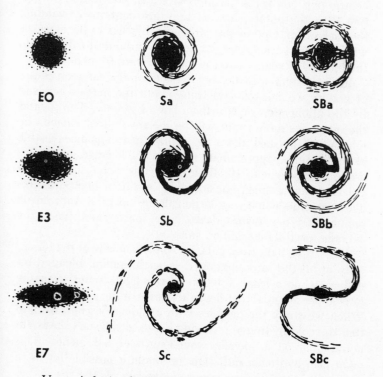

V-1. *A basic classification of the extragalactic nebulae, or galaxies, by E. P. Hubble.*

theorizing, no perfectly satisfactory explanation has yet been advanced to account for the continued existence of spiral arms in such a large percentage of galaxies. Current thinking tends to the belief that magnetic fields in space may have a lot to do with maintaining a spiral structure in star systems, but it is too early yet to say anything definite on this subject. It is worth noting, however, that the effects of magnetic fields are entering more and more into the theoretical discussions of certain features of our universe, and the importance of such considerations has only been realized in recent years.

One thing we do know about the galaxies is that, like immense celestial pin-wheels, they are rotating about their centres, and where spiral arms are present, the arms trail, according to most investigators. As in the solar system the central portions of the galaxies have a shorter period of rotation than the outer parts, so they are continually winding themselves up. One of the problems that has to be solved is why the spiral arms have not been wound out of existence in the billions of years since the galaxies were formed.

In any system of bodies revolving around a common centre of gravity we can tell something about the masses involved by the application of Newton's law of gravity. The greater the mass, the more rapid will be the revolution. Hence, the motions of the stars about the centres of the galaxies enable us to determine approximate masses. The average galaxy has a mass equivalent to 10,000 million suns. Some small dwarf galaxies have a mass considerably less than one-tenth this average value, while very large galaxies, like the Andromeda nebula and our own galaxy, have masses ten times the average, or 100,000 million suns.

The visible light from galaxies consists mostly of the luminosity of all the stars contained in each system, blended together, while a small fraction of the light comes from the interstellar material that lies in the arms of the spiral galaxies. When we study the galaxies with a radio telescope we find that the cold hydrogen gas lying between the stars sends out a radiation on a specific wave-length of 8.3 inches. This eight-inch hydrogen radiation has made it possible for us to trace out the spiral arms in our own galaxy, as the gas always lies thickest along the arms.

But there is another type of radio energy emitted by both our galaxy and many of the other systems. It originates from a roughly spherical volume, or halo, considerably larger than the visible disk of stars that makes up a galaxy as we see it in photographs. In other words a galaxy has about twice as big a diameter when viewed with a radio telescope as when photographed. It is now believed that this invisible halo radiation comes from an immense cloud of electrons, that is, small, negatively charged particles. These acquire high energies from the cosmic rays of space and such electrons, if placed in a magnetic field, will produce radiation. Hence, the halo radiation from a galaxy gives evidence of two phenomena associated with a galaxy: a cloud of high energy electrons, and a general magnetic field.

I have already noted that the majority of galaxies show a spiral structure, while most of the remainder, about twenty per cent, are elliptical objects with no evidence of spiral arms. However, the elliptical galaxies look very much like the centres of the spiral galaxies minus the arms. Suppose we examine more closely the differences between the elliptical and the spiral star systems.

We can start by looking at the types of stars involved. The term giant refers to a star which has a very high absolute luminosity, in other words a light source with a high candle power, and this generally means a relatively large mass as well. The sun is located in one of the spiral arms of our own galaxy, and in the general neighbourhood of the sun we find some very luminous blue-giant and supergiant stars with high surface temperatures. Along with these we have other types of stars such as red giants, yellow stars of average brightness like the sun, red dwarfs, and white dwarfs, and so on.

When the individual stars in the elliptical galaxies were first studied, astronomers were surprised to find there were no blue giants at all in these systems. The brightest stars were the red giants, and these gave the elliptical systems a slightly redder colour than the spirals. It was also found that the central cores of the spiral galaxies were like the elliptical galaxies, and contained no blue giant stars. Some other interesting differences turned up. The elliptical galaxies, and the central parts of the spiral galaxies, contained practically no gas or dust among the stars, while the spiral arms in galaxies had large amounts of both gas and dust.

Thus, we find in space two completely contrasting arrangements of matter. On the one hand we have the spiral arms of galaxies with many types of stars, including blue giants, and quantities of gas and dust between the stars. On the other hand we have the elliptical galaxies and the central cores of the spirals, with no blue giants and little gas or dust. For convenience in reference the two types of stellar associations have been named Population I and Population II. Population I occurs chiefly in spiral arms and corresponds to what we find in our portion of space, where both blue giants and gas and dust are present. Population II is what we find at the Galactic centre, in the centres of other spiral galaxies, and in the elliptical systems. Here neither blue giant stars nor gas and dust are found. The late ·Walter Baade, of the Mt. Wilson and Palomar Observatories, was chiefly responsible for developing this very important concept of the two types of stellar communities.

It is natural to ask whether there is any explanation for the two populations in space. The origin of this phenomenon must be very basic, and must depend on the way star systems have evolved from the original state of matter. There are many puzzles still to be solved in this connection but on certain facts there is general agreement.

Population II lacks the bright blue giant and supergiant stars. Stars of this type are radiating energy at a very high rate, and they are using up their resources of nuclear fuel so fast that they cannot be very old compared to objects like the sun. These bright blue stars are considered to be the youngest members of the stellar company. It is a very significant thing that gas and dust in any quantity are missing from exactly the same formations that have no blue giants. This lends weight to the hypothesis that stars condense out of the gas and dust of space, and it is logical to find very young stars where there is a good supply of this star-forming material, but no young stars where this material has all been used up. We thus have the picture of Population II as consisting only of middle-aged and very old stars that have existed for thousands of millions of years, while Population I contains both the old and the young, and has many regions where even now stars are being born. The great swirling mass of gas and dust that centres around the nebula in the constellation Orion is such a region.

But we are not yet certain of the reason why some galaxies contain nothing but an aging population while others have in addition the younger, more varied, and active population of the spiral arms. The best guess at present is that the answer will be found when we consider the action of one galaxy on another. We will come back to this point a little later. In the meantime it may give us some satisfaction to realize that the sun, although itself a middle-aged star, is a member of the younger and more virile type of population in our galaxy. The division of stars into populations is a statistical procedure and in the case of many individual stars it may be difficult or impossible to decide which population they belong to.

I have said a lot about galaxies as individual units, and it is time we paused for a moment to review the contents of an average galaxy. Let us take the typical spiral system. At the centre we have a massive core formed of very old stars and around this a flattened disk of spiral arms, with an over-all diameter somewhere in the range between 10,000 and 100,000 light-years or more. The stars in this disk exhibit a great variety, not only in colour and size but also in behaviour and in association with their neighbours. We find rapidly pulsating white or yellow stars and others that are red and vary slowly in luminosity. Some stars emit great quantities of gas, either steadily or in tremendous flares and outbursts. Many stars pair up with a companion, and we have every conceivable combination of two or more stars revolving about mutual centres of gravity. Often the tidal forces in these systems become so extreme that the stars are deformed, and great streams of gas spiral out into space and envelop the surrounding region. Ghostly shells of gas around certain stars appear as remnants of past activity, and bright and dark nebulosities lie thick along the spiral arms.

Then we have the larger associations of stars: clusters like the Pleiades, the Hyades, the Double Cluster of Perseus, and others, most of them lying near the basic plane of a galaxy.

And there is another kind of star cluster that is not confined to the general plane of a galaxy. I refer to the globular clusters, spherical associations of some 100,000 stars each. These are distributed widely like the outer framework of a star system, and it was a study of the globular clusters which first suggested to the American astronomer Harlow Shapley the great extent of our own galaxy. In photographs of the closer galaxies the globular clusters can be seen like little hazy dots grouped around each star system. And outside the globular clusters there is an invisible halo of atoms and electrons, extending out into space beyond the visible portion of the system. Such is a typical galaxy.

What about the relations of the galaxies to each other. When we study their distribution in space we find a definite tendency for them to cluster together. This is somewhat analogous to the behaviour of stars, and as a matter of fact, of men and of atoms as well. Our own galaxy belongs to a local cluster of at least seventeen star systems. Apart from ours I have already mentioned five of these systems, the Andromeda nebula and its two elliptical companions, and the two Magellanic Clouds. The seventeen galaxies of the local group occupy a somewhat elongated volume of space roughly two million light-years long. We can best visualize the spacing by adopting a scale of one inch to 10,000 light-years. Now, take seventeen disk-shaped objects of assorted sizes ranging from a twelve-inch cake plate for the Andromeda galaxy, and an eight-inch dessert plate for our own system, down through saucers and coins of various sizes to the heads of small thumb tacks for the smallest galaxies. Suspend these at random in a room ten by twenty feet in size, placing the two largest plates near opposite ends of the room, and you have a scale model of our local cluster of galaxies.

Other clusters of galaxies are larger and contain more members. The closest large cluster outside our local group is called the Virgo cluster because it lies in the direction of the constellation Virgo, the Virgin. Almost in the same general direction is the much more distant Coma cluster, named after the little constellation of Berenice's Hair. A scale model of the central part of the Coma cluster could be made by taking the same assorted plates, saucers, coins, and thumb tacks we used before, and scattering 500 of them in a hall fifty feet square with a very high ceiling.

Twenty or more clusters of galaxies have now been studied, and these range in distance out to those where the brightest galaxies of the cluster can just be photographed with the 200-inch telescope as tiny hazy dots on the negatives. Taken by themselves we would not know what these tiny dots were but fortunately we have a steady progression of photographs from those of the nearby galaxies, where we can study individual stars, down through small and fainter images with less and less detail to the minute records of the most distant galaxies that can be detected.

This question concerning the distance of the galaxies is very difficult. It is possible to determine the relative distances of the various clusters of galaxies by tabulating the apparent size and brightness of the most prominent members of the cluster. Although individual galaxies vary greatly in size and type there seems to be a fairly uniform upper limit of absolute brightness for the big ones in a cluster. The fainter these appear the more distant the cluster. But to arrive at the absolute distances of the galaxies is a much bigger problem. During the last ten years our estimate of the distances of these clusters of galaxies has been steadily going up, even though the fundamental observations upon which these distances are based have not been altered.

We must make the assumption that the physical characteristics of the galaxies at the limits of observation are the same as those in our own neighbourhood. From the evidence available this seems a sound hypothesis, at least in the first approximation. The latest estimate of the distance of the Virgo cluster, the closest to us, is about fifty million light-years while the Coma cluster is just under 300 million light-years away. The light of the Coma cluster, observed today, has been on its way to us for close to 300 million years, and we see this group of galaxies as it was when the carboniferous forests of tree ferns flourished on earth long before the age of the dinosaurs.

But the Coma cluster is among the three or four closest clusters of galaxies. The others are much further away and have distances extending up to several billions of light-years.

And yet we may be recording systems far beyond this visible limit. The apparent paradox arises as a result of the use of radio telescopes, which record the invisible radio waves from the universe around us. I have already mentioned several sources of radio waves from space. There is our own sun for example, and there are the atmospheres of some of the planets. Then there is the hydrogen gas in our star system that is broadcasting on a radio wave-length of 8.3 inches, and we receive a more general type of radio energy from the Milky Way and from the electron halo enveloping the Milky Way. But some of the strongest radio signals come from none of these sources. As soon as radio astronomers started to make a general survey of the sky in various radio wave-lengths they detected many sources of radio waves that were very small and had a fixed position among the stars. These were called "radio stars", and for most of them there was no visible object in the direction in space from which the radio waves seemed to come.

Unfortunately radio telescopes are not able to fix the position of radio sources with the accuracy possible in optical work. This adds to the problem of identification. The first radio star to be recognized was found in 1944 by the pioneer radio astronomer, Grote Reber. It is located in the constellation Cygnus the Swan, and has been named Cygnus A. When the position of Cygnus A had been determined to a reasonable accuracy with the world's most powerful radio telescopes, then the 200-inch telescope on Mt. Palomar was used to examine this region of the sky, and a very faint peculiar galaxy was found at just the right position. This object had two central cores close together, and it seemed likely that here was an example of two galaxies in direct head-on collision.

Apparently colliding galaxies are very efficient broadcasting stations, since in the radio wave-lengths these two galaxies are radiating a quarter of a million times as much energy as they would if not in collision. The stars in galaxies are so far apart relative to their own diameters that there is small chance of any stars colliding, even if two galaxies pass directly through each other. But the gas and dust of the two systems will meet at high velocity, and the energy of this impact seems to produce very strong radio waves. The correctness of this interpretation was checked by analyzing the light from the colliding galaxies of Cygnus A with the spectroscope. The spectrum was found to contain bright lines of the type that could only be produced by a very hot, highly excited gas.

It should be noted here that a number of astronomers, including a group in the U.S.S.R., do not accept the collision hypothesis as an explanation of the intense radio emission from peculiar galaxies. An alternative view is that these are young galaxies of complex structure. The abnormally strong radio-wave intensity is assumed to result from the explosions of large numbers of supernovae in these systems.

Collisions of galaxies are not an unexpected event. Suppose we return to our scale model of a large cluster of galaxies. We had 500 objects ranging from a foot in diameter down to the size of thumb tacks, all in a fifty-foot hall. Each galaxy has its own individual motion, and under these conditions an occasional traffic accident is bound to happen. We see many galaxies in apparent contact, or linked by long nebulous streamers like extensions of spiral arms. These streamers probably originate from tidal action at the time of near misses.

And now we return to the problem I mentioned earlier— why do the elliptical galaxies have no dust or gas? Perhaps the collisions are responsible as, after a few collisions, most of this material would be swept up or dispersed out of the systems. It is very significant that the gas-free elliptical galaxies are most common near the congested centres of large clusters, where collisions would be most frequent. On this view the spiral galaxies are those which have never had a collision, or at least have had very few collisions.

The peculiar galaxies of Cygnus A turn out to be over 700 million light-years away. The most distant object of this type yet identified may have the tremendous distance of 6,000 million light-years, and this seems near the limit of the present optical instruments. It is estimated that roughly a billion galaxies can be photographed with the 200-inch telescope. But of all the radio sources only a small fraction have been identified. Some can be explained by various types of sources in our own system, but a growing body of evidence indicates that most of the unidentified radio stars are very faint galaxies, possibly in full or grazing collisions, and these may never appear in optical telescopes. At the present time there is no good way of determining their distances by radio observations, but many are likely to be further away than the limits to which we can see with the 200-inch telescope. Already radio astronomy, the youngest branch of astronomical research, seems to have outstripped the other branches in surveying the universe.

The well-known Horsehead Nebula in the constellation of Orion is an example of the almost starless areas which appear in certain regions of the sky. The theory that these areas are due simply to an absence of stars has given way in the twentieth century to the theory that they are caused by obscuring matter which prevents visual observation of objects lying beyond it. The existence of such matter has only recently been proved. Sir Arthur Eddington, who died in 1944, is quoted by Otto Struve as comparing it to a ghost and astronomers to a guest in a haunted room who remarked, "I do not believe in ghosts but I am afraid of them." Radio astronomy is able to penetrate to regions where optical astronomy is barred and one of its contributions has been to throw "light" on the "darkness" caused by interstellar matter.

Interstellar dust may not only obscure stars and galaxies completely. It may also disperse or dim their light or make it appear redder than it otherwise would appear. It plays another, more constructive part in modern cosmology. Many astronomers now believe that cosmic dust and gas are the stuff out of which stars originate.

THE DUST AND GAS OF SPACE

PETER M. MILLMAN

MOST OF THE mass of our universe that is not in the stars
exists as gas and dust between the stars. Estimates of the
total quantity of this interstellar material range all the way
from five per cent to fifty per cent of the total mass in the
universe. If the steady-state model of the universe is correct,
gas may account for much more than fifty per cent of the
total mass. The word gas refers to matter where the individual atoms or molecules are separated and move independently of each other. The word dust is used to refer to
matter in the form of small solid particles with dimensions
considerably larger than those of atoms and molecules.

In speculating on the origin of stars it is usual to assume
that initially they developed from concentrations in a large,
diffuse cloud of gas. This suggests that a gas cloud was the
original, or at least an earlier, state of matter, and that the
stars evolved from it. On the other hand our sun is continually projecting streams of gas into the solar system, and
other stars, much brighter than the sun, are even more active
in this regard. Obviously then some of the matter we now
find between the stars originated in the stars. As a matter of
fact interstellar material with this type of origin may be
quite important in our study of the evolution of the universe.
It is quite possible that some of the heavier elements owe
their origin chiefly to nuclear reactions that have taken place
inside stars.

Most of the stars appear the same year after year. If they
do change, the process is so slow that even centuries of observation would show no great difference. But every now and
again a bright star suddenly appears where no object was
previously visible. This is a so-called new star, or nova. The
name is a bit misleading as the star has been there all the

time, generally very faint and visible only in a large telescope. But all at once it reaches an unstable point in its development, and within a few hours it increases in luminosity to over 50,000 times its previous brightness. Such an event is an explosion of truly cosmic proportions. At its brightest a nova shines with an absolute luminosity something like 100,000 times that of the sun.

A bright nova appeared in the constellation Perseus in February, 1901, and another in Aquila during June, 1918. These both became as bright as any of the stars we see except for Sirius, the Dog Star. But after a couple of months they faded back into obscurity again. Analysis of the light of these novae with the spectroscope showed that when they exploded they threw off great shells of bright gas that moved outward at speeds up to 2,000 miles per second. Many years after the original outbursts the remnants of these gas shells could still be seen in the telescope as areas of faint nebulosity around the two stars (Figure V-2).

Tremendous as these nova outbursts are, we sometimes see an explosion in space which is 10,000 times more powerful. This is called a supernova and the brightest supernova can shine with a light equivalent to 1,000 million suns. On November 11, 1572, a star that could be seen in broad daylight suddenly appeared in the constellation Cassiopeia. This was a supernova and was studied in detail by that most assiduous observer of the heavens, the Danish astronomer Tycho Brahe. Unfortunately, this event occurred before the telescope was invented and so our knowledge of Tycho's Star, as it is called, is restricted to what could be observed with the naked eye. The star faded slowly and remained visible for nearly a year and a half, after which it was too faint to be seen without instrumental aid. Now, nearly four centuries later, we cannot identify it as there are a number of very faint stars in the position described by Tycho.

However, looking in a different part of the sky, we can still see the remains of another bright supernova of the past. In the constellation of Taurus the Bull, near the tip of one of the bull's horns, we see an object consisting of weirdly shaped filaments of gas. This seems to bear some resemblance to a crab, and so it has been called the Crab nebula. Now the old

M1 (CRAB NEBULA)

NOVA PERSEI

M57 (RING NEBULA)

NGC 6543

M97 (OWL NEBULA)

NGC 7009 (SATURN NEBULA)

V-2. Examples of associations of gas showing some degree of
symmetry and generally associated with a single star near the
centre.

records of both the Chinese and the Japanese state that in approximately this same position a very bright new star appeared in the sky in the year A.D. 1054. It reached a brightness equal to Jupiter and then eventually faded away. Careful observations, made over the last fifty years, have shown that the Crab nebula is gradually expanding at a rate which indicates that it originated at a point near its centre 900 years ago. This pretty well confirms the hypothesis that the Crab nebula is the remains of the medieval supernova. The speed of expansion of the nebula is 800 miles per second, and its diameter is now almost four light-years, that is roughly the distance from the solar system to the nearest star. Think of an explosion big enough to fill a space of this volume!

Both types of nova explosions occur because a star loses the balance between its nuclear energy production and the radiation of this energy into space. In the case of the ordinary nova the event is probably more superficial and associated chiefly with the outer layers of the star. In the case of the supernova it is deep seated and originates in the star's central core. It is suspected that most novae are repeaters, and blow off their outer layers at intervals of a million years or so, while it is not likely that a star can be a supernova more than once. As far as we know only a small percentage of the stars become novae. In our own star system, or galaxy, it is estimated that some twenty or thirty nova explosions occur every year, but supernova explosions are much rarer and according to latest calculations we probably have only two or three of these every century. A large percentage of the latter will be hidden by obscuring matter and will not be seen from our position in the galaxy.

There is another class of objects in space which may be closely related to the exploding stars and their clouds of gas. Here and there we find a hazy, symmetrical form of a circular or oval shape. About 500 of these objects are known and they are called planetary nebulae, not because they have any physical connection with the planets but because many of them look something like faint planets when seen in small telescopes. Actually a planetary nebula is a complex or multiple gas shell with a very faint star at the centre. The best known is the Ring nebula in Lyra, while among the others are the Owl nebula, the Saturn nebula, the Dumb-bell nebula, and so on (Figure V-2). In each case, the name gives an indication of the general appearance.

To fully understand what these objects are it is necessary to analyze their light. The familiar lines of hydrogen and helium were easily identified in their spectra. But the surprising thing was that most of the light showed a pattern of colours never before observed. In particular there were two strong lines in the blue-green and three in the violet that were present in the light of practically every nebula, and there was not the slightest hint as to what element might produce them. Astronomers began to talk about the possibility of nebulium, a new element that might exist only in the nebulae.

Then, thanks largely to the work of I. S. Bowen at the Mt. Wilson Observatory in California, it was realized that the unrecognized type of light was produced by well-known, familiar atoms shining in very unusual conditions—at least unusual as far as our experience on the surface of the earth is concerned. The strongest of the unidentified bright lines in the planetary nebulae were produced by three atoms, oxygen, nitrogen, and neon.

It may seem strange that these three familiar atoms remained unrecognized for such a long time. As a matter of fact they had all assumed very excellent disguises. In a neon sign on earth the neon atom shines with a red light while in the nebulae its chief radiation is a rich violet colour. Oxygen turned out to be the element producing the two strong blue-green lines and the other two strong lines in the violet.

Why do we not observe this type of light when we study neon and oxygen atoms in the laboratory? The most important factor is one of size. The planetary nebulae have diameters ranging up to half a light-year. The important difference between the gas in the laboratory and the gas which is shining in the nebulae is that on earth we can only experiment with a very small volume of gas in a glass tube, while out in space we are looking through a sphere or shell of gas two million million miles across. Under these conditions we can see certain colours or wave-lengths of light which stand only a very small chance of occurring. Physicists, accustomed to working in laboratories, called these colours forbidden lines, but the emission of these wave-lengths is not actually impossible, only highly improbable. When we look through a million million miles of gas enough atoms in the long column will be shining with the very improbable light to be seen. On the other hand the atoms in space are so widely separated that often they will not shine with the light we are accustomed to see from atoms in the laboratory.

Although the stars at the centres of the planetary nebulae are inconspicuous to the eye, it is these peculiar stars which provide the energy which makes the nebulae luminous. These stars are very strong in ultra-violet light, invisible in our telescopes. Ultra-violet light has high energy and this energy is pumped into the atoms of the nebular gas, making it possible for them to fluoresce with light in the visible part of the spectrum.

The gas clouds we have been discussing are in the form of shells around very hot stars, and it is logical to assume that they originated in these stars at some time in the past. In fact, in the case of some of the novae, we have been able to observe the actual formation of gas shells.

But the material in these shells represents only a very small percentage of the dust and gas in space. By far the greater part appears either as bright or as dark clouds of irregular outline, many of these looking remarkably like the clouds in our own atmosphere. In distant space we even see clouds with a silver lining. One important difference between the clouds in space and those on earth is the time scale. Our local clouds are transitory and change their form every few seconds, while the space clouds look much the same century after century. This is not because they are not in motion—the space clouds may have turbulent velocities of five miles per second or more. It is simply that their distances from us are so large that even these velocities will not have any great effect on their shape over intervals of many years, and as a result we have plenty of time to study them in detail.

Most of the bright and dark clouds or nebulae of irregular outline are found in and near the Milky Way. Some have been named after their chance resemblance to certain forms.

Thus among the bright clouds we have the North America nebula, the Network nebula, and the Pelican nebula, while some of the dark clouds are called the Cone nebula, the Coalsack, and the Horsehead nebula. The southern part of the Milky Way seen in summer, that runs from Cygnus down through Sagittarius, is divided into two by a dark lane known as the Great Rift. This is an immense cloud of obscuring matter relatively close to the solar system, and it hides the light of the stars behind it. In some areas the dark clouds of space are completely opaque, and allow no visible light to penetrate from the far side. Others only dim the light of the stars behind them, and in this case the stars usually look redder than normal.

Is it possible to learn anything about the material in these absorbing clouds? Before I answer this question I want you to think of a somewhat similar situation on earth. Sometimes we have a cloud that completely obscures the sun. At other times we may have a fog bank overhead, which dims the brilliance of the sun but still allows us to see it quite clearly as a white disk. Again, when the sun sinks to the horizon on a clear day, it may be dimmed to a fiery red disk as it sets. These various effects are due to a phenomenon we call the scattering of light.

In the case of the dense cloud all the light from the sun is scattered and none of it gets through the cloud directly to reach our eyes. All we see is the general luminosity of daylight. The fog on the other hand scatters some of the sunlight, but the rest gets through and reaches the eye, so we see the sun's disk dimmed. In this case all the colours of light are scattered in the same proportion and the colour of the sun is not materially changed. However, in the third case, when the sun is near the horizon on a clear day, the blue light is scattered much more than the red light with the result that most of the blue light does not reach our eyes and the sun looks red. This is called selective scattering, that is certain wave-lengths of light are affected more than others. It has been found that dust particles bigger than one-thousandth of an inch in diameter scatter all colours equally, but when the particles are 10 to a 1000 times smaller than this, the blue light is scattered twice as much as the red. For even smaller sizes, corresponding to atoms and molecules, the blue light may be scattered ten to twenty times more than the red light.

Most of the scattering of starlight by the dust of space seems to be of the type that would be produced by particles between a thousandth and a millionth of an inch in size. Recent work has suggested that particles considerably smaller than this may also be present, and that some dust particles may have an elongated or needle-like shape. Whatever the exact form of the dust, it is believed that small particles are formed out of the gas of space by a tendency of the atoms of hydrogen, carbon, nitrogen, and other elements, to clump together and to build up larger units. This process may be assisted by particles formed in the atmospheres of cool stars.

The dust reveals itself in another way, which has a good analogy here on earth. On a foggy night you see a glow around every street light since the fog particles reflect light. In the same way dust clouds in space near bright stars reflect the light of these stars. A beautiful example of this is the little cluster of stars called the Pleiades, or the Seven Sisters. Long-exposure photographs of this cluster show hazy clouds around all the brighter stars. When we analyze the light of these misty halos we find that it is the same as that of the stars, which indicates that it is reflected light. And just as in the case of the street lights, the brighter the stars, the greater the distance to which the illumination extends. The brightest stars in our system will illuminate this interstellar material out to a distance of over thirty light-years from the star. However, an average star like our sun will only illuminate it out to a distance of a quarter of a light-year. Dust that does not happen to be near enough to a star to be illuminated remains as a dark cloud, and photographs show that some of these dark masses of dust have relatively sharp edges, the Horsehead nebula being the most famous example of this.

We have all heard the expression "where there's smoke there's fire." In space at large this could be paraphrased by saying "where there's dust there's gas," since the close association of dust clouds and gas clouds is clearly indicated by astronomical observations. If, as suggested earlier, dust is forming out of gas, it is not exactly surprising that we find both in the same regions of the universe.

The gas of space can be recognized in a number of ways. We have already seen how the ultra-violet light from hot stars will cause the emission of visible light in an extended shell around the star. The same effect is found in the irregular gas clouds. If they happen to be near hot stars the atoms in the gas will be excited, and will shine in the same way as does the gas in a planetary nebula. The best example of this is the great nebula in Orion that marks the jeweled sword hilt near the belt of the Hunter. This is one of the nebulous objects that can be seen quite well with small telescopes, and in photographs it looks just like the great swirling turbulent mass of gas it is. Four blue stars with high surface temperatures are located near the centre of the Orion nebula, and these provide a large portion of the energy that keeps it shining.

Throughout the universe hydrogen is the commonest element. The hydrogen atom is the simplest atom and consists of one positive electrical charge and a negative charge, or electron, to balance it. In most parts of space the hydrogen atoms are cold and dark and in a state of very low energy, but near the hot stars there is enough energy to remove the electrons from the hydrogen atoms. This hot hydrogen is said to be ionized, and when the wayward electrons rejoin the ionized hydrogen atoms, the characteristic light of hydrogen is given out. This process is going on continuously in regions of space near the hot stars. Whether a gas cloud in space shines with its own light or not depends on the surface temperatures of the stars embedded in it. If we find stars hotter than 18,000° Kelvin, the gas near them will flouresce with the characteristic atomic radiations I have already described. For the cooler stars below 18,000° there is not enough energy to excite the gas to shine, and here we see only the reflected starlight from the dust clouds, as was noted in the Pleiades.

It is natural to inquire as to just how concentrated this space material is. According to the standards we are accustomed to, it is very rarified indeed. Let us start with the air we breathe at sea level as a standard for comparison. It is roughly one-thousandth the density of water. At a height of sixty miles above the earth the density of the atmosphere is one-millionth the density of the air at sea level. We can produce a density ten million times smaller still with good vacuum pumps in a physics laboratory. But the density of a typical gas cloud in space is ten million times rarer than this laboratory vacuum, while the average density of space dust is lower still, probably not much more than one per cent of the gas density. If you have been keeping track of the powers of ten in what I have just listed you will find that the average density of gas in the plane of the Milky Way is equal to the density of water divided by ten raised to the twenty-third power, while the density of dust is that of water divided by ten raised to the twenty-fifth power.

Even so, however, space is far from empty. Suppose we take a typical cubic yard of space in the plane of the Milky Way. On the average we will find in this cube about five million hydrogen atoms. The number of helium atoms present is somewhat uncertain but they are probably next to hydrogen in abundance. There will be roughly 1,000 atoms each of oxygen, nitrogen, and carbon, while magnesium and silicon, and possibly sodium and neon also, contribute 100 atoms each. Then there will be smaller quantities of other elements, some simple molecules, and a large number of electrons. The dust is much less evident; there is only one grain in every thousand of our cubic yards. Yet even this small amount is quite sufficient to cause the obscuration and reddening we see in our galactic system.

The interstellar gas shows a tendency to gather into clouds of higher density than the average, and in certain areas of space it is possible that stars are forming out of the gas. The region of the great Orion nebula is quite likely a place where stars are being born at the present time, as here we find a large number of very luminous and hot stars of the type believed to be relatively young.

The gas in space does not produce visible obscuration in the same way as the dust particles, but its effect can be seen when we study starlight with the spectroscope. The spectrum of a star, like the spectrum of the sun, consists of a band of colour covering the entire range from violet to red. But on this band we find certain missing wave-lengths or colours that appear as dark lines on a bright background. These are characteristic of specific atoms which are in the outer layers or atmosphere of the star, and which are interposed between us and the hotter lower layers of the star. Starlight, when analyzed, turns out to be quite complex. If we have atoms in space between us and a star, they also may add their contribution to the star spectrum in a similar way to atoms in a very extended stellar atmosphere. We can usually identify the features added by the space gas, as the lines will look somewhat different to those originating in the star itself, and will give a different velocity in the line of sight. The calcium and sodium atoms in space show up particularly well in this way and have been studied in detail by astronomers in both the United States and Canada.

The stars, and the clouds of dust and gas in our galactic system, have their own individual motions, but over and above this there is a general motion of the whole system. Both stars and interstellar matter show the same basic rotation about the distant centre of our star system. In fact it was the motions of the stars which first clearly demonstrated that there was a distant massive centre to the galaxy. Radial velocity observations of stars and gas clouds, made at the Dominion Astrophysical Observatory near Victoria, B.C. by J. S. Plaskett and J. A. Pearce, played a vital role in charting the position of this centre, and in finding the relation of the sun to it.

The problem of locating the centre of the galaxy is not an easy one. With optical telescopes it is not possible to see it as there is too much dust in the way. We have to deduce where the centre is by a study of the star motions in our immediate neighbourhood. I think you will be able to visualize this more easily if you imagine yourself at an amusement park where there is a ride that consists of a series of concentric tracks upon which a large number of small cars all go round in the clockwise direction. You get on a car partway out from the centre to the edge. It's a very foggy night so you can't see the centre of the ride, but you do see the cars near you. You note that those on your right seem to be passing you as a result of being on a shorter track. At right-forward they move almost directly away from you while to right-rear they are approaching. On the other hand, you keep about the same distance from the car immediately ahead but you approach or overtake the cars to left-forward, pass the cars to your left, and move away from cars to left-rear. If you carefully measure the relative motions of all the cars around you, you can draw some conclusions about the distance of the centre of the ride from your particular car even though you never see the centre itself.

This is the type of reasoning that led to a knowledge of the fact that the solar system, along with all the other stars and clouds in our part of space, is moving at a speed of over 130 miles per second in the direction of Cygnus, the Northern Cross or Swan. This general motion is part of the rotation around the centre of our star system, and takes place in the plane of the Milky Way. The centre is 26,000 light-years away towards the constellation Sagittarius. It will take us well over 200 millions years to make one complete circuit, and like the cars on the midway ride we are all moving clockwise when viewed from the top or north side of the Milky Way.

The general conclusions just mentioned were reached over thirty years ago as a result of the optical study of stars within a few thousand light-years of the sun. During the last ten years they have been verified by a completely independent series of observations made with radio telescopes. It was in the spring of 1951 that Harold Ewen, a graduate student at Harvard University, first recorded the radio signals from hydrogen atoms in space, using a strangely shaped horn that looked like a futuristic model of *His Master's Voice*. We have seen that most of the atoms in space are cold, and do not either emit or absorb light in the visible part of the spectrum; hence, they are invisible. But the cold hydrogen atoms do, once in a long while, send out energy in the radio spectrum on a wave-length of 8.3 inches. There are several million hydrogen atoms in each cubic yard of the space clouds, so even if each hydrogen atom emits radiation only at very long intervals, there will always be some atoms broadcasting on this wave-length.

By recording this eight-inch radiation, and studying its

velocity variations over the sky, the hydrogen clouds of our galactic system have been mapped out. The wonderful part about this method of charting the galaxy is that the dust clouds, which hide the light of the galactic centre in optical light, are transparent to the hydrogen eight-inch radio wavelengths. Hence, it has been possible to observe directly the centre of our system, and to map out the long spiral condensations of hydrogen gas that encircle this centre (Figure

50,000 light years

V-3. *Clouds of hydrogen gas in our galaxy, adapted from plots by J. H. Oort, G. Westerhout, and G. W. Rougoor, at the Leiden Observatory. The position of the sun is indicated by a cross.*

V-3). The stars show a tendency to cluster along these arms of gas, and the sun itself is located in one.

The whole flattened disk of gas and dust and stars forming our galaxy has a diameter of about 80,000 light-years, and a mass of some 100,000 million suns. The old "pathway of the gods" has in truth acquired vast proportions, and our entire solar system is but a tiny speck in this vastness.

Reference has previously been made to Sir Arthur Eddington and to the present article. He was born at Kendal, Westmoreland, England in 1882. At 15, he entered Owens College, Manchester, where he became a student of Arthur Schuster, a distinguished astronomer of a past generation. In 1902, he entered Trinity College, Cambridge; in 1906 became chief assistant to Sir F. W. Dyson, the astronomer royal; in 1913, was elected Plumian professor of astronomy at Cambridge; and in 1914 director of the observatory there. That same year he published Stellar Movements and the Structure of the Universe, which created a new subject—stellar dynamics. 1916 saw the beginning of Eddington's research on the internal constitution of the stars. He introduced the principle that the chief agent in the transport of heat from the inner to the outer regions of a star was not convection but radiation and that radiation pressure plays an important part in supporting the weight of superincumbent material. His discovery was an important factor in the development of the mass-luminosity relationship and in the modern theory of stellar evolution.

Eddington's observation of the deflection of light during an eclipse has previously been mentioned. He here tells the story of that observation, which with other similar observations helped prove Einstein's relativity theory, thus limiting the previously-held universality of Newton's law of gravitation. It is a chapter from his great work, Space, Time and Gravitation.

WEIGHING LIGHT

SIR ARTHUR EDDINGTON

> Query 1. Do not Bodies act upon Light at
> a distance, and by their action bend its Rays,
> and is not this action *(caeteris paribus)*
> strongest at the least distance?
> NEWTON, *Opticks.*

WE COME NOW to the experimental test of the influence
of gravitation on light.

It must be understood that there were two questions to
answer: firstly, whether light has weight (as suggested by
Newton), or is indifferent to gravitation; secondly, if it has
weight, is the amount of the deflection in accordance with
Einstein's or Newton's laws?

It was already known that light possesses mass or inertia
like other forms of electromagnetic energy. This is manifested in the phenomena of radiation-pressure. Some force
is required to stop a beam of light by holding an obstacle
in its path; a searchlight experiences a minute force to recoil
just as if it were a machine-gun firing material projectiles.
The force, which is predicted by orthodox electromagnetic
theory, is exceedingly minute; but delicate experiments have
detected it. Probably this inertia of radiation is of great
cosmical importance, playing a great part in the equilibrium
of the more diffuse stars. Indeed it is probably the agent
which has carved the material of the universe into stars of
roughly uniform mass. Possibly the tails of comets are a
witness to the power of the momentum of sunlight, which
drives outwards the smaller or the more absorptive particles.

It is legitimate to speak of a pound of light as we speak
of a pound of any other substance. The mass of ordinary
quantities of light is however extremely small, and I have

calculated that at the low charge of 3*d*. a unit, an Electric Light Company would have to sell light at the rate of £140,000,000 a pound. All the sunlight falling on the earth amounts to 160 tons daily.

It is perhaps not easy to realise how a wave-motion can have inertia, and it is still more difficult to understand what is meant by its having weight. Perhaps this will be better understood if we put the problem in a concrete form. Imagine a hollow body, with radiant heat or light-waves traversing the hollow; the mass of the body will be the sum of the masses of the material and of the radiant energy in the hollow; a greater force will be required to shift it because of the light-waves contained in it. Now let us weigh it with scales or a spring-balance. Will it also weigh heavier on account of the radiation contained, or will the weight be that of the solid material alone? If the former, then clearly from this aspect light has weight; and it is not difficult to deduce the effect of this weight on a freely moving light-beam not enclosed within a hollow.

The effect of weight is that the radiation in the hollow body acquires each second a downward momentum proportional to its mass. This in the long run is transmitted to the material enclosing it. For a free light-wave in space, the added momentum combines with the original momentum, and the total momentum determines the direction of the ray, which is accordingly bent. Newton's theory suggests no means for bringing about the bending, but contents itself with predicting it on general principles. Einstein's theory provides a means, viz. the variation of velocity of the waves.

Hitherto mass and weight have always been found associated in strict proportionality. One very important test had already shown that this proportionality is not confined to material energy. The substance uranium contains a great deal of radioactive energy, presumably of an electromagnetic nature, which it slowly liberates. The mass of this energy must be an appreciable fraction of the whole mass of the substance. But it was shown by experiments with the Eötvös torsion-balance that the ratio of weight to mass for uranium is the same as for all other substances; so the energy of radio-activity has weight. Still even this experiment deals only with bound electromagnetic energy, and we are not justified in deducing the properties of the free energy of light.

It is easy to see that a terrestrial experiment has at present no chance of success. If the mass and weight of light are in the same proportion as for matter, the ray of light will be bent just like the trajectory of a material particle. On the earth a rifle bullet, like everything else, drops 16 feet in the first second, 64 feet in two seconds, and so on, below its original line of flight; the rifle must thus be aimed above the target. Light would also drop 16 feet in the first second*; but, since it has travelled 186,000 miles along its course in that time, the bend is inappreciable. In fact any terrestrial course is described so quickly that gravitation has scarcely had time to accomplish anything.

The experiment is therefore transferred to the neighbourhood of the sun. There we get a pull of gravitation 27 times more intense than on the earth; and—what is more important—the greater size of the sun permits a much longer trajectory throughout which the gravitation is reasonably powerful. The deflection in this case may amount to something of the order of a second of arc, which for the astronomer is a fairly large quantity.

In Figure V-4 the line *EFQP* shows the track of a ray of light from a distant star *P* which reaches the earth *E*. The main part of the bending of the ray occurs as it passes the sun *S*; and the initial course *PQ* and the final course *FE* are practically straight. Since the light rays enter the ob-

V-4.

* Or 32 feet according to Einstein's law. The fall increases with the speed of the motion.

server's eye or telescope in the direction *FE*, this will be the direction in which the star appears. But its true direction from the earth is *QP*, the initial course. So the star appears displaced outwards from its true position by an angle equal to the total deflection of the light.

It must be noticed that this is only true because a star is so remote that its true direction with respect to the earth *E* is indistinguishable from its direction with respect to the point *Q*. For a source of light within the solar system, the apparent displacement of the source is by no means equal to the deflection of the light-ray. It is perhaps curious that the attraction of light by the sun should produce an apparent displacement of the star away from the sun; but the necessity for this is clear.

The bending affects stars seen near the sun, and accordingly the only chance of making the observation is during a total eclipse when the moon cuts off the dazzling light. Even then there is a great deal of light from the sun's corona which stretches far above the disc. It is thus necessary to have rather bright stars near the sun, which will not be lost in the glare of the corona. Further the displacements of these stars can only be measured relatively to other stars, preferably more distant from the sun and less displaced; we need therefore a reasonable number of outer bright stars to serve as reference points.

In a superstitious age a natural philosopher wishing to perform an important experiment would consult an astrologer to ascertain an auspicious moment for the trial. With better reason, an astronomer to-day consulting the stars would announce that the most favourable day of the year for weighing light is May 29. The reason is that the sun in its annual journey round the ecliptic goes through fields of stars of varying richness, but on May 29 it is in the midst of a quite exceptional patch of bright stars—part of the Hyades—by far the best star-field encountered. Now if this problem had been put forward at some other period of history, it might have been necessary to wait some thousands of years for a total eclipse of the sun to happen on the lucky date. But by strange good fortune an eclipse did happen on May 29, 1919. Owing to the curious sequence of eclipses a similar opportunity will recur in 1938; we are in the midst of the most favourable cycle. It is not suggested that it is impossible to make the test at other eclipses; but the work will necessarily be more difficult.

Attention was called to this remarkable opportunity by the Astronomer Royal in March, 1917; and preparations were begun by a Committee of the Royal Society and Royal Astronomical Society for making the observations. Two expeditions were sent to different places on the line of totality to minimise the risk of failure by bad weather. Dr. A. C. D. Crommelin and Mr. C. Davidson went to Sobral in North Brazil; Mr. E. T. Cottingham and the writer went to the Isle of Principe in the Gulf of Guinea, West Africa. The instrumental equipment for both expeditions was prepared at Greenwich Observatory under the care of the Astronomer Royal; and here Mr. Davidson made the arrangements which were the main factor in the success of both parties.

The circumstances of the two expeditions were somewhat different and it is scarcely possible to treat them together. We shall at first follow the fortunes of the Principe observers. They had a telescope of focal length 11 feet 4 inches. On their photographs 1 second of arc (which was about the largest displacement to be measured) corresponds to about $\frac{1}{1500}$ inch—by no means an inappreciable quantity. The aperture of the object-glass was 13 inches, but as used it was stopped down to 8 inches to give sharper images. It is necessary, even when the exposure is only a few seconds, to allow for the diurnal motion of the stars across the sky, making the telescope move so as to follow them. But since it is difficult to mount a long and heavy telescope in the necessary manner in a temporary installation in a remote part of the globe, the usual practice at eclipses is to keep the telescope rigid and reflect the stars into it by a coelostat—a plane mirror kept revolving at the right rate by clockwork. This arrangement was adopted by both expeditions.

The observers had rather more than a month on the island to make their preparations. On the day of the eclipse the weather was unfavourable. When totality began the dark disc of the moon surrounded by the corona was visible through cloud, much as the moon often appears through cloud on a night when no stars can be seen. There was nothing for it but to carry out the arranged programme and hope for the best. One observer was kept occupied changing the plates in rapid succession, whilst the other gave the exposures of the required length with a screen held in front of the object-glass to avoid shaking the telescope in any way.

> For in and out, above, about, below
> 'Tis nothing but a Magic *Shadow*-show
> Played in a Box whose candle is the Sun
> Round which we Phantom Figures come and go.

Our shadow-box takes up all our attention. There is a marvellous spectacle above, and, as the photographs afterwards revealed, a wonderful prominence-flame is poised a hundred thousand miles above the surface of the sun. We have no time to snatch a glance at it. We are conscious only of the weird half-light of the landscape and the hush of nature, broken by the calls of the observers, and beat of the metronome ticking out the 302 seconds of totality.

Sixteen photographs were obtained, with exposures ranging from 2 to 20 seconds. The earlier photographs showed no stars, though they portrayed the remarkable prominence; but apparently the cloud lightened somewhat towards the end of totality, and a few images appeared on the later plates. In many cases one or other of the most essential stars was missing through cloud, and no use could be made of them; but one plate was found showing fairly good images of five stars, which were suitable for a determination. This was measured on the spot a few days after the eclipse in a micrometric measuring-machine. The problem was to determine how the apparent positions of the stars, affected by the sun's gravitational field, compared with the normal positions on a photograph taken when the sun was out of the way. Normal photographs for comparison had been taken with the same telescope in England in January. The eclipse photograph and a comparison photograph were placed film to film in the measuring-machine so that corresponding images fell close together*, and the small distances were measured in two rectangular directions. From these the relative displacements of the stars could be ascertained. In comparing two plates, various allowances have to be made for refraction, aberration, plate-orientation, etc.; but since these occur equally in determinations of stellar parallax, for which much greater accuracy is required, the necessary procedure is well-known to astronomers.

The results from this plate gave a definite displacement, in good accordance with Einstein's theory and disagreeing with the Newtonian prediction. Although the material was very meagre compared with what had been hoped for, the writer (who it must be admitted was not altogether unbiassed) believed it convincing.

It was not until after the return to England that any further confirmation was forthcoming. Four plates were brought home undeveloped, as they were of a brand which would not stand development in the hot climate. One of these was found to show sufficient stars; and on measurement it also showed the deflection predicted by Einstein, confirming the other plate.

The bugbear of possible systematic error affects all investigations of this kind. How do you know that there is not something in your apparatus responsible for this apparent deflection? Your object-glass has been shaken up by travelling; you have introduced a mirror into your optical system; perhaps the 50° rise of temperature between the climate at the equator and England in winter has done some kind of mischief. To meet this criticism, a different field of stars was photographed at night in Principe and also in England at the same altitude as the eclipse field. If the deflection were really instrumental, stars on these plates should show relative displacements of a similar kind to those on the eclipse plates. But on measuring these check-plates no appreciable displacements were found. That seems to be satisfactory evidence that the displacement observed during the eclipse is really due to the sun being in the region, and

---

* This was possible because at Principe the field of stars was reflected in the coelostat mirror, whereas in England it was photographed direct.

is not due to differences in instrumental conditions between England and Principe. Indeed the only possible loophole is a difference between the night conditions at Principe when the check-plates were taken, and the day, or rather eclipse, conditions when the eclipse photographs were taken. That seems impossible since the temperature at Principe did not vary more than 1° between day and night.

The problem appeared to be settled almost beyond doubt; and it was with some confidence that we awaited the return of the other expedition from Brazil. The Brazil party had had fine weather and had gained far more extensive material on their plates. They had remained two months after the eclipse to photograph the same region before dawn, when clear of the sun, in order that they might have comparison photographs taken under exactly the same circumstances. One set of photographs was secured with a telescope similar to that used at Principe. In addition they used a longer telescope of 4 inches aperture and 19 feet focal length. The photographs obtained with the former were disappointing. Although the full number of stars expected (about 12) were shown, and numerous plates had been obtained, the definition of the images had been spoiled by some cause, probably distortion of the coelostat-mirror by the heat of the sunshine falling on it. The observers were pessimistic as to the value of these photographs; but they were the first to be measured on return to England, and the results came as a great surprise after the indications of the Principe plates. The measures pointed with all too good agreement to the "half-deflection," that is to say, the Newtonian value which is one-half the amount required by Einstein's theory. It seemed difficult to pit the meagre material of Principe against the wealth of data secured from the clear sky of Sobral. It is true the Sobral images were condemned, but whether so far as to invalidate their testimony on this point was not at first clear; besides the Principe images were not particularly well-defined, and were much enfeebled by cloud. Certain compensating advantages of the latter were better appreciated later. Their strong point was the satisfactory check against systematic error afforded by the photographs of the check-field; there were no check-plates taken at Sobral, and, since it was obvious that the discordance of the two results depended on systematic error and not on the wealth of material, this distinctly favoured the Principe results. Further, at Principe there could be no evil effects from the sun's rays on the mirror, for the sun had withdrawn all too shyly behind the veil of cloud. A further advantage was provided by the check-plates at Principe, which gave an independent determination of the difference of scale of the telescope as used in England and at the eclipse; for the Sobral plates this scale-difference was eliminated by the method of reduction, with the consequence that the results depended on the measurement of a much smaller relative displacement.

There remained a set of seven plates taken at Sobral with the 4-inch lens; their measurement had been delayed by the necessity of modifying a micrometer to hold them, since they were of unusual size. From the first no one entertained any doubt that the final decision must rest with them, since the images were almost ideal, and they were on a larger scale than the other photographs. The use of this instrument must have presented considerable difficulties—the unwieldy length of the telescope, the slower speed of the lens necessitating longer exposures and more accurate driving of the clock-work, the larger scale rendering the focus more sensitive to disturbances—but the observers achieved success, and the perfection of the negatives surpassed anything that could have been hoped for.

These plates were now measured and they gave a final verdict definitely confirming Einstein's value of the deflection, in agreement with the results obtained at Principe.

It will be remembered that Einstein's theory predicts a deflection of $1''.74$ at the edge of the sun*, the amount falling off inversely as the distance from the sun's centre. The simple Newtonian deflection is half this, $0''.87$. The final results (reduced to the edge of the sun) obtained at Sobral and Principe with their "probable accidental errors" were

$$\text{Sobral} \quad 1''.98 \pm 0''.12,$$
$$\text{Principe} \quad 1''.61 \pm 0''.30.$$

* The predicted deflection of light from infinity to infinity is just over $1''.745$, from infinity to the earth it is just under.

It is usual to allow a margin of safety of about twice the probable error on either side of the mean. The evidence of the Principe plates is thus just about sufficient to rule out the possibility of the "half-deflection," and the Sobral plates exclude it with practical certainty. The value of the material found at Principe cannot be put higher than about one-sixth of that at Sobral; but it certainly makes it less easy to bring criticism against this confirmation of Einstein's theory seeing that it was obtained independently with two different instruments at different places and with different kinds of checks.

Those who regard Einstein's law of gravitation as a natural deduction from a theory based on the minimum of hypotheses will be satisfied to find that his remarkable prediction is quantitatively confirmed by observation, and that no unforeseen cause has appeared to invalidate the test.

The most basic problem facing astronomy, perhaps the most basic facing all science, is that of the origin of the universe. In the most primitive societies men wondered about it; the great religions have offered their own explanations; philosophers have pondered it; the most sophisticated theorists of our day fail to agree on a satisfactory explanation. It may be, indeed, that the human mind is incapable of comprehending the concepts necessary to a solution, but it has never been the attitude of science to acknowledge the possibility of such defeat.

Three main theories, discussed in the following article, are currently under consideration by cosmologists. They raise such all-encompassing questions as whether the universe always did and always will continue to exist, whether it undergoes cycles of expansion and contraction, whether matter is constantly being created, or whether the universe was created at some definite moment in time and at some later moment will eventually die. Advances toward a solution of the problem must await further observation, not only with the tools at hand but with the new tools and methods discussed throughout this book.

Fred Hoyle was born in Yorkshire in 1914 and in 1939 won a prize fellowship at St. John's College, Cambridge, where he

later became a professor. As Plumian professor of astronomy, he
teaches in England and does research at the Mt. Wilson and
Palomar Observatories in California. He is one of the leading
proponents of the steady-state theory and his article thus under-
standably emphasizes the evidence in its favor.

WHEN TIME BEGAN

FRED HOYLE

THROUGHOUT the centuries man, gazing at the night
sky in wonder, has never ceased to speculate about the
larger aspects of the universe around him. How and when
and why did it all begin and will there be an end? I shall
here describe three different theories which attempt to probe
these mysteries of time and space and matter. They will be
referred to as the Explosion Theory, the Expansion-Contraction Theory and the Steady-State Theory. Before we
begin this cosmological exploration, however, we must understand the background common to all three theories.

Our modern ideas concerning the larger aspects of the
universe are both more detailed and more consistent than
those of former ages. Observations can now be made, with
both radio and visual telescopes, that were impossible a
decade ago. We are even beginning to overcome the handicaps imposed on us by the terrestrial atmosphere, through
the use of instruments mounted in satellites. And our recent
advances in particle physics now enable us to calculate accurately how matter behaves under the extremely varied
conditions found throughout the universe.

Space is populated by vast galaxies of stars. The Milky
Way, of which the earth is part, is such a galaxy. The
galaxies tend to be distributed in groups, sometimes in big
groups with as many as a thousand galaxies, sometimes in
small groups of only two or three galaxies. Our galaxy belongs to a small collection known as the local group. It has
only two main members, the Milky Way and the famous

galaxy, M-31, which is seen through the constellation of Andromeda—a configuration of Milky Way stars. If you know exactly where to look, you can see this second galaxy with the naked eye on a dark, clear night.

About a thousand million galaxies lie within the range of the Hale 200-inch telescope on Mt. Palomar in California. They can be observed at the stupendous distance of some 30,000,000,000,000,000,000,000,000 (30 sextillion) miles. Almost certainly our terrestrial telescopes do not mark the limit of the universe; the galaxies may be strewn through space without limit.

The galaxies move around within their particular group, and sometimes two of them collide at high speed. In such a collision the component stars rarely hit each other, because they are small and the distances between them great. But the galaxies also contain huge clouds of gas, and these clouds do collide.

In such an encounter the gas moves with violent turbulence, and becomes intensively hot. A colossal emission of radio waves then seems to result. A radio station on earth, with an output of 100 kilowatts, is considered fairly powerful. Two such colliding galaxies observed in the constellation of Cygnus emit some 10,000,000,000,000,000,000,000,000,000,-000,000,000 (10 decillion) kilowatts.

Here we come to the most crucial point. Observations indicate that the different clusters of galaxies are constantly moving apart from each other. To illustrate by a homely analogy, think of a raisin cake baking in an oven. Suppose the cake swells uniformly as it cooks, but the raisins themselves remain of the same size. Let each raisin represent a cluster of galaxies and imagine yourself inside one of them. As the cake swells, you will observe that all the other raisins move away from you. Moreover, the farther away the raisin, the faster it will seem to move. When the cake has swollen to twice its initial dimensions, the distance between all the raisins will have doubled itself—two raisins that were initially an inch apart will now be two inches apart; two raisins that were a foot apart will have moved two feet apart. Since the entire action takes place within the same time interval, obviously the more distant raisins must move apart faster than those close at hand. So it happens with the clusters of galaxies.

The analogy brings out another important point. No matter which raisin you happen to be inside, the others will always move away from you. Hence the fact that we observe all the other clusters of galaxies to be moving away from us *does not mean that we are situated at the center of the universe.* Indeed, it seems certain that the universe has no center. A cake may be said to have a center only because it has a boundary. We must imagine the cake to extend outward without any boundary, an infinite cake, so to speak, which means that however much cake we care to consider there is always more.

This brings us to the Explosion Theory. In expansion, as we have seen, the clusters of galaxies move apart from each other. It can therefore be argued that space is becoming emptier as time goes on. The same argument suggests that space was formerly more densely occupied. Indeed, if the universe has always been in a state of expansion, space must once have been jammed tight with galaxies. Astrophysicists have calculated that the universe was apparently packed tight roughly eight or nine billion years ago.

According to an entirely different line of reasoning, the ages of stars inside our own galaxy can be determined by considering the nuclear processes within them. By this calculation the oldest stars also originated about eight or nine billion years ago. The agreement between the two methods of calculating is highly interesting. It would appear that the universe originated nearly ten billion years ago, and that our galaxy was formed about a billion years later.

The essential concept is that universal matter was originally in a state of very high density, enormously greater than the density of the galaxies today. This original matter we assume to have been explosive. The whole universe expanded rapidly, its initial state of very high density lasting only a few minutes. In time the continuing expansion produced less and less density. After almost a billion years of expansion and decreasing density, the clusters of galaxies formed. They have since continued to move apart and will go on moving apart throughout eternity.

Thus, according to the Explosion Theory, the universe was born a definite time ago. The state of dispersal caused by the explosion will never cease in this theory. The galaxies will continue to move apart from each other until, in the ultimate limit in the future, space will present a uniform, featureless emptiness. All activity inside the galaxies will ultimately cease. The stars will no longer shine. All sources of energy will be exhausted.

Until very recently, astronomers and physicists thought this theory could be supported by a further powerful argument. The 100 or so known chemical elements possess curious regularities in the abundances with which they exist in nature. These regularities indicate that some process of building from hydrogen, the simplest element, has been at work. But if complex elements have been formed from the simplest, if carbon, oxygen, iron, have been "made," the great question is how?

At first thought it seemed as if the first few minutes of universal explosion provided the ideal conditions for the creation of complex elements—that is, extreme density combined with extreme heat. In short, it looked as if the complex elements might be relics of the earliest period in the history of the universe.

Flaws in this argument soon appeared, however. In the first place, it contains hypotheses that contradict our knowledge of nuclear physics. Moreover, it would lead us to expect to find the same proportions of complex atoms in all stars. For if the process that originated complex atoms were truly universal, there should be no purely local variations of composition. Yet such local variations are marked. The oldest stars to have formed in our galaxy have been found to possess very low concentrations of the complex atoms, much lower than in middle-age stars—the sun, for example. This strongly suggests that production of the complex atoms takes place inside the stars and has nothing to do with the early history of the universe.

We must therefore turn the whole question inside out and ask why no nuclear relics remain from the early superdense state of matter, if indeed there ever was a superdense state. A satisfactory technical answer can be given, provided the early state was even hotter than we formerly thought. For we now know that a still-higher temperature, instead of promoting fusion, prevents hydrogen from fusing to produce complex elements. This realization led to a modification of the Explosion Theory. It is called the Expansion-Contraction Theory.

Some astronomers think that the original explosion of the superdense material may not have been sufficiently violent to produce a complete dispersal. They believe that the clusters of galaxies are moving apart from each other at a markedly declining rate, and that eventually expansion will cease altogether. Gravitational attraction will then cause the clusters to start moving together. This means that the universe will pass into a phase of contraction. The clusters will approach each other at ever-increasing speeds until the galaxies collide. Still further contraction will cause even the stars to collide. As a consequence of the greatly rising temperature that accompanies such a strong compression, the complex atoms will disintegrate and be transformed back into hydrogen. The stage will thereby be set for a reversal of the contraction process, and another universal expansion.

Here, then, is a very different picture—a cyclic universe, with expansion and contraction alternating. During expansion, galaxies and stars are formed. Hydrogen supplies energy inside the stars and is gradually changed into complex elements. During contraction, the galaxies and stars are disrupted, and the complex elements are broken down by the high temperature generated at the stage of greatest compression. Each cycle is similar to the previous one, and there is no limit to the number of cycles. Each cycle lasts roughly thirty billion years. The universe is now about half-way through an expansion phase.

According to the Expansion-Contraction Theory, the amount of matter in the universe is finite. Even the volume of space itself is finite, in somewhat the same way as the area of the surface of a sphere is finite. During expansion, all space swells up like an expanding balloon. During contraction, space collapses literally to a point.

The third theory—the Steady-State Theory—differs in

almost all essentials both from the Explosion Theory and from the Expansion-Contraction Theory. The first two theories rest on the assumption that all matter now existing also existed in the past. The argument for a superdense state of the universe disappears if this assumption is false. It is therefore important to examine the possibility that much of the matter now in existence was not in existence in the past, and that much of the matter of the universe that will be in existence in the future is not in existence today.

What do the physicists say about this question? They consider no particle of matter permanent. One particle can be changed into another; new particles can be created. These processes take place partly through fields of force associated with the atomic-nuclear particles, partly through the electromagnetic field. These are the fields responsible for holding the atomic nuclei together, and for propagating all forms of electromagnetic disturbance, such as light, X rays and radio waves.

Such impermanence scarcely seems important in the problem of the expansion of the universe, however, for here we have to consider impermanence, not in the nuclear or electromagnetic field, but in the gravitational field—the field that brings a parachutist back to the ground, that holds the earth in its orbit around the sun. It is the main controlling field of the cosmos. But modern physicists can tell us very little about the properties of gravitation. They have been unable to gather adequate information from experimental laboratory work.

Gravitation is difficult to study in the laboratory, because in the laboratory we are limited to small quantities of matter. These small quantities suffice to produce the full impact of the nuclear and electromagnetic fields. Indeed, the nuclear field can be studied in a single atom by itself. In order to assess the full impact of gravitation, however, we would have to measure the gravitational forces of the entire universe, because all the atoms in the universe add their gravitation contributions together. Thus gravitation cannot be studied piecemeal; it must be measured in its totality. No satisfactory way of doing this has yet been found.

So, lacking adequate information from the laboratory, we have no choice but to weigh the two possibilities—first, that particles have permanence in the gravitational field; second, that they have impermanence. The Explosion Theory and the Expansion-Contraction Theory demand permanent particles because they exclude the possibility of the continuous creation of matter. The Steady-State Theory requires impermanent particles because it postulates such a continuous creation.

Einstein's general theory of relativity provides a powerful framework within which the possibility of impermanence can be tested. But if we accept that framework, we are not free to formulate the hypothesis of impermanence exactly as we might like. In return for the advantages it offers, the relativity theory imposes constraints.

These constraints can be met. As they are met, it emerges that impermanence must take the form either of a steady creation of matter or of a steady annihilation, but it cannot take the form of both together. We cannot have creation in one part of the universe and annihilation in another. The creation of matter is linked to the expansion of the universe. According to Einsteinian mathematics, space cannot accommodate more than a certain fixed average density of matter. Therefore, we cannot have a steady creation of matter without a steady expansion of the universe. Conversely, we cannot have a steady annihilation without a contraction of the universe. Obviously, expansion and contraction of space cannot take place at the same time—just as a balloon cannot be simultaneously inflated and deflated.

We are thus faced with the alternatives of creation plus expansion or of annihilation plus contraction. In theory we must weigh both these alternatives, because every physical hypothesis considers two possible ways of viewing the direction of time—the case where time runs forward into the future in the usual sense, and the case where time runs backward into the past. An analogy might be found in unrolling a strip of carpet from beginning to end—from the past through the present to the future; reverse the process and you go from the end to the beginning, or from the future to the past. In practice, when we restrict ourselves to the usual sense of past and future, the relativity theory gives us just the one possibility—that of the creation of matter allied firmly to the expansion of the universe.

The maintenance of a constant average density of matter in space leads to the Steady-State Theory, first discussed by Prof. Hermann Bondi, Prof. Thomas Gold and myself some ten years ago. Because the density remains constant, the condensation of clusters of galaxies should apply to the present and future as well as to the past. More recently, Gold and I have been exploring the possibility that the matter in space may be extremely hot, and that the formation of galaxies arises from a cooling process within localized blobs of material. The pressure inside the blobs is thereby reduced below that existing in the still-hot surrounding material. This causes strong compression of the blobs. In proceeding on this assumption we find that many of the difficulties formerly encountered in trying to understand the genesis of galaxies disappear. We also find that the cooling process may be associated with the production of cosmic radio waves and with the origin of cosmic rays. We tend to believe that such a cooling is going on at present in many of the distant radio sources observed by radio-astronomers, and that in these sources we are observing a phase in the process of formation of new galaxies.

In the Steady-State Theory the clusters of galaxies expand apart, but as they do so new galaxies are born, and at such a rate that their average density in space remains unaltered with time. The individual clusters change and evolve, but the universe itself, viewed on the large scale, does not change. Thus the old problem of the beginning and end of the universe does not arise at all in the Steady-State Theory, for the universe did not have a beginning and it will not have an end. Every cluster of galaxies, every star, every atom, had a beginning, but the universe itself did not.

The perceptive reader may here find himself pondering the density of the distant galaxies in an ever-expanding universe without an end. As we demonstrated in our raisin-cake analogy, the more distant the galaxy, the faster it will move away from the observer. This relationship between distance and velocity is an observable fact and is measured by the so-called "red shift," by which certain wave lengths of the light from a given star shift across the spectrum. A similar shift, in the sound spectrum, is noticed when the pitch of a train whistle decreases as the train moves away from a listener. The speed of the distant galaxy continues to increase until, presumably, it exceeds the speed of light— 186,000 miles per second. At that point the light emanating from the stars in the galaxy is being carried away at a velocity exceeding its return speed, and the galaxy as an observable fact is lost to us forever.

These, then, are the dominant hypotheses concerning the structure of the universe. The decision among them rests with observation. As an example, it would be of great interest to know whether new galaxies are being formed at the present time. If new galaxies are being formed, the Explosion Theory and the Expansion-Contraction Theory would be suspect because they do not provide for such creation. If new galaxies are not being formed, the Steady-State Theory becomes untenable.

Although many such observational tests are being actively worked on, it must be realized that cosmological observations are very difficult to make. The tests are all concerned with objects that lie very far away from us. This forces the observer to work near the limit of reliability of his instruments. In these circumstances only great persistence and care, combined with fine judgment, will separate the genuine from the spurious. A decision among the different theories, therefore, is not an issue that can be hastened. Only the slow evolution of astronomy will enable us to reach an unambiguous decision.

In the meantime we must fall back on philosophic criteria for distinguishing between the different pictures presented by astronomical theory. Such criteria are by no means to be decried, so long as it is clearly understood that observational tests must take priority, once the appropriate observational results become available.

The Explosion Theory gives us the picture of the universe as an explosion from a superdense state of matter. Many people are specially attracted to this hypothesis because it requires a definite moment of creation for the whole universe. According to this theory, the universe is not a self-operating concern. It has to be started, much as one might switch on a huge machine. There are many questions relating to this hypothesis that we can never hope to answer, for many of the present-day characteristics of the universe depend on the precise manner of the "switching on" process. There is also a philosophic undercurrent of an existence outside the universe that touches on religion, a feature that seems attractive to some and unappealing to others.

The Expansion-Contraction Theory and the Steady-State Theory are similar in that they both present the universe as a fully self-operating system. There is no moment of origin, time extends backward into the past as far as we care to consider it. Otherwise these two theories are very different, the one depending on permanence and the other on impermanence of particles in the gravitational field.

Space and time play very different roles in the three theories. In the Explosion Theory, space is infinite, while time is finite toward the past and infinite toward the future. In the Expansion-Contraction Theory, time is infinite in both the past and future, but space is finite. In the Steady-State Theory, space and time are both infinite. Moreover, space and time have a still deeper connection in the Steady-State Theory. This is a point of such considerable interest as to be worth a short diversion.

The concept of the equivalence of spatial observers has been used in cosmology for many years. This simply means that observers situated at widely different points of space will observe exactly the same large-scale structure of the universe—that the universe has no point of space from which things look any different than they do from other points of space. An observer in a distant galaxy would see large-scale features entirely similar to those that we ourselves observe. This important condition is satisfied in both the Explosion Theory and the Expansion-Contraction Theory provided *one crucial requirement is met*—that the observers look at the universe at the same moment of time. Equivalence is lost in these theories if this proviso is not satisfied because time is linked with nonrecurring cosmological changes. An evolving universe, in which space becomes progressively less dense with matter, must present different aspects to an observer viewing it at different moments of time. *But equivalence is still maintained in the Steady-State Theory even if observers look at the universe at different times,* for there is a continuing pattern of development. A universe which maintains its general cosmological structure through the continuous creation of matter will present the same aspect to observers at any moment of time.

This wider interpretation of equivalence provides one of the strongest aesthetic reasons for preferring the Steady-State Theory. Moreover, the whole progress of modern physics has been closely bound up with the discovery of relations that are independent of the special position of the observer. For this reason alone, I feel that it would be most surprising if the Steady-State Theory, with its compelling space-time equivalence, should turn out to be wrong.

I would like to present my own point of view on all these questions, to give my reasons for preferring the Steady-State Theory to its rivals. These reasons are for the most part philosophical in character. But first there is one purely scientific point that must be mentioned. In the Steady-State Theory all observable features of the universe must be the consequences of processes that are going on all the time: We cannot take refuge in the argument that things were different in the past, as it is possible to do in the other theories. This means that every feature of the universe must be susceptible to the principle of observational investigation. Thus the Steady-State Theory aims to place observation on a very much firmer footing than is the case in rival theories.

Considerations of elegance and economy also appear to be highly relevant. In both the Explosion Theory and the Expansion-Contraction Theory all matter is supposed to have been in a hot superdense condition. Yet, as we have seen, this condition cannot have promoted any nuclear reactions. The superdense state of matter must be designed specifically to prevent nuclear reactions from taking place. Indeed, the universe must be constructed in a way that hides from us all direct evidence of the existence of this singular state. Personally I find it difficult to place much credence in this very negative supposition. It would seem to be more natural to believe that a superdense state never existed at all.

In the Expansion-Contraction Theory we are asked to think of expansion and contraction following each other in a never-ending series. During expansion, matter becomes organized into galaxies, stars, planets, living creatures. During contraction the galaxies, stars, and so on, are entirely disintegrated in preparation for the succeeding phase of expansion. Each cycle is exactly similar to the preceding cycle. Nothing new ever happens from cycle to cycle, and it is just this that seems uninspired and inelegant. This is an aesthetic rather than a scientific objection, but it may be worth adding that scientists are more concerned with aesthetics than is commonly supposed!

What then of the Steady-State universe? This third picture might seem at first sight to contain a similar inelegance. But it turns out that there is an important sense in which this is not so. I would like to begin the explanation of this point with another diversion.

In recent years physicists have come to pose a very important question: How deep are the laws of physics? How far must one dig before nothing basically new remains to be discovered, before the level of absolute truth is revealed? Twice during the past seventy years scientists have believed themselves within sighting distance of the ultimate laws of physics. On both occasions their optimism was unfounded. The tendency is now rather to ask: Are there any ultimate final laws of physics? Might it not be that however deep one digs, there are always still deeper levels of subtlety to be uncovered? Nowadays the trend is to answer the last question affirmatively, to believe that no end will be found to the intricacy of the laws of physics.

Such a point of view makes sense in the Steady-State Theory but not, I think, in the other theories. In the Expansion-Contraction Theory, for instance, we have a universe that is entirely finite—a finite amount of matter, finite space, a finite time of cycling. It seems to me most doubtful whether such a universe could possibly accommodate laws of an infinite complexity. The situation is better in the Explosion Theory. Here we could possibly have an infinite universe with infinite laws—but one in which only a finite fragment of the laws was discoverable. For in the Explosion Theory there is but one single generation of galaxies. The stars and the living creatures in these galaxies live only for a finite time of a few tens of billions of years. Hence any understanding gained by living creatures must always remain finite. Digging beyond a certain finite depth would manifestly be impossible.

The situation is otherwise in the Steady-State Theory. Here it is possible to accumulate knowledge indefinitely, to dig to any depth, however deep. Here we have an unending series of generations of galaxies. When a particular galaxy dies, the knowledge that has been gained by creatures in it can (in principle!) be passed to a nearby younger galaxy. This process can be repeated without end, so that in the long run knowledge can be piled up to any required degree. Here we have a universe that is infinite, not only in its obvious physical characteristics but also in its intellectual possibilities.

Although it may not be of the most consuming scientific importance, we as human beings cannot avoid being engrossed by the problem of whether other intelligent beings, similar or dissimilar to ourselves, exist in space. There is evidence that life of a low order does exist elsewhere in our solar system, but attempts to communicate with extraterrestrial beings have so far met with failure. By statistical methods a strong case can be made for the supposition that intelligent life does exist in other star systems. In the following article, a distinguished astronomer explains why he believes it to be more than a possibility. Born at Nashville, Missouri in 1885, Harlow Shapley did research at Mt. Wilson under George Ellery Hale, and became professor of astronomy at Harvard and director of the Harvard College Observatory in 1921. He is noted for his work in photometry and spectroscopy, and in the use of cepheid variables as measuring tools and in cosmology. He is a widely known lecturer and author.

LIFE ON OTHER WORLDS

HARLOW SHAPLEY

THE STARS are composed of the same stuff as that which constitutes the sun and is found in the earth's crust. They are built of the same materials as those that compose terrestrial organisms. As far as we can tell, the same physical laws prevail everywhere. The same rules apply at the center of the Milky Way, in the remote galaxies, and among the stars of the solar neighborhood.

In view of a common cosmic physics and chemistry, should we not also expect to find animals and plants everywhere? It seems completely reasonable; and soon we shall say that it seems inevitable. But to demonstrate the actual presence of organic life in other planetary systems is now impossible for us because the stars are so remote and we, as earth-bound searchers of the sky, are yet too feeble in the face of stellar realities. To establish, however, through statistical analysis the high probability of planets suitable for living organisms is not difficult. A statistical argument, as a matter of fact, is more convincing than would be a marginal observation.

It will clarify the discussion if we start with two routine reminders: (1) by life we mean what here we terrestrials recognize as life—a biochemical operation involving carbon and nitrogen and making use of water in the liquid state (Other kinds are imaginable; e.g., one where silicon replaces carbon, or where sulphur's participation is like that of oxygen. Such is imaginable, but unlikely); and (2) Mars and Venus are therefore the only other planets of our solar system that are at all suitable for living organisms. The evidences are good that Martian life is low and lichen-like, if it exists at all, and the surface of Venus is an unsolved

344

problem, with the odds against living organisms because of
the lethal chemistry of the atmosphere.

Among the many definitions of life is the cold rigid version: "material organizations perpetuating their organization." The emphasis is on "perpetuating." We might better
put it: "the perpetuation by a material organization of its
organization." The definition can quite properly refer both
to individuals and to species, and also to societies. They are
all alive. They all die, if we suitably define death. The
lively deathless atoms of our breath and bodies, however,
are not, in this defining, alive.

Life is tough, tenacious, and also persistent when we give
it time to adjust to varying environments. We find it in
geysers and hot springs. Some flowers bloom under the
snow. Both plants and animals on occasion endure for long
periods on hot deserts. Some seeds can withstand desiccation
and extreme cold indefinitely. Life as we know it on the
earth has wide adaptability; but there are limits, and one of
these limits is the heat and radiation near a star's surface,
where the molecules constituting protoplasm would be
dissociated.

In our consideration of the spread of life throughout the
universe, we must therefore immediately drop all thoughts of
living organisms on the trillions of radiant stars. The flames
of the sun are rich in the lively atoms of oxygen, carbon,
hydrogen, nitrogen, and calcium—the principal constituents
of living matter—but physical liveliness and organic living-
ness are quite different behaviors. At the surfaces of some of
the cool stars, like Antares and Betelgeuse, and in the cooling
sunspots, we find a few familiar molecules, in addition to
the scores of kinds of atoms; but there is nothing that is as
complicated and tender as the proteins—those molecular
aggregates that underlie the simplest life. And of course the
stars harbor no water in the liquid state.

The stars are out of it, therefore, and they probably
represent more than half of all the material in the universe.
Most of the rest is believed to be in the form of interstellar
gas, with a bit of dust. The dust is of the sort that shows up
as meteors, when in collision with the earth's atmosphere,

and appears also as remote dark nebulosities that interrupt and make patchy the glow of the Milky Way. No life exists on these minute meteoric specks, or on the relatively larger meteorities, and for several reasons. Among the reasons: (1) the masses are too small to hold gravitationally an atmosphere (even our moon cannot maintain the oxygen and carbon dioxide necessary for breathing animals and plants); (2) moreover, the meteors out between the stars are too cold for liquid water; and (3) they are all too unprotected against the lethal ultraviolet radiation from hot stars.

How about life on the comets? The same general argument holds as for meteors and meteorites, since the comets are simply assemblages of dusty and fragmented meteoric materials, infused with escaping gases. In addition, most of the large comets of the solar system are, when brightest, too near the sun for living organisms and the rest of the time too frigidly remote in the outer parts of their orbits.

In our search for life we are therefore left with the planets, and those on which it can occur and survive must be neither too near their stars nor so remote from them that the cold is unrelieved. They should not be too small to hold an oxygen atmosphere, unless we are content to settle for primitive anaerobic life. (A few types of low organisms thrive in the absence of elemental oxygen.)

The life-bearing planets must also have nonpoisonous atmospheres, salutary waters, and agreeable rocky crusts; but given time enough, organisms could no doubt become adjusted to environments that would be poisonous and impossible for life such as that now developed on the earth.

Finally, the propitious planets that are suitable in size, temperature, and chemistry must also have orbits of low eccentricity. Highly eccentric orbits, like those of most comets, would bring their planets too near the star at periastron a part of the year, and then too far out at apastron. The resulting temperature oscillations would be too much for comfort, perhaps even too much for the origins and persistence of early life. Also, in the interests of avoiding too great differences in temperature from night to day, it would be best if the planets rotate rapidly and their rotational axes be highly inclined (as is ours) to their orbital planes.

With the foregoing requirements in mind we ask if there are many really suitable planetary systems, and the companion question: How are planets born?

In the beginning, as they say, was chaos. Or at any rate, soon after the explosive beginning of the expanding universe there was chaos, if we accept the theory of the Primeval Atom as proposed by Canon Lemaître—a theory that visualizes the original assemblage of the matter and energy of the whole universe in one body, a single superatom. In those chaotic early times, some five to ten billion of our years ago, the average material density was of course very high; the stars were near together; many galaxies interpenetrated, if galaxies at that time existed as organizations, and if not, the forming protogalaxies overlapped. Collisions and secondary explosions must have been frequent in those crowded, chaotic times. Masses of flying gas in the cold of space quickly liquified, solidified, cooled into planet-like bodies, with a wide range of sizes. Shattering and exploding bodies produced dust grains and gases from which later stars were born. All that action seems logical, if we accept the hypothesis of a tight little universe before the cosmic expansion had spread it out. Moreover, better hypotheses are hard to come by.

Whether or not there was in the beginning a single primeval "atom" that contained all, there can be little doubt that the now dispersing galaxies with their billions of stars were densely crowded together in the remote past. It is highly significant that the age of the earth's crust, measured by the radioactivity in the rocks, is much the same as the measured age of the expansion.

The supernatural deities of various sorts, rather than "accident" or astrophysical operations, were in ancient times given credit for the origin of the earth; but also the assumption that it always had existed was not uncommon. Many of the rationalizations, developed to account for the origin of the inclusive system of sun, planets, satellites, asteroids, comets, and interplanetary dust, are now wholly discredited. Some theories included the origin of the sun; others assumed its prior existence before the planets appeared. Most of the theories are of recent date—a natural consequence of the great accumulation of relevant scientific data in the past few decades, and of the increasing population of ingenious speculators. The new knowledge built up by the world's astronomers in the past forty years is many times that of all times before.

The following list of fifteen hypotheses, arranged in approximate chronological order, represents the thoughts of speculative scientists from Israel, Germany, France, Australia, India, America, England, Russia, Sweden, and Holland. This geographical distribution shows the wide spread of curiosity about man's physical place in the universe.

1] The Mosaic cosmogony, and similar early religious doctrines.

2] Nebular hypothesis, the famous long-enduring Kantian-Laplacian theory.

3] Partial disruption of the sun by a comet, with the production of planets.

4] Solar eruptions providing planet-building "planetesimals."

5] Capture of the planets by the sun from space or from other stars.

6] Tidal disruption of the sun by a passing star, providing gaseous filaments that condense into planets (variant of 4).

7] Glancing collision of stars (variant of 6).

8] Break-up of one component of a binary star by a third passing star.

9] Explosive fission of the hypothetical protosun.

10] Disruption of an unstable pulsing variable star (cepheid).

11] Revival of the nebular hypothesis, bolstered by modern theories of dust and gas accretions.

12] Electromagnetically produced condensations in a contracting nebula (variant of 2).

13]   Nova explosion in a binary system providing circulating planetoidal fragments.

14]   Revival of the hypothesis of cold planetesimals operating in a nebulous medium (combination of variants of 4, 11, and 12).

15]   Primeval explosive chaos and the Survival of the Conforming—my "hypothesis of desperation."

All of these theories could be described in detail. Some of them overlap. A few have been rejected on the basis of obvious failings or because they are not complete hypotheses. For example, Nos. 1, 3, 4, 5, 9, and 10 are out. Nos. 2 and 6 are weak. This leaves Nos. 7, 8, 11, 12, 13, 14, and 15. We should observe that several different methods may be responsible for planetary origins. We do not need to search out only one method to the exclusion of all others.

The general conclusion at this moment must be that not one of the theories is entirely satisfactory. The best of them need further development. Many do not easily account for the following observed regularities and arrangements:

(a) The nine major planets revolve in the same direction around the sun.

(b) The sun and, so far as known, most of the planets and satellites rotate on their axes in the same direction.

(c) The inclinations of the planetary orbital planes are such that the over-all system (excluding comets) is exceedingly flat.

(d) The smaller planets, except Pluto which may be an escaped satellite of Neptune, are relatively near the sun; the greater planets are all from five to thirty times the earth's orbital radius from the sun.

(e) The satellite systems of Jupiter and Saturn have characteristics simulating those of the planetary system of the sun.

(f) Apparently the chemical content of the earth, probably also of the other planets, is similar to that of the sun, when allowance is made for escaping atmospheres.

(g) The distribution of angular momentum in the planetary system appears fatal to many of the hypotheses; the sun rotates too slowly, or the planets too fast to allow for a common origin—unless protective subhypotheses hurry to their assistance.

The foregoing theories, with two or three exceptions, can be classed as either catastrophic or as calmly accretional. In other words, the planets were born of violence or of slow building up through the accumulation of material. The former generally visualizes the earth, or at least the proto-earth, as once hot from surface to center; the latter visualizes the earth's surface as never wholly molten, although, as the mass grew from accretion, the center naturally heated up and affected the outer strata.

What do these theories imply with respect to the prevalence of earthlike planets? If the contracting-nebula type of origin of stars is accepted, and the stars are held to result mainly from the condensation of cold clouds of gas and dust with the planets coming along as a by-product, then we must assume that planets like those we know, similar in mass, temperature, and chemistry, are the natural and common product of an evolving universe.

We must always remember that our sun is a very ordinary sort of star. One hundred thousand of the brightest million stars are essentially identical with the sun. The sun and the aforementioned 100,000 stars like it have no exceptional position in the Milky Way system; they are in the outer part of what appears to be a typical large spiral galaxy in a Metagalaxy where there are thousands, perhaps millions, of galaxies of the same spiral type. The sunlike stars (most of them) also have a history dating back to those turbulent planet-breeding early times. The evidence is increasing, therefore, for an abundance of habitable planets.

There is, however, in all theories of origin one important deterrent to the universal formation and retention of planets with the suitable requirements for life. That hindrance lies in the common existence of numerous double and multiple stars. A century ago double stars were considered something of a rarity. With the increase of optical power and of skill in discovering binaries and multiples, the picture has changed.

We now believe that forty per cent or more of the stars are in pairs or triples. Of the fifty-five stars known to be within one hundred trillion miles of the earth, only thirty-one are single stars and companions may yet be found for some of them. In a two- or three-star system, planets within the zone of liquid water are highly improbable. The gravitational rules are against it. Orbits would be unstable. We must accept as hospitable only single stars, and perhaps very wide doubles where a stable planetary orbit around one component might be permitted by the other star. Probably we should also exclude the highly populated centers of globular star clusters if we want long endurance for a system of planets.

By taking the contracting-nebula hypothesis (say, No. 14), we would choose the one that probably is most favorable to the formation and preservation of planets. But suppose we accept instead one of the collisional hypotheses; not the cometary-collision suggestion, for the comets we know are relatively too small in mass to be a potent factor in stellar catastrophe. The collision of two or more stars might now be very unproductive of planetary systems because of the infrequency of such collisions. At the present time our sun and its neighbors, and this holds for all single stars not in the center of clusters or the nuclei of galaxies, are so remote from each other that collisions are well-nigh impossible. Twenty-five trillion miles separate our sun from its nearest known stellar neighbor, Alpha Centauri. Any given star, although it be moving at the average relative speed of twenty-miles a second, would course around the galaxy for millions of years without collision or near approach. If we insisted that planetary systems could arise only through the collision or very near approach of mature stars in a fully developed galaxy like ours, we would need to subscribe to the belief that our own "accident" may have been unique—one time only in the whole galaxy—and we the offspring of that remote improbable event! We should then answer: "We *are* alone; we are the special care of whatever omnipotence is concerned in caring for rare accidents."

But two observations quickly weaken or defeat that conclusion. The first is that we do not limit our thoughts only to this galaxy of 100,000,000,000 stellar bodies that are always attracting but safely avoiding each other; we must consider the increase in the chance of collision somewhere provided through the circumstance that there are billions of other galaxies within our telescopic reach, and possibly trillions beyond our direct knowing. All of these systems must be considered when we examine the probability of life as a cosmic phenomenon. If only one galaxy in a hundred has had a planet-producing collision among its stars, there would be millions of such collisions.

The other and more potent contribution to the defeat of our isolationism (on the hypothesis that only collisions can produce planetary systems suitable for life) is the relatively new and well-established evidence that the Metagalaxy is expanding. The actual observation is that galaxies are receding in all directions from each other and that the average density of matter in metagalactic space is steadily decreasing. We need only turn that observation backward and conclude that yesterday the galaxies were closer together than today, that a million years ago they were still nearer each other, and that a few billion years ago they were all tightly packed together, intermingled, overlapping. They were far back toward the stage dramatically described as Canon Lemaître's "Primeval Atom." In the early days collisions and disruptive near approaches must have been millions of times more frequent than would be possible now. In the whole wide world of galaxies there must have been by one method or another innumerable planetary systems established—precariously at first because of the interference of other stars, but ever more safely as the universe expanded.

On the basis of our sampling census of stars in our galaxy, and our sampling of galaxy population out to the limit attainable by present telescopes, we can readily compute that there are more than 10^{20} stars in the universe, each one competent of course through radiation to maintain the photochemical reactions that are the basis of plant and animal life. Perhaps only a few per cent of these are single stars with planetary potentialities. Perhaps only a few per cent of these few developed in such a way (nebular contraction) or had such a suitable experience in the past (collisional) that they would now possess persisting planets. Perhaps only a few per cent of these that succeed in having stable-orbited persisting planets would have one or more at the right distance from the central star; and of these rightly placed planets but one per cent have an orbit of suitable circularity to maintain sufficiently equable temperatures. We could go on with further restrictions to a few of the few of the few, because nonpoisonous airs and waters are also required, and that particular activity of carbon, oxygen, hydrogen, and nitrogen that we call "living" must get started. We could by such restrictions reduce the number of stars with livable and actually "inhabited" planets to nearly a nothing.

All these restrictions, however, get us practically nowhere in isolating ourselves as something unique and special, for there are too many stars. Three undeniable factors have entered our consideration—the ordinariness of our sun which has accomplished the creation of life on this planet; the evidence of the universality of the kind of chemistry and physics we know here; and the existence of more than 10^{20} opportunities for life, that is, the existence of more than one hundred thousand million billion stars.

Let us look once more at large numbers and work this argument over again. Suppose that because of doubling, clustering, secondary collisions, and the like, only one star in a thousand has a planetary system. Personally I would think that one in fifty would be a better estimate, and many of those who believe in the nebular contraction theory of stellar formation would say that at least one out of ten stars has planets. But to be conservative, we say that only one out of a thousand has a planetary system, and then assume that but one out of a thousand of those stars with systems of planets has one or more planets at the right distance from the star to provide the water and warmth that protoplasm requires. In our solar system we have two or three planets in such an interval of distance. Further, let us suppose that only one out of a thousand of those stars with planets suitably distant has one large enough to hold an atmosphere; in our system we have at least seven planets out of nine with atmospheres. That will reduce our suitable planet to a one in a billion chance.

Let us make one other requirement of our suitable planet: the chemical composition of air and water must be of the sort that would develop the naturally arising complex inorganic molecules into the organic. Perhaps that happens but once in a thousand times?

Assembling all four of the one to a thousand chances (all grossly underestimated, I believe, but in the effort to establish our uniqueness in the world, and hence our "importance," we are making it as hard as possible to find other habitable planets), we come to the estimate that only one star out of 10^{12} meets all tests; that is, one star out of a million million. Where does that high improbability of proper planets leave us? Dividing the million million into the total number of stars, $10^{20} \div 10^{12}$, we get 10^8—that is, a hundred million planetary systems suitable for organic life. This number is a minimum, and personally I would recommend its multiplication by at least a thousand times, possibly by a million.

To state a conclusion: The researches of recent times have enriched and clarified our concepts of habitable planets. Through discovering the true stellar nature of the spiral "nebulae," through the sounding of star-and-galaxy populated space to such great depths that the number of knowable stars rises to billions of times the number formerly surmised, and through the discovery of the expansion of the universe with its concomitant deduction that a few billion years ago the stars and planetary materials were much more densely and turbulently crowded together than in the present days of relative calm, we have strengthened our beliefs with respect to the existence of other "worlds." The present concept includes the identifying of our own world as the surface of planet No. 3, in the family of a run-of-the-mill yellowish star, situated in the outer part of a typical galaxy that contains billions of typical stars—this "home galaxy" being one item in an over-all system, the Metagalaxy, that numbers its galaxies in the multibillions.